KU-557-149

THIN-WALLED STRUCTURES:
DEVELOPMENTS IN THEORY AND PRACTICE

This volume is based on papers presented at the N. W. Murray Symposium held at Monash University, Australia on 3–4 November 1988

#22490738

THIN-WALLED STRUCTURES: DEVELOPMENTS IN THEORY AND PRACTICE

THE N. W. MURRAY SYMPOSIUM

Edited by

I. B. DONALD

Department of Civil Engineering
Monash University, Clayton,
Victoria, Australia

Reprinted from
Thin-Walled Structures
Vol. 9 Nos 1–4

ELSEVIER APPLIED SCIENCE
LONDON and NEW YORK

ELSEVIER SCIENCE PUBLISHERS LTD
Crown House, Linton Road, Barking, Essex IG11 8JU, England

Sole Distributor in the USA and Canada
ELSEVIER SCIENCE PUBLISHING CO., INC.
655 Avenue of the Americas, New York, NY 10010, USA

© 1990 ELSEVIER SCIENCE PUBLISHERS LTD

British Library Cataloguing in Publication Data

Thin-walled structures.
1. Thin walled structures
I. Donald, I. B. II. Murray, N. W. (Noel Williams) *1928–*
624.1'77

ISBN 1-85166-458-0

Library of Congress Cataloging-in-Publication Data

N. W. Murray Symposium (1988 : Monash University)
  Thin-walled structures : developments in theory and practice : the
N. W. Murray Symposium/edited by I. B. Donald.
    p.   cm.
  Papers presented at the N. W. Murray Symposium held at Monash
University, Australia, 3–4 November 1988.
  Includes bibliographical references.
  ISBN 1-85166-458-0
  1. Thin-walled structures — Congresses. I. Donald, I. B.
II. Title.
TA660.T5N2 1988
624.1'7—dc20   89-48680

No responsibility is assumed by the publisher for any injury and/or damage to persons or property as a matter of products liability, negligence or otherwise, or from any use or operation of any methods, products, instructions or ideas contained in the material herein.

Special regulations for readers in the USA

This publication has been registered with the Copyright Clearance Center Inc. (CCC), Salem, Massachusetts. Information can be obtained from the CCC about conditions under which photocopies of parts of this publication may be made in the USA. All other copyright questions, including photocopying outside the USA, should be referred to the publisher.

All rights reserved. No part of this publication may be reproduced, stored in a retrieval system, or transmitted in any form or by any means, electronic, mechanical, photocopying, recording, or otherwise, without the prior written permission of the publisher.

Printed in Great Britain by Galliard (Printers) Ltd, Great Yarmouth

D
624.177
THI

HS

ANDERSONIAN LIBRARY

1 4. MAR 91

UNIVERSITY OF STRATHCLYDE

Foreword

by Sir Louis Matheson

It is a great disappointment to me that I shall be abroad when this symposium, to celebrate my old friend and colleague Noel Murray's sixtieth birthday, is held. Ian Donald has agreed that I should write a page or so which he, or someone, might read. It is fitting that this should be done because I have probably known Noel for longer than anyone else here.

Our work together dates from 1952 when I was at the beginning of my nine years as Beyer Professor at Manchester. Although funds for building up the Department were beginning to be available, finding good staff to spend them on was difficult. I had come to Manchester from Melbourne and I knew most of the civil professors in Australia quite well. It occurred to me that some of them might have bright students who would like to spend a few years in England. Frank Bull in Adelaide produced Noel and, a year or so later, John Lavery in Brisbane sent John Nutt, now head of the Ove Arup office in Sydney. That was a real flash of inspiration because it was certain that no Australian professor would send anyone who was not first class — and so it turned out.

Noel proved to be not only extremely competent as a theoretician and experimenter but to have a taste for dangerous occupations in his leisure time. I was terrified that I should lose him. In the 'random walk' through his life he mentions taking up rock climbing, which can be pursued to good effect on the millstone grit faces in the Pennines; he played rugby and I fancy that there was a motor bike somewhere in his life. When he turned up one day with a broken collar-bone I was delighted that he would be safe for a couple of months at least.

He stayed at Manchester for about five years, I think, and completed a

ANDERSONIAN LIBRARY

brilliant Ph.D. in which his command of mathematical methods played a considerable part. He also took one of Professor Lighthill's courses on applied mathematics, which Lighthill used as an argument for prescribing the course for engineering students generally. I had to disabuse him of the idea that there were many Noel Murray's among our students.

I saw Noel only occasionally after he left to go first to Sheffield and later to G.E.C. at Erith but when he applied to this infant university as senior lecturer in charge of civil engineering I was delighted and advised Professor Ken Hunt to look no further.

Noel's 'random walk' does not say much about his first few years at Monash when he must have been fully preoccupied with organising the civil engineering course, getting his department built, designing the strong floor and so on. His taste for dangerous sports had not diminished, though, and after cracking the infant rugby fifteen for some time he took up skiing while still occasionally indulging his taste for mountain climbing. His promotion to the chair was not only an acknowledgement of what he had already done, at Monash and elsewhere, but a recognition of his capacity for future success. This Symposium is a celebration of how well we chose and of the significance of the achievements of Professor Noel Murray.

Preface

The N. W. Murray Symposium — 'Thin-walled Structures: Developments in Theory and Practice' was organised by Professor Noel Murray's colleagues at Monash University in Melbourne to mark his 60th birthday and his many outstanding contributions to the profession of structural engineering, particularly in the area of thin-walled structures. The Symposium was an acknowledgement of his role in founding and developing the Department of Civil Engineering at Monash from its tentative beginnings in 1960 to the large, active, nationally and internationally respected teaching, consulting and research group of the 1980s.

Invitations to attend and present keynote papers were sent to four European colleagues of Noel's, all of whom had collaborated with him on research projects. The organisers wish to express their gratitude to Professors Patrick Dowling, Imperial College of Science and Technology, London, Norman Jones, The University of Liverpool, Liverpool, Georg Thierauf, The University of Essen, Essen, West Germany and Alastair Walker, The University of Surrey, Guildford, for giving of their valuable time and expertise. The opportunity was also taken to present a showcase of Australian contributions to the field of thin-walled structures, sixteen local authors and groups of authors contributing papers on a range of topics, testifying to the strength and breadth of Australian activity in this important branch of modern structural engineering.

The Symposium was unanimously agreed by all participants to have been a signal success and a fitting tribute to its eponymous dedicatee. This success could not have been achieved without the generous sponsorship of ESSO Australia Ltd., Gutteridge, Haskins and Davey,

Ove Arup and Partners and the Australian Institute of Steel Construction, all of whom are gratefully acknowledged here.

The Organising Committee:

Ian Donald (convenor)
Mario Attard
Raphael Grzebieta
Mick O'Brien
Kay Smith

Contents

KEYNOTE ADDRESS

SESSION 1

SESSION 2

SESSION 3

SESSION 4

SESSION 5

List of Contributors

L. R. ALLEN
  Leonard Allen and Associates, 1 Hodgson Street, Heidelberg, Victoria 3084, Australia

M. M. ATTARD
  Department of Civil Engineering, Monash University, Clayton, Melbourne, Victoria 3168, Australia

I. D. BENNETTS
  BHP Melbourne Research Laboratories, 245–273 Wellington Road, Mulgrave, Victoria 3170, Australia

S. BILD
  Bild Consulting Engineers, D-5800 Hagen, FRG

R. S. BIRCH
  Impact Research Centre, Faculty of Engineering, University of Liverpool, PO Box 147, Liverpool, L69 3BX, UK

M. A. BRADFORD
  School of Civil Engineering, The University of New South Wales, Kensington, New South Wales 2033, Australia

B. A. BURGAN
  Sir Frederick Snow (International) Ltd., PO Box 9806, Amman, Jordan

A. J. DAVIDS
  Wargon Chapman Partners, Consulting Engineers, Sydney, New South Wales, Australia

P. H. DAYAWANSA
Department of Civil Engineering, Monash University, Clayton, Victoria 3168, Australia. Present address: *BHP Melbourne Research Laboratories, 245–273 Wellington Road, Mulgrave, Victoria 3170, Australia*

P. J. DOWLING
Department of Civil Engineering, Imperial College of Science and Technology, London SW7 2BU, UK

P. GRUNDY
Department of Civil Engineering, Monash University, Clayton, Melbourne, Victoria 3168, Australia

R. H. GRZEBIETA
Department of Civil Engineering, Monash University, Clayton, Melbourne, Victoria 3168, Australia

G. J. HANCOCK
School of Civil and Mining Engineering, University of Sydney, Sydney, New South Wales 2006, Australia

A. HOLGATE
Department of Civil Engineering, Monash University, Clayton, Melbourne, Victoria 3168, Australia

G. L. HUTCHINSON
Department of Civil and Agricultural Engineering, University of Melbourne, Parkville, Victoria 3052, Australia

H. M. IRVINE
School of Civil Engineering, The University of New South Wales, Kensington, New South Wales 2033, Australia

N. JONES
Impact Research Centre, Faculty of Engineering, University of Liverpool, PO Box 147, Liverpool, L69 3BX, UK

P. W. KEY
School of Civil and Mining Engineering, University of Sydney, Sydney, New South Wales 2006, Australia. Present address: *Starch International Limited, Melbourne, Victoria, Australia*

P. W. KNEEN
Department of Structural Engineering, University of New South Wales, Kensington, New South Wales 2033, Australia

M. K. KWOK
Department of Mechanical Engineering, University of Surrey, Guildford, Surrey GU2 5XH, UK

S. C. W. LAU
Ove Arup and Partners, Consulting Engineers, Sydney, New South Wales, Australia

R. LAWTHER
School of Civil Engineering, The University of New South Wales, Kensington, New South Wales 2033, Australia

M. MAHENDRAN
Department of Civil Engineering, Monash University, Clayton, Melbourne, Victoria 3168, Australia

R. E. MELCHERS
Department of Civil Engineering and Surveying, The University of Newcastle, Newcastle, New South Wales 2308, Australia

N. W. MURRAY
Department of Civil Engineering, Monash University, Clayton, Melbourne, Victoria 3168, Australia

K. J. R. RASMUSSEN
School of Civil and Mining Engineering, University of Sydney, Sydney, New South Wales 2006, Australia

M. SALAHELDIN
Department of Civil and Mining Engineering, University of Wollongong, Wollongong, New South Wales 2500, Australia

L. C. SCHMIDT
Department of Civil and Mining Engineering, University of Wollongong, Wollongong, New South Wales 2500, Australia

L. K. STEVENS
Department of Civil and Agricultural Engineering, University of Melbourne, Parkville, Victoria 3052, Australia

G. THIERAUF
Department of Civil Engineering, Universität Essen,
Universitätsstrasse 15, D 4300 Essen 1, FRG

N. S. TRAHAIR
School of Civil and Mining Engineering, University of Sydney, Sydney,
New South Wales 2006, Australia

C. TURNELL
BHP Steel International Group, Level 12, Forest Centre,
221 St. George's Terrace, Perth, Western Australia 6000, Australia

A. C. WALKER
Department of Mechanical Engineering, University of Surrey, Guildford,
Surrey GU2 5XH, UK

KEYNOTE ADDRESS

Thin-Walled Structures **9** (1990) 1–28

A Ramble through the Life of a Down-Under Academic

Noel Murray

Department of Civil Engineering, Monash University, Clayton, Victoria 3168, Australia

When my colleagues asked me to write this article about my 'life's work' I wondered how one set about describing what is really just a random walk. But all good papers state their aim in the first paragraphs; mine is to describe mostly how I have arrived where I am with my research and not to sound too boring or pompous in the process. I decided that it might be more interesting for the reader if the article were not exclusively about technical matters. The first important question about where does one begin seemed to be answered most simply by 'at the beginning'.

In order to do research one has to have an education and that is where the random walk starts. At the age of nine I seemed to wake up from a child's dream world and found that I was milking seven cows each twice a day, by hand, on my father's 10-hectare farm at a place called Yundi in South Australia. 'Place' is the correct word to use, because it had a 3-metre square, galvanized iron shed as its local store (open for 2 h/d) and a small single-roomed school with about 10 children and one teacher. It certainly was not a village and few South Australians had even heard of it, much less knew where it was. Although I liked the cows individually I did not like milking them and realized that by joining the Australian Navy it might be possible to escape this work for the rest of my life. At the height of World War II and at the age of 13 I wrote and sent a form to the naval authorities to enrol in their officer training school. Their reply came back months later and informed me that I was too old.

Although this was a disappointment it gave me some sense of maturity and I sought other ways of escaping from those seven cows. At about this time I was at Morphett Vale Higher Primary School while my older brother was attending Adelaide High School and was about to enter Adelaide University. I knew little of what one did at university but it

1

Thin-Walled Structures 0263-8231/90/$03·50 © 1990 Elsevier Science Publishers Ltd, England. Printed in Great Britain

seemed plausible to study medicine there and then enter the Navy as a ship's surgeon, thus avoiding the cow bails forever. It was a daring scheme but when I mentioned university and medicine to my father his taciturn response was that in his judgement he did not see me as the sort of person who would like to spend six years at a university. He urged me to take up engineering which required only four years. When one is 13 years old, six years is half of one's life over again, and it seemed an eternity so I followed his advice.

After two years at Adelaide High School I entered Adelaide University in 1945 with a scholarship of £A150 ($A300) per annum generously donated by the government during wartime to enable it to keep up the supply of engineers for 'The Front'. Fortunately for me and all concerned, my military abilities were never put to the test but I still had this awful hankering to go to sea. During two university long vacations I worked as deckhand and cook on sailing ships which were carting grain from outlying ports to Port Adelaide for the overseas trade. It was very hard physical work and a bit hazardous but I did not mind that. My successor on the *Leillateah* (Fig. 1) was washed overboard and never found. In 1959 she capsized and only one person survived.

Four years at university were great fun but they seemed to confirm the rectitude of my father's judgement and I left for North Queensland, having no desire to see the inside of a university again. This was no reflection upon Adelaide University where the staff had been superb; I

Fig. 1. The *A.S. Leillateah*, built of huon pine in 1891, was 66 ft × 19·2 ft × 5·7 ft and 45 tons gross. Here she is rigged as a schooner but in 1946 she was rigged as a ketch.

had sat at the feet of many eminent scholars, the most famous of whom was probably Sir Douglas Mawson, but that phase of my life was over. In North Queensland I was put in charge of two percussion drilling rigs which were being used to investigate the underground water resources potential of the Herbert River Basin. In Australia the consumption of beer became a national sport but at that time in Ingham it was taken up with religious fervour by nearly everyone. I decided that as a beer drinker I would never become famous internationally or indeed nationally so in my free time I would disappear into the beautiful tropical jungle in that area and sit there reading books on mathematics. Although the animals in the jungle accepted this as a legitimate pastime, the inhabitants of Ingham appeared to have problems with it.

My confidence with the manipulation of the integral calculus improved to the point where I decided to return to Adelaide University for post-graduate research work. As there were no scholarships in those days I had to use my savings, which were only just sufficient if nothing went wrong. Things, of course, did go wrong; a motorcycle accident put my leg in plaster for three months but I survived financially by doing hand calculations for a surveyor. The research project in the field of photo-elasticity gave me a good understanding of stress analysis, as did the personal tuition from the staff (I was their only research scholar), in elasticity, stability and theoretical soil mechanics. This grounding in the fundamentals of structural theory has been a great personal asset ever since.

In 1952, at the end of the project, an enquiry came to Adelaide from Professor Louis Matheson of Manchester, UK, who needed an Assistant Lecturer. Not only did this give me the opportunity to work towards a PhD but it enabled me to travel overseas. An obliging aunt loaned me the money for the fare but it was nearly two years before I could save enough from the stipend of £450 per annum to repay her.

In September 1952 I embarked on the SS *Mooltan* whose cargo seemed to be mainly graduates making their way to the UK for further studies or to gain industrial experience. The majority were staying in Oxford, Cambridge and London. Perhaps my suspicions should have been aroused when I met only two or three who were going to Manchester. I arrived in Manchester Central Station on a gloomy October day. In the city everything appeared to be black or dark grey (Fig. 2) and at first I wondered why the Mancunians didn't all migrate to Australia. Although not as badly bombed as some other cities, parts of Manchester were still like wastelands of building rubble sprinked here and there with terraced houses still standing and occupied. Moss Side, just behind the university, was one such area and there I took dinner, bed and breakfast with a

Fig. 2. First impressions of Manchester's skyline in 1952.

Brazilian landlady, one cat, and one bath per week, all up £3.15.0. After tax, National Health and superannuation payments this left me with £1 per week.

At the university three of us shared an office and Doris, the cleaning lady, whose accent I had heard before only from British comedians on the radio. I lectured on elementary structural mechanics to all of the first-year engineering students, many of whom were older than me.

But now was to begin my research work. Professor Matheson suggested three topics, namely, the application of computers to structural analysis, wire ropes, and secondary stresses in braced frameworks. By 1952 Manchester University had attracted some brilliant staff such as Professors J. Lighthill, F. C. Williams and M. Polanyi, Dr Alan Turing and many others. A computer had been built but I didn't know much about it or what it could do. The available booklet for it was made of fairly rough duplicated sheets which at first were mumbo-jumbo to me. The instructions for the computer were all in machine language, a typical one looking something like a/?*b;!. I struggled with the sheets and after three months I succeeded in writing a program for converting strain gauge rosette readings into principal stresses. I decided that computing was even more tiresome than milking cows.

It took me some time to find out what secondary stresses were. I didn't like to ask Professor Matheson because I was a bit shy about being a colonial and of my ignorance in these matters. During a long search in the library I eventually found a book which mentioned them. It explained that a bridge truss was usually made by joining members together, forming a series of triangular spaces. In the analysis of such a bridge truss it was assumed that at their ends the members were all pinned together, whereas in reality they are nearly always rigidly joined.

When the tension members stretch and the compression members decrease in length, all by very small amounts, the shape of each of the triangular spaces changes. If the members are pinned together they carry only axial forces and the small changes in the angles of the triangles are accommodated by swivelling about the pins. However, when the members are rigidly joined the small changes in length of the members can only be accommodated by bending of the members. Bending of the members gives rise to bending stresses which had been called the 'secondary stresses', the 'primary stresses' being the simple axial stresses. In some trusses these secondary stresses were shown to be quite large, often exceeding the primary stresses in magnitude.

A simple method for their calculation had already been evolved but nobody seemed to have any ideas about their significance. Would their presence cause premature collapse of a truss? This problem appealed to me more than the wire ropes topic because the latter was, I felt, too specialized.

I set about designing a rig for manufacturing what I thought would be perfect specimens. I now realize that such an aim is impossible to achieve but it seemed to be important at the time, and I was disappointed that the truss members ended up not being straight and that the joints had some eccentricity. The first model truss I made became firmly locked into the jig because of the shrinkage of the welds as they cooled; it could not be extracted intact and I had to cut it to pieces in the jig. However, these problems were solved and some good specimens rolled off the production line. As I did not have access to electrical resistance strain gauge apparatus, I devised ways of measuring joint rotations and curvatures at points along the members by using mirrors and mirror pairs. Deflections at key points were measured with dial gauges. Figure 3 shows a view of the set-up. The willing help of the technical staff was an essential element in carrying the experimental part of the project through to a successful conclusion. Despite the primitive apparatus by today's standards, the experimental results were very precise and I was happy with them.

By about late 1953 Drs Ken Livesley and D. B. Chandler had each produced, by means of the Manchester computer, tables of so-called stability functions, the latter's work being an extension of the former's and taking into account the size of the joint. These tables enabled the elastic behaviour of my models to be predicted. This is simply the behaviour of the frames when the loads are small and the levels of stress have not reached the point where the steel deforms permanently, i.e., yields. By using these stability functions the rotations of the joints of the frames and the deflections and curvatures of the members, all of which

Fig. 3. Testing a triangular framework (see Fig. 4). Mirrors were used to measure joint rotations, mirror pairs to measure curvature of the members, and dial gauges to measure deflections.

were non-linear and which I was measuring in the laboratory, could be reproduced using pure theory. It was a beautiful thing to observe. But the elastic behaviour was only one half of the story and perhaps the most important piece in the jigsaw puzzle was the load at which a frame collapses. The collapse stage involves yielding of the steel, and during this phase the steel behaves rather like a piece of chewing gum. During the war and afterwards Professor J. F. Baker and his team at Cambridge had developed the plastic theory of structures and applied it to many beam and column (rectangular) frameworks. The obvious step was to apply it to my simple braced frameworks. The only modification which had to be introduced was the introduction of the effect of an axial force upon the moment-carrying capacity of the members. The presence of an axial stress σ in a member of rectangular cross-section reduces its full bending moment capacity M_p by a factor $1 - (\sigma/\sigma_0)^2$, i.e.

$$M_p' = M_p\left[1 - \left(\frac{\sigma}{\sigma_0}\right)^2\right] \tag{1}$$

where σ_0 is the yield stress of the steel and M_p' is the reduced moment capacity.

The application of this approach to my models resulted in another theoretical curve which gave information about the way they collapsed as plastic mechanisms. Figure 4(a) shows for one framework the two theoretical curves superimposed on one another and the way the experimental points follow the elastic curve at the start of loading, depart from it when some part of the frame starts to yield, and then become asymptotic to the plastic collapse line.

What one is doing in applying this technique is simply replacing the idealized stress–strain curve of the steel (Fig. 4(b)) by a pair of lines — the elastic AB and the so-called rigid-plastic CD (Fig. 4(a)). These lines form a kind of framework around the curve which describes the actual behaviour of the framework. The approach is simple and straightforward because it means that a steel structure can be analysed largely by using two existing and well-established theories, viz., the elastic and rigid-plastic theories. Thus a research worker can concentrate on one theory or the other at a given time and, as I found out later, to a certain extent this eases the whole problem of the direction of a research team. I was to return to the technique years later.

Life at Manchester improved for me as time went on. In the department I had become lecturer, I was a resident tutor in St Anselm Hall in Victoria Park and I had taken up rock-climbing. Altogether I stayed in Manchester for five years, by which time I saw beauty in the subtle shades of greys and blacks, the misty skies and the endless rows of red-bricked terraced houses. I had made many close friends.

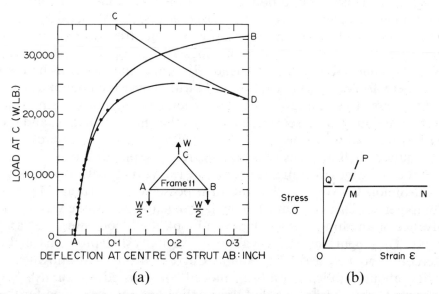

Fig. 4. (a) Curve AB is derived using elastic theory and curve CD by using rigid-plastic theory. (b) Elastic theory assumes σ–ε follows OMP while for rigid-plastic theory it follows OQMN.

Quite out of the blue I was approached by Professor Jim Duncan of the Mechanical Engineering Department at Sheffield University to join him in establishing a stress laboratory. Jim had been a lecturer at Adelaide when I was there and later moved to Manchester where he had conducted research on optical methods of experimental stress analysis, especially applied to tube-plates for boilers. He was a meticulous experimenter, he had a good grasp of theory, it was a field I knew fairly well, and Sheffield was closer to the rock-climbs, so I moved to the other side of the Pennines. During the two years at Sheffield my research centred mainly on the analysis of plates, pressure vessels and three-dimensional photo-elastic stress analysis using the frozen-stress technique.

At this time the British government had plans to build 19 nuclear power stations and various consortia had been formed to achieve this programme. I was asked by Dr Ray Hicks, head of the structural investigation section of the GEC–Simon Carves consortium, to join his team in Erith, Kent. The purpose of his section was to develop advanced theoretical and experimental techniques for analysing the stresses in the large pressure vessels and other components which formed the primary gas circuits of nuclear power stations. I joined them in 1959 and soon found myself on a very steep learning curve. The theory of thin shells is rather complicated and there was much to learn in a short space of time. Unfortunately most of the design work was being done in another section using the British standard boiler code of the day. That document was never intended to be applied to the enormous vessels (20-metre diameter spheres with 75–100 mm thick plates) which the firm was building. So, many problems were referred to our specialist group, usually after the difficulties had raised their ugly heads. Typical of the problems handed to us were devising ways of lifting and turning over the bottom quarter (with a mass of 350 tonnes) of the Hunterston reactor, of sealing the joint in the 5 m diameter vessel which contains the charge machine, and the earthquake analysis of the Tokai-Mura reactor in Japan. These problems all required shell analysis of a high degree of sophistication.

Perhaps the most fortunate factor in the two years I spent at Erith with GEC–Simon Carves was that the firm possessed a Ferranti Mercury Computer which used Autocode as its language. Autocode was far in advance of anything else available and took the blood, sweat, toil and tears out of programming. I was able to solve many shell problems on the Mercury, and because GEC–Simon Carves had a most enlightened policy about publication I was indeed encouraged to publish my research findings. I believe that their policy not only was good for the profession but helped the firm commercially.

They were busy and exciting days but leavened by Ray Hicks's superb leadership. Ray was a model railway enthusiast. His hobby was pursued with great single-mindedness. He attended painting classes with me one evening a week essentially so that he could paint the scenery for his layout. His other 'night off' was spent at a model railway club at Orpington, but he left soon after joining because he thought that the other members were very strange, being interested only in 'playing trains', whereas he was a constructor. He regaled us with wonderful stories after his trips to Japan — it appears that even the inscrutable Japanese have their fair share of strange and over-enthusiastic model railway buffs.

One day Ray called me to his office and said that I should find another job. As I was his deputy I thought that I or one of my engineers must have made some terrible blunder. It turns out that it was just friendly advice based upon his personal concern for my future. He felt that it would be in my own interests to gain further experience elsewhere as he thought that I had 'learned it all'. I couldn't see this myself but I took his advice and applied for a senior lectureship at Monash University when it was advertised shortly afterwards. As I had been away from Australia for nine years it seemed to be a good opportunity and I was fortunate in being appointed. The vice-chancellor of this brand new university, which at that time didn't even have students, was Dr Louis Matheson who had supervised my PhD at Manchester.

Starting up a new university is like waking up and finding yourself flying an aircraft, never having undergone instruction. There's nobody who can tell you how to do it and everything is happening at once. Life was so busy that a decade would have slipped by almost unnoticed had it not been for the stimulation I received in working with Ross McLeary on the problem of shells bursting in gun barrels and with Anusorn Intarangsi on the finite element analysis of pipelines with mitre bends. Then on 15 October 1970, while under construction, West Gate Bridge collapsed. This incident was to change my research field from mainly shells, pressure vessels and pipelines to that of thin-walled steel structures. The collapse was a direct tragedy for 35 families but indirectly for many more who were injured or whose reputation was tarnished.

In my capacities as one of the two advisors to the City Coroner (Professor Len Stevens was the other) and advisor to the subsequent Royal Commission, I had ready access to the remains of the bridge and was able to bring back to our well-equipped laboratory large-scale panels for testing and research purposes. Some of the work was needed because large sections of the bridge, which was a box girder, were still standing and questions as to its adequacy were of paramount importance.

The work for the Coroner went on for only about four weeks; my duties were to collect and record as many details as possible. It was obvious that the transverse splice connecting the boxes was the key element whose buckling had triggered the collapse. It is unfortunate that the story of the technical reasons for the collapse of West Gate Bridge has never been told. The report of the Royal Commission does not even contain a drawing of the splice referred to above, and the body of the report itself concentrates almost entirely upon the communication problems which existed between the various parties prior to the collapse. Given the state of our legal system the story may never be told.

After testing segments of the bridge containing the splice, I started testing large panels without a splice taken from the upper deck of the collapsed span. All of the tests had to be done as thoroughly but as expeditiously as possible in order to provide as much information for the Royal Commission as possible. I was fortunate in being able to call on the services of Bob Runge as Laboratory Manager and of Henry Puszka, a Senior Technical Officer. The vital results could not have been obtained in time without their strong support on the technical side and their dedication to the aims of the project.

The splice connection was analysed theoretically and remarkable agreement with experimental results was obtained. Because failure occurred by means of a fairly simple plastic mechanism, I simply 'dredged up' the approach described earlier, namely analysis of the splice first as an elastic element and then as a plastic mechanism. The plastic hinges were all oriented at right angles to the direction of longitudinal loading so the analysis in this case was straightforward. Equation (1) was used because the presence of the axial stress reduced the plastic moment capacity of the plating.

The plain stiffened panels were tested as wide columns with pin ends, the axial force being applied by ten 100-tonne hydraulic jacks. The panels themselves were flat plates stiffened longitudinally with parallel bulb plates which were pointing upwards during the tests (Fig. 5). Such a structure can buckle as a column either upwards or downwards. In the first case (Mode 1), because of the overall bending, the plate carries higher compressive stresses than the free edges of the stiffeners; in the second case (Mode 2) the reverse applies, i.e. the free edges of the stiffeners carry the highest compressive stress. Several important observations were made as follows.

(a)   In Mode 1 the plate first developed elastic buckles in a chequerboard pattern which evolved into a plastic mechanism (Fig. 6) as deflections became larger.

(b)   In Mode 2 the free edges of the stiffeners first developed a shape

Fig. 5. A stiffened plate being tested as a wide pin-ended column. The plate has buckled locally in a chequerboard pattern and the stiffeners twist in sympathy.

Fig. 6. Another stiffened plate after collapse, showing the plastic mechanism developed in the plate (Mode 1). The white lines show the position of the longitudinal stiffeners or the plastic hinges in the mechanism.

like a snake wriggling along. This elastic buckle then developed
into a plastic mechanism which tripped the stiffeners sideways
and caused collapse (Fig. 7). This mode of collapse was sudden
and with very little warning.

(c) In the plastic mechanisms some of the plastic hinge lines were
inclined to the direction of thrust. Thus eqn (1) could not be used
and it became apparent that the moment capacity of an inclined
hinge would have to be derived before the plastic mechanisms
could be analysed to determine their plastic collapse lines.

(d) Whereas the Mode 2 plastic mechanisms could be approximated
readily as spatial mechanisms (in a mechanical engineering
sense), those of Mode 1 contained whole regions which were
yielding (i.e. deforming) in-plane. The former were classified as
'true mechanisms' and the latter as 'quasi-mechanisms'.

(e) Tests were also carried out on flat plates constrained by
longitudinal knife edges instead of stiffeners. Figure 8 (left) shows
a so-called 'flip-disc' mechanism which developed when b/t
exceeded 70. With b/t less than 50 a roof mechanism developed
(right). The reason for the existence of two mechanisms had to be
explained.

(f) Comparison between the elastic and plastic behaviour of the

Fig. 7. An alternative failure mode for a stiffened plate occurs when the edges of the
stiffeners carry the highest stress. The stiffeners trip sideways suddenly (Mode 2).

compression members in the braced frameworks I had tested at Manchester and that of these wide columns showed that in the former case there was no significant deformation of the cross-section of the members but in the latter case there was. The West Gate panels failed by first buckling locally at roughly mid-length, which caused a global buckle the length of the panel to develop. It was recalled that the members of the framework developed simple plastic hinges and global plastic mechanisms, but in contrast to this the stiffened panels collapsed by developing a complicated local plastic mechanism at mid-length which served a similar purpose as a simple plastic hinge at that point. By observation in this way a terminology was developed, e.g., local buckle, global buckle, local plastic mechanism, global mechanism, and so on. A simple hinge was one in which the cross-section did not deform — these are the hinges which we introduced to our undergraduates in ordinary plastic analysis of frameworks.

However, the most important term of all, viz., thin-walled structure, remained undefined. Originally a thin-walled structure was said to be one in which the dimensions of the plate elements were small compared to the overall dimensions of the cross-section. This left open the question of how small, so it was not a satisfactory answer. Finally it was decided that it was best to define a thin-walled structure as one in which the shape of the cross-section changes substantially during collapse. This implies that local elastic buckling and the ensuing local plastic mechanism are the essential features determining the behaviour of the structure. This way of looking at thin-walled structures enabled me to formulate a research programme which could be handled by my research students over a period of many years.

In the first place a compendium of experimental results was required. Ken McLeod, Walter Michelutti and Dennis de George tested many different stiffened plates under different combinations of axial and transverse loading. One remarkable series of tests on 14 nominally identical panels, each tested with different combinations of axial and transverse loading, revealed three different mechanisms of failure. At the switch-over points between these mechanisms there were large and sudden changes in the load carrying capacity.

Nelson Fok then tackled the elastic analysis of stiffened plates using the finite difference technique which was quite easily able to cope with the inevitable initial imperfections of the models. He devised an experimental technique for measuring the actual imperfections of the plate and feeding them directly into a computer which he had

Fig. 8. Identical plates tested in compression: the one on the left was constrained longitudinally by three pairs of knife edges while that on the right had five pairs, resulting in a lower b/t ratio and a different plastic mechanism.

programmed to solve the well-known Marguerre equations. It was a beautiful piece of research, but then Nelson is a meticulous worker. He has refurbished his own house, having made much of the furniture himself, and has made many domestic electronic gadgets.

A further impetus to the elastic behaviour of stiffened plates was given by the visit of Professor Georg Thierauf to Monash. Mainly at his instigation and because of his untiring drive, a computer program called PLATE was developed. It used the finite strip technique of Y. C. Cheung and enabled us, for any given cross-section of stiffened plate, to define the buckling load, buckling mode, and conditions under which the latter would or would not be initiated by local buckling. Between us we brought out a book of tables for designers of stiffened plates. We felt that the tables would be more useful to designers than a computer program because there were problems with interpretation of computer output unless one was an 'expert'. Also designers can more quickly look through a series of tables than put up a computer program and feed in the large number of variables required.

During Georg's stay we visited the ski slopes at Mount Buller, and we even made a trip to Mount Hutt and other nearby slopes in New Zealand. There Georg slipped and dislocated his shoulder, and this involved a trip of 50 km to the 'local' doctor. Not only was this somewhat traumatic for Georg but when we found the doctor he turned out to be quite new to the

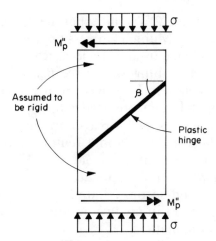

Fig. 9. In thin-walled structures the fold lines (hinges) are usually inclined to the direction of stress. A new theory had to be developed to enable plastic mechanisms (e.g. Figs 6 to 8) to be analysed.

game. Not only did he have to read up his textbook on the subject (in front of Georg), but also without an anaesthetic Georg had to instruct him on how the joint should be put back, calling on his experience from a previous dislocation. The same grit, determination and stoicism was shown by Georg in seeing that our book was eventually published.

I want to leave the elastic theory for a time at this stage and go back in time to follow the thread of the development of the plastic theory. The vital piece missing until 1973 was the relationship between axial stress σ and applied moment M_p'' of a given piece of plate (Fig. 9) when the plastic hinges were inclined to the direction of axial stress. A crude head-on approach seemed appropriate. Just as in the theory used to derive eqn (1), it was again assumed that there was a central core of material which devoted itself to carrying the axial stress, and the remaining outer 'skins' took it upon themselves to carry the bending moment acting across the hinge line. It was found that this gave a simple equation for the moment capacity, M_p'':

$$M_p'' = M_p' \sec^2\beta = M_p \left[1 - \left(\frac{\sigma}{\sigma_0} \right)^2 \right] \sec^2\beta \qquad (2)$$

where β is the angle shown in Fig. 9. In deriving this equation the effects of the shear and normal stresses which one would find from a simple Mohr's circle analysis of the plate were ignored. A much later and more thorough analysis showed that for practical purposes these effects could be ignored and that eqn (2) would give almost the same results. In order to verify the validity of eqn (2) a small experiment was carried out while I was on sabbatical leave at Munich University. A small rectangular bar of mild steel was strengthened in some regions, leaving unreinforced strips which became the plastic hinges. The $\sec^2\beta$ law was shown to be of sufficient accuracy. The help I received from Professor K. Latzin and Georg Thierauf is gratefully acknowledged.

That occasion was my first real trip to Germany and as it was for more than three months I learned a lot about Teutonic thoroughness. I had to queue with 'guest-workers' at 7 a.m. at the *Polizeipräsidium* for my *Erlaubnis*, at the *Krankenhaus* for a medical checkup, at the *Zollamt* to be cleared by Customs, and so on. I found that one morning per week during the last two months of my five-month stay was sufficient to deal with these bureaucratic matters.

The $\sec^2\beta$ law was applied to the stiffener (Mode 2) and flip-disc mechanisms referred to earlier. The roof mechanism was analysed by assuming that the longitudinal strips which covered the end gables of the 'roof' yielded in pure compression (but at the ultimate stress of the steel because of the large strains in these regions). There were also compression and tension yield zones in the stiffeners so as to allow the mechanism to deform. A subsequent refinement, also developed while I was in Munich, took into account the strength of the small bulb at the free edge of the bulb-flat. The paper shows that these bulbs are far too small to strengthen stiffened plates significantly.

The next step was a fairly obvious one, viz., to apply the rigid-plastic theory to thin-walled structures other than stiffened panels, i.e. to channels, boxes, etc., when loaded as beams or columns. Khoo Ping Sen tested a whole range of structures and we developed the plastic collapse lines for them. The main result from this project was to find that the bilinear technique could be applied but that the experimental curves usually lay above the theoretical plastic collapse line. Tests also showed clearly that the plastic collapse line based upon a local plastic mechanism lay much closer to the experimental results than that based upon a simple plastic hinge (i.e. no deformation of the cross-section) (Fig. 10). In other words these results from many different kinds of structures showed that the definition presented earlier of a thin-walled structure is valid for axial loads, at least.

With a view to showing that the approach could be used for a more complicated loading combination, Mahedeva Mahendran tested two series of square box sections each with various ratios of axial load P to torque T. The first series had a b/t ratio of 78 which was on the low side and from Khoo's experiments we knew would fail with a roof mechanism. Figure 11(a) shows how the mechanism is transverse to the

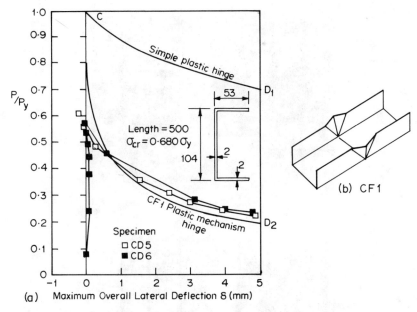

Fig. 10. Theoretical and experimental results of a channel column are compared. It is seen that the local plastic mechanism must be used and not the simple plastic theory.

axis when the specimen is loaded as a column ($T = 0$) but spirals around it; as T increases the angle of the spiral increases. A similar result is seen (Fig. 11(b)) for the second series ($b/t = 158$) which failed with a flip-disc mechanism. Mahendran developed theoretical analyses for both of these mechanisms. Some of this work is described in another paper at this Conference.

The intriguing question of why two mechanisms should have developed still remained. I thought back to some work I had done years ago when looking into the effects of initial dishing (imperfection) of isolated plates. In order to analyse their behaviour in the elastic range I had derived three closed-form solutions to the Marguerre equations:

$$\nabla^4\Phi + Et(y''w^{\cdot\cdot} - 2y'^{\cdot}w'^{\cdot} + y^{\cdot\cdot}w'' + w''w^{\cdot\cdot} - w'^{\cdot 2}) = 0 \qquad (3)$$

$$D\nabla^4 w - [\Phi^{\cdot\cdot}(y + w)'' - 2\Phi'^{\cdot}(y + w)'^{\cdot} + \Phi''(y + w)^{\cdot\cdot}] - Y = 0 \quad (4)$$

where

y is the initial shape of the plate,
w is its additional deflection during buckling,
t is its thickness,
E is its Young's modulus value,
Y is its lateral load per unit area,

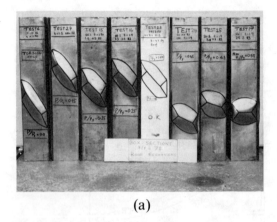

(a)

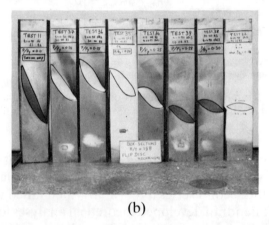

(b)

Fig. 11. Two series of hollow box columns, (a) with $b/t = 78$ and (b) with $b/t = 158$, tested with axial load only on the right, with torque only on the left, and with various combinations in between.

D is its bending rigidity, and
Φ is a stress function defining the in-plane loading before buckling.

At the time I had found that for a given plate with a given value of y the point at which the maximum stress occurred switched from the middle of the plate to the edge as b/t increased. If this was also true in stiffened plates, box columns, etc., then it seemed that once yielding commenced either at the central point (for low b/t) or at the edge (for higher b/t) the plastic mechanisms became attached to these points and grew outwards from them. This was indeed verified by Mahendran who ran through the parameters on the computer showing that, for plates with the magnitudes of initial dishing found in practice and with b/t less than 50, a roof mechanism was sure to develop, and for b/t in excess of 70 a flip-disc would develop. In between these values the magnitude of the initial dishing was the deciding factor. I thought back to the experiments of Walter Michelutti. The sudden switches in failure load were linked to the plastic collapse line which in turn was determined by where yielding commenced and thus which plastic mechanism developed. The pieces of the jig-saw puzzle were beginning to come together.

Although Mahendran had carried out both a plastic and an elastic buckling analysis of his box sections (in the elastic case we extended the finite-strip work done previously with Georg Thierauf to cover not only in-plane axial loading but also in-plane shear and in-plane transverse loading so we could analyse buckling due to torsion), generally speaking, most of the students had worked either on elastic behaviour or on plastic behaviour. In an attempt to 'bring it all together' I suggested to Tony Lau that he should investigate a channel which was loaded as a cantilever (Fig. 12) but with the load causing both bending and twisting. This turned out to be an interesting little project, especially when the plastic behaviour was analysed. It is perhaps an interesting exercise for the reader *a priori* to try to imagine what form the plastic mechanism might take. In this case the chances of guessing correctly are not good. For the compression tests of similar specimens with a channel cross-section, Khoo had found five different mechanisms, so one learns to be cautious about guessing. It was found that at the built-in end the web under the load (yes, it really is the web in this case!) tripped sideways like the stiffeners in a Mode 2 collapse of a stiffened plate. The remainder of the cross-section was then sufficiently flexible as an elastic member to allow the cantilever to bend downwards through large distances without much increase in the size of the plastic regions. In other words the plastic

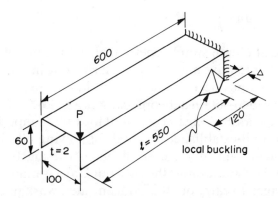

Fig. 12. An eccentrically loaded cantilever develops a local buckle and then fails in an interesting way which does not require a complete plastic mechanism.

mechanism didn't embrace the whole cross-section. This same effect was noticed by Mahendran. In many cases the box sections in his series developed local plastic mechanisms only on two sides even when the angle of twisting was quite large.

I would now like to return to the elastic theory to describe briefly another fascinating phenomenon which we picked up again through laboratory tests. Peduru Dayawansa ('Daya' to everyone) worked in an area we hadn't touched at that stage, viz., the large-deflection elastic behaviour of stiffened plate panels. This is a topic in which membrane effects arise when the panel buckles into a dished shape, the plate elements between the stiffeners buckle and the stiffeners can simultaneously deform like long buckling columns. All of these buckling modes can interact, i.e. influence one another.

Daya started by building a special-purpose testing machine into which the models of stiffened plate panels, made by gluing together pieces of sheet Acrylonitrile Butadiene Styrene (ABS), could be fitted. The machine was a screw device which controlled axial shortening. The out-of-plane deflections of the panels were measured using a Moiré fringe technique which produced a contour map of the out-of-plane deflections showing the hills and valleys of the surface of the plate. For small deflections the panels behaved as expected, i.e., the plate strips between the stiffeners buckled into roughly square shapes (Fig. 13(a)). However, when the deflections increased an irregular pattern developed (Fig. 13(b)). Daya carefully measured these shapes from the Moiré fringe patterns and found that the deflection of a strip of plate between a pair of adjacent stiffeners always consisted of the sum of three basic shapes (Fig. 14). Thus at any stage of loading the shape of a plate strip between two stiffeners could be described by the expression

$$w = C_1 \sin \frac{\pi x}{b} \sin \frac{m \pi z}{L} + C_2 \sin \frac{\pi x}{b} \sin \frac{\pi z}{L} + C_3 \sin \frac{\pi z}{L} \tag{5}$$

where C_1, C_2 and C_3 are simply coefficients which are functions of the applied load, their relative magnitudes determining how much of each of the three basic shapes occurs at any given load.

We then decided to obtain a theoretical solution for C_1, C_2 and C_3 using an energy method and taking into account the initial imperfections of the plate. This is a well-established method for solving all kinds of elastic buckling problems but in the case of plates the algebra can become overwhelming. This was almost the case but Daya is made of pretty stern stuff and managed to carry out this concentrated work in over 100 pages by squaring long expressions, taking term by term second derivatives and then doubly integrating over the whole plate strip. I checked his

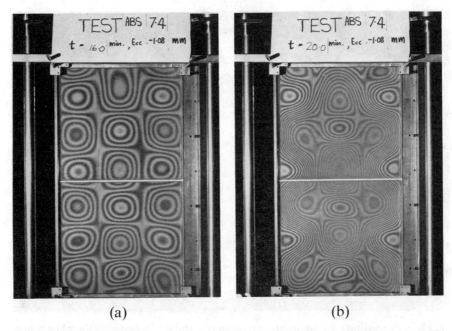

(a)   (b)

Fig. 13. (a) For small deflections a stiffened ABS sheet buckles as the full-scale panel in Fig. 5. (b) Continued loading resulted in a complex deflected shape which had three main components (Fig. 14).

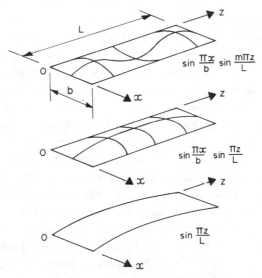

Fig. 14. The buckled plate in Fig. 13(b) had three main components which interact in a complicated way (see eqn (5) and Fig. 15).

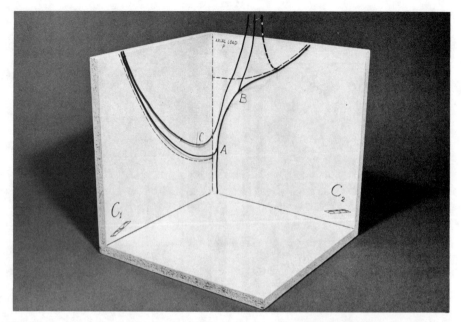

Fig. 15. A three-dimensional graph of P versus C_1 and C_2. A perfectly flat plate follows the dotted line to the bifurcation point near A. With an initially deformed plate the bifurcation points at A and B move towards each other. With larger initial deformation the curve C detaches so C_1 buckles cannot form.

work term by bitter term. It took me weeks but I found no errors. In the end Daya had arrived at a nice cubic equation which he was able to apply to any rectangular plates.

As this work was fairly complicated and difficult to explain to others, we made up the models such as that shown in Fig. 15. These are simply three-dimensional graphs with the applied load P plotted along the vertical axis. Along the horizontal axes we have the coefficients C_1 and C_2 which then indicate at any point how much we have of the associated basic buckling modes in eqn (5). For the purposes of explanation we fixed how much of initial shape C_3 there was to be. The lines which form tree-like structures in Fig. 15 were made with soft copper wire and show what are called 'equilibrium paths'. They show the load–deflection characteristics, i.e. how much C_1 and C_2 mode there is for any applied load P (C_3 is held at a known value), of a given plate. Thus one can start at any point in the C_1–C_2 plane (the coordinates of this starting point are the amount of initial imperfection) and using the theory (solving the cubic equation) form up a tree-like path. In this path there are branching points, the so-called bifurcation points, where the structure can follow one branch or the other. At a bifurcation point it is usual for one branch to be stable while the other is unstable. The stable path is like that up a valley while the unstable path is like that along an arête. In the model shown in Fig. 15 it was found that if a plate has sufficient initial imperfection of the C_3-type it is possible to suppress the C_1-type buckles altogether. The C_3-type buckling shape has the lowest buckling load associated with it so it is an advantage if it can be suppressed. The suppression occurs in an interesting way. As greater values of initial C_3-type imperfection are introduced the first and second bifurcation points move towards one another until finally they coalesce and the two branches join and detach from the main trunk. To demonstrate this phenomenon in the laboratory we made a series of box-columns. Figure 16 shows one pair which had identical cross-sections at mid-height but that with the tapered shape did not buckle there (where the b/t had its greatest value) but towards the end. Furthermore it carried about 40% more load than that with straight sides. Each of these results was predicted by theoretical analysis before the experiments were carried out,

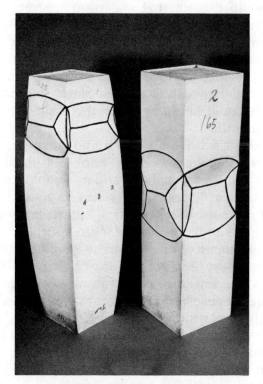

Fig. 16. Hollow box columns. Paradoxically, the one on the left buckles at the end where b/t has its least value. The bulging suppresses the local buckling mode and increases the load capacity (see Fig. 15).

but nevertheless it was an exciting moment when the tests confirmed the theory.

This brings us to the current situation in our research programme into conventional thin-walled structures at Monash. The bilinear technique has worked well for this class of structure. The reason why this has been so was pointed out in a recent paper presented in Yugoslavia. In the case of thin-walled structures it is usually found that the point of first yield on the elastic curve lies quite close to the point where it intersects the plastic collapse line. In other words, for many thin-walled structures the load at which yielding commences can be taken as a good approximation to the collapse load. This is an observation but it has not been proved generally.

At the beginning I said that my life has been a random walk. I seem to stumble into things on the way by accident. Professor Norman Jones of the Department of Mechanical Engineering at Liverpool University and Editor of the *International Journal of Impact Engineering* wrote to me in 1982 saying that he had read some of our Monash work and suggested I write a paper for a forthcoming conference in Liverpool on crashworthy structures. I should explain that crashworthy structures are ductile structures designed specifically to minimize damage to property and people. An example is a crash barrier on the roadside. Mild steel is ductile and it has an enormous capacity to absorb the energy of an impacting mass provided it is formed into a suitable structure. My paper for the conference showed how simple plastic mechanisms in thin-walled structures could be analysed so that their capacity to absorb energy can be quantified.

This conference acted like a catalyst and when I returned I found Raphael Grzebieta looking for a topic. Raphael is the father of triplets, three strong and healthy young boys, and no doubt he is used to things crashing around him at all hours. So it seemed a good line of research in which he could make use of his practical knowledge. We started with a simple pin-ended column of rectangular cross-section. Although this is of little practical interest it enabled us to develop simple theoretical models and to compare their behaviour with their real counterparts in the laboratory. These tests also helped Raph to develop and purchase experimental equipment which could record these extremely high-speed events. When mild steel is strained at a high rate the yield stress increases according to the well-known Cowper–Symonds Law. This law suggested that for the strain rates we measured the yield stress would be about 50% higher than that obtained from a slow test. In our theory the yield stress was therefore enhanced by 50% and we obtained quite good agreement between theory and experiment. Figure 17 shows how a strut behaves; *ab* represents elastic buckling and along *bc* the specimen is developing a

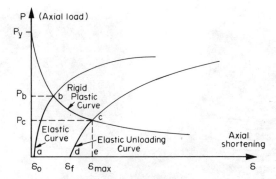

Fig. 17. The behaviour of a pin-ended column under an impact load *P* can be explained by combining the elastic and rigid-plastic theories just as in Fig. 4.

plastic hinge at mid-height until the hammer comes to rest at *c*. The area directly under *abc* represents the energy absorbed by the specimen in bringing the hammer to rest, while *cd* is an elastic curve arising from the spring-back of the specimen as the hammer is removed, i.e. lifted off the specimen.

Our crashworthy research then split into a number of strands. Raph built a large drop hammer (1 tonne dropping through up to 3 m — even his triplets were most impressed with it) and started investigating the energy absorption characteristics of thin-walled cylinders. Two plastic mechanisms develop, depending mainly upon the radius to thickness ratio (*R/t*). One is a beautiful axisymmetric mechanism and the other looks like the old-fashioned accordion (we call it the diamond pattern) (Fig. 18).

One of my own themes is an investigation of the plastic mechanisms developed in square box-columns. Again two different mechanisms may form depending upon the *b/t* ratio. It was pointed out earlier that for low *b/t* a box-column will develop a roof mechanism (Fig. 11(a)). Continue crushing it and the mechanism shown in Fig. 19(a) is obtained. For higher *b/t* a flip-disc mechanism develops and when it is crushed it becomes the mechanism shown in Fig. 19(b). The close folding at the hinges in Fig. 19(a) suggests a very efficient means of absorbing energy. This single tube would be sufficient to absorb the energy of the average domestic car travelling at 15 km/h. In other words, instead of damaging the whole of the front of one's car in a minor collision, all of the damage could be concentrated into a cheap throw-away element such as a tube. Low speed accidents cost the community an enormous amount of money — in Victoria the bill is estimated at about $A400 million per annum — so there are real gains to be made from this work. At the time

Fig. 18. Thin cylinders develop an axisymmetric (left) or a diamond (right) plastic mechanism depending upon the radius to thickness ratio.

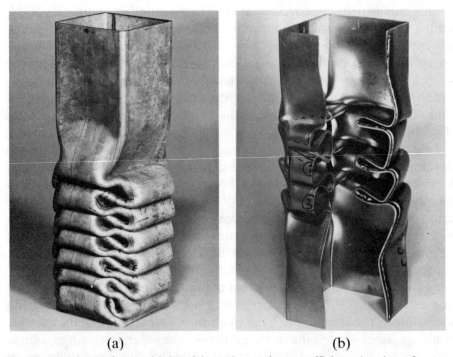

(a)   (b)

Fig. 19. (a) A box-column with low *b/t* can be used as an efficient absorber of energy when crushed as shown. (b) For higher *b/t* a column develops a flip-disc mechanism which crushes into a different, less efficient absorber.

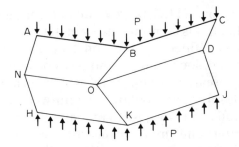

Fig. 20. Isometric view of the basic element of the plastic mechanism shown in Fig. 19(a).

of writing I am developing a non-extensional theoretical analysis of the mechanism shown in Fig. 19(a). The basic unit of this mechanism is shown in Fig. 20 where it is seen that the corner develops a hinge which rolls until the unit flattens.

We were fortunate in being able to arrange a visit from Norman Jones for July and August 1987. During his stay Norman, Raph, Daya and I tested a number of different bumper bars in order to establish their energy absorbing capacities. Visits were made to local car wreckers who were most cooperative and gave us a variety of bumper bars. Tests confirmed the results of some similar work in Britain, namely that the term bumper bar is a misuse of the English language. Even at speeds of 2 km/h many bumper bars are useless and allow the expensive parts of the car to be damaged. Part of the problem is that they are thin-walled structures, flattening on the slightest impact and losing most of their desirable structural properties.

The random walk goes on and there is far too much to be done in the next five years before I must retire from the university. This is how it should be. It is fortunate for us lesser mortals that the Einsteins of this world don't discover it all and therefore there are a few crumbs left to pick over. The reader might well ask now what has been the benefit of all this activity. For me personally I have benefitted in many ways. I have not milked a cow in the past 37 years. But of more importance, the work has brought me into contact with many outstanding scholars around the world. I have had the privilege of supervising some extraordinarily bright young researchers. They have given me their full support and I have learned much more from them than they from me. Nothing worthwhile could have been achieved without their dedication.

The benefit to society is more difficult to define. The department in which I work had been started from nothing in 1961 and in 27 years it has built up a high profile and an excellent international reputation in both teaching and research. I was particularly pleased with the results of recent reviews by the CTEC (a government committee) and by the university itself. Each was complimentary in the extreme. Thus, I believe that society has benefitted by the constant stream of graduates at bachelor, master and doctor levels who have been well trained.

The Monash research group with which I am associated has developed a philosophy for looking at thin-walled and crashworthy structures. Hopefully the work will gradually seep into the profession and result in safer and more economic designs. In the field of crashworthy structures perhaps these effects will be more obvious, more immediate and more dramatic because property damage and personal injuries are so expensive.

I have been very fortunate to have worked at Monash. I can't think of a better way of spending one's life although at times it hasn't been easy. I have been very lucky to have such excellent academic, technical, secretarial and research student colleagues.

In closing I would like to thank my colleagues for their help over the years and for giving me this opportunity to get a few things 'off my chest'. Finally, I am greatly honoured to have this symposium named after me. It is a singular honour and I wish to thank all of those who have contributed to it. Special mention should be made of Professor Ian Donald and his organizing committee who have done so much work.

SESSION 1

Thin-Walled Structures **9** (1990) 29–60

Dynamic and Static Axial Crushing of Axially Stiffened Cylindrical Shells

R. S. Birch & Norman Jones

Impact Research Centre, Faculty of Engineering, University of Liverpool, PO Box 147, Liverpool L69 3BX, UK

ABSTRACT

The axial impact of cylindrical tubes, which incorporate axial stiffeners, is examined in this paper. For comparison purposes, the effect of static loading is also studied. An examination is made into the influence of stiffener depth (T), number of stiffeners (N) and the effect of placing the stiffeners externally or internally.

The experimental results on mild steel specimens show that there are considerable differences between the static and dynamic modes of failure, and that an optimum T/D ratio may exist for a given value of N.

NOTATION

A Cross-sectional area of stiffener
A^* A/bH
b Circumferential spacing of stiffeners on the mid-surface of a cylindrical shell
D Mean diameter of a cylindrical shell
D' External diameter of a cylindrical shell
h Mode length
H Shell wall and stiffener thickness
L Initial length of a specimen
N Number of stringers
P Axial load

Thin-Walled Structures 0263-8231/90/$03·50 © 1990 Elsevier Science Publishers Ltd, England. Printed in Great Britain

$\hat{P}$ Peak load
P_{m} Mean load
Q_{i} Impact energy
t Time
T Stiffener depth
v Velocity
V_{i} Impact velocity

δ Overall axial deformation

1 INTRODUCTION

An analysis of the static plastic progressive buckling of plain unstiffened circular tubes was carried out by Alexander[1] and Pugsley and Macaulay[2] while recent studies in the dynamic range are reported in Refs 3 and 4.

Engineers make use of structural stiffening as a means of improving the strength of lightweight structures. Stiffened tubular structures are common in various vehicles. For example, aircraft and road or rail coaches may be idealised as tubes stiffened by stringers (axial) and rings (circumferential). Buckling of such structures no longer takes on the simple geometric form which may develop in the compression of a plain tube.[1-4] Moreover, collapse under a dynamic loading may be very different from the static case.

Theoretical studies into the dynamic elastic behaviour of stiffened cylindrical shells have been reported by Fisher and Bert[5] and Simitses and Sheinman,[6] while the dynamic plastic buckling of an axially stiffened cylinder was examined by Jones and Papageorgiou.[7] It was concluded in Ref. 7 that, for the particular parameters studied, an optimal response occurs for internal stiffeners with rectangular cross-sections when the non-dimensional parameter A^* equals $\frac{5}{16}$, approximately. The theoretical analysis also found that it is more efficient to place these stiffeners on the outside of a tube.

Pugsley[8] examined the axial impact of idealised railway coach structures, which were, in effect, square tubes reinforced with axial stringers. The concept of a solidity ratio was proposed as a means of comparing the mean loads for tubes with various cross-sections. Macaulay and Redwood[9] examined the behaviour of rods, square tubes and small-scale models to gain insight into the effect of axial impact on railway coaches. They found important differences between the static and dynamic buckling behaviour and recognised a velocity effect with two components, geometrical and strain rate. Lowe et al.[10] also found differences between the static and dynamic crumpling behaviour during their investigations into the axial impact of small-scale model motor coaches.

There is a shortage of experimental test results on the influence of stiffeners on the dynamic plastic response of thin-walled structural members. A series of controlled tests on axially stiffened cylindrical mild steel tubes is reported in this paper.

2 SPECIMEN MANUFACTURE

A series of axial impact and static crushing tests were carried out on specimens manufactured from commercial structural mild steel tubing (seam welded) having an outside diameter D' of 64 mm, a wall thickness H of 1·58 mm, a length L of 150 mm, and with stiffeners as shown in Fig. 1. Table 1 shows the basic test matrix and specimen coding. Four depths of stringer were examined, with non-dimensional ratios T/D of 0·07, 0·12, 0·23 and 0·37, and each of these was tested using four equally spaced stringers. The effect of having eight and twelve equally spaced stringers was examined using the smaller T/D ratios of 0·07 and 0·12. Difficulties in manufacturing these test specimens meant that only four stringers could be mounted externally with a minimum ratio of 0·12.

Several manufacturing methods were considered, such as riveting or spot welding.[8-10] However, the use of discontinuous joints could introduce unwanted side effects during the plastic collapse of small-scale tubular specimens. Therefore, a manufacturing technique based on uniform and continuously welded joints was adopted.

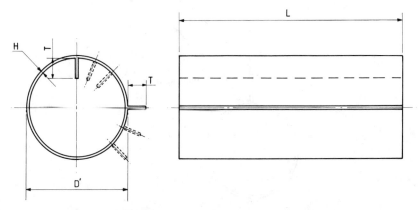

Fig. 1. Specimens with internal or external stringers. N = number of equally spaced stringers; D = mean tube diameter $D' - H$.

TABLE 1
Test Matrix and Specimen Coding

T/D ratio	Number of stiffeners[a]			
	0	4	8	12
0	NF00	—	—	—
0·07	—	IF416	IF816	IF1216
0·12	—	EF49		
		IF49	IF89	IF129
0·23	—	EF44		—
		IF44	—	
0·37		EF42		
	—	IF42	—	—

[a]N indicates no stiffening; EF indicates external stiffening; IF indicates internal stiffening.

The manufacturing method commenced with a cut length of tube which formed the basic specimen cylinder. Longitudinal strips were also cut from the wall of another length of the same tube and lightly rolled flat to form the stringers. In the case of the externally stiffened tubes, these strips were welded to the outside of the tube using argon arc welding, as shown in Fig. 2. A drawback to this construction method was the presence of a small fillet weld between the stiffener and a tube. Also, due

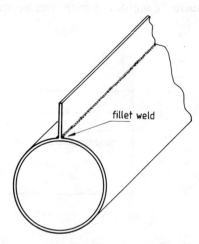

Fig. 2. Method of mounting external stringers. The stringer is mounted directly onto the tube surface and welded into position.

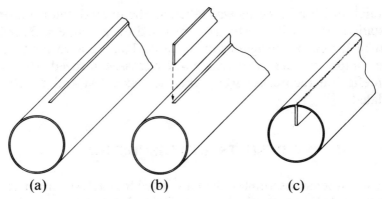

Fig. 3. Method of mounting internal stringers: (a) a slot is cut axially along the tube blank; (b) the stringer is then placed into this slot; (c) both stringer and tube are fused together and the tube end is then machined off.

to the difficulties in welding, it was not possible to have a stiffener depth less than 5 mm ($T/D = 0·08$).

Internal stiffening was achieved by machining longitudinal slots along the tube blank with a width slightly larger than the stringer thickness, as shown in Fig. 3. The stringers were then inserted into these slots, with the outer edge protruding 0·25 mm above the outside surface of the tube, and fused using argon welding. No filler rod was necessary and fillets on the inside of the tube could be kept to a minimum. This method was highly successful for stiffener depths greater than 3 mm.

Heat distortion during all welding operations was minimised by passing cool air through the tube section. To ensure uniformity, all specimens were fully annealed as a single batch in a vacuum furnace, together with the tensile test specimens taken from the wall of the tubing material.

3 TEST PROCEDURE

All tests were performed on the main drop hammer rig in the University of Liverpool Impact Research Centre with a constant tup mass of 67·6 kg. Five tests were performed on each cross-section using drop heights from 2·16 m to 7·145 m. A laser Doppler velocimeter (LDV)[11] was used to record the tup velocity–time history during each impact test, which was processed to provide a load–time record. Mean loads were calculated using the point of zero tup velocity as the datum.

After each test, the overall length of a specimen was carefully re-measured, taking an average of several readings. The difference between the initial and final lengths was taken as the overall deformation δ.

A static compression test was performed on a single stiffened tube specimen for each configuration in Table 1 using a 25 tonne Dartec tensile/compression testing machine with a crosshead speed of 0·05 mm/s. Load/deflexion recordings were taken for each test and a mean load calculated.

4 RESULTS AND DISCUSSION

The basic dimensions and test data are listed for each specimen in Table 2. Sample laser Doppler velocimeter (LDV) velocity–time recordings and derived load–time histories are presented in Figs 4 to 15. The photographs in these figures show the deformed specimens arranged from left to right with increasing impact velocity or energy (original specimen on the far left side), since these tests were conducted using a constant tup mass.

The results from the static tests are also listed in Table 2. Photographs of each specimen are presented in Figs 16(a) to 17(d) together with their respective load–deformation recordings.

4.1 Unstiffened case

It is evident from Fig. 4 that dynamic loading of the plain tubes causes the specimens to collapse in the classic symmetric or concertina mode of failure with a mode length h of 8 mm.[1-4]

The static buckling of a plain tube is illustrated in Fig. 16(a) and shows almost exactly the same mode of failure, but with a slightly longer mode length of 10 mm. However, a second static test, shown in Fig. 16(b) and carried out under the same conditions, resulted in the diamond or 'lobed' mode of failure which was not observed in any of the dynamic cases in Fig. 4. Here the diamond mode has a rather longer mode length and is discussed in Refs 3 and 4.

4.2 Four internal stringers

The effect of placing four internal stringers with $T/D = 0·07$ is demonstrated in Fig. 5 which shows that for the same initial impact energy there is a marked decrease in deformation compared with the corresponding plain tubes in Fig. 4. The same drop height was used in the corresponding tests in Figs 4 and 5 which gives the same initial kinetic energy. However, the specimens with axial stiffeners deform less

TABLE 2
Basic Specimen Dimensions and Test Results

Code	Type of stringer	Stringer depth	Number of stringers	Impact velocity	Permanent deformation	Mean load	Peak load
		T (mm)	N	V_i (m/s)	δ (mm)	P_m (kN)	$\hat{P}$ (kN)
1NF00	Plain	0	0	6·25	19·8	53·2	115
2NF00	Plain	0	0	7·93	33·2	51·2	111
3NF00	Plain	0	0	9·23	49·2	50·1	96
4NF00	Plain	0	0	10·60	64·8	52·7	89
5NF00	Plain	0	0	11·70	80·4	49·7	78
6NF00	Plain	0	0	static	47·5	38·6	77
7NF00	Plain	0	0	static	48·0	34·2	84
1IF42	Internal	23·3	4	6·29	11·7	81·1	167
2IF42	Internal	23·1	4	7·95	19·2	83·9	161
3IF42	Internal	24·1	4	9·32	27·2	—	—
4IF42	Internal	23·2	4	10·60	37·1	—	—
5IF42	Internal	23·5	4	11·70	42·6	—	—
6IF42	Internal	23·0	4	static	23·0	65·1	126
1EF42	External	24·7	4	6·28	7·6	115·2	179
2EF42	External	24·2	4	7·93	15·6	—	—
3EF42	External	24·3	4	9·28	28·2	78·3	176
4EF42	External	24·0	4	10·60	32·4	—	—
5EF42	External	24·2	4	11·55	40·1	85·9	159
6EF42	External	24·0	4	static	48·0	51·8	110
1IF44	Internal	15·1	4	6·23	13·0	72·5	136
2IF44	Internal	14·4	4	7·93	20·0	—	—
3IF44	Internal	14·8	4	9·28	28·8	81·7	156
4IF44	Internal	14·8	4	10·60	37·8	—	—
5IF44	Internal	14·8	4	11·70	46·2	—	—
6IF44	Internal	14·0	4	static	48·5	53·1	118
1EF44	External	15·7	4	6·25	9·5	87·9	171
2EF44	External	15·7	4	7·91	17·0	83·9	179
3EF44	External	16·0	4	9·40	25·6	86·6	175
4EF44	External	15·6	4	10·61	33·7	79·9	169
5EF44	External	15·9	4	11·70	44·4	82·3	141
6EF44	External	15·0	4	static	48·5	50·2	112
1IF49	Internal	7·4	4	6·25	14·3	—	—
2IF49	Internal	7·6	4	7·93	21·6	—	—
3IF49	Internal	7·6	4	9·32	33·4	—	—
4IF49	Internal	7·5	4	10·60	43·6	69·6	192
5IF49	Internal	7·4	4	11·61	52·6	71·7	116
6IF49	Internal	7·0	4	static	32·0	53·9	114

(continued)

R. S. Birch, Norman Jones

TABLE 2—*contd.*

Code	Type of stringer	Stringer depth	Number of stringers	Impact velocity	Permanent deformation	Mean load	Peak load
		T	N	V_i	δ	P_m	$\hat{P}$
		(mm)		*(m/s)*	*(mm)*	*(kN)*	*(kN)*
1EF49	External	7·8	4	6·56	11·5	77·1	159
2EF49	External	7·6	4	7·93	20·1	—	—
3EF49	External	7·4	4	9·30	30·9	74·4	142
4EF49	External	7·7	4	10·53	36·3	83·7	128
5EF49	External	7·6	4	11·59	44·1	77·5	121
6EF49	External	7·0	4	static	48·5	42·6	96
1IF89	Internal	7·5	8	6·26	9·5	77·4	192
2IF89	Internal	7·7	8	8·07	21·6	68·0	161
3IF89	Internal	7·7	8	9·19	32·0	54·7	178
4IF89	Internal	7·4	8	10·53	51·1	48·0	188
5IF89	Internal	7·3	8	11·66	71·4	46·7	183
6IF89	Internal	7·0	8	static	28·0	53·6	116
1IF129	Internal	7·5	12	6·24	6·6	—	—
2IF129	Internal	7·7	12	7·93	14·4	93·5	195
3IF129	Internal	7·7	12	9·16	24·4	66·5	187
4IF129	Internal	7·7	12	9·90	23·0	104·1	222
5IF129	Internal	7·0	12	static	38·0	44·4	124
6IF129	Internal	7·6	12	11·69	44·1	—	—
1IF416	Internal	4·2	4	6·25	14·1	—	—
2IF416	Internal	4·1	4	7·92	24·7	72·1	120
3IF416	Internal	4·3	4	9·27	35·8	62·9	120
4IF416	Internal	3·9	4	10·48	43·4	70·4	125
5IF416	Internal	4·0	4	11·51	61·8	61·5	125
6IF416	Internal	4·0	4	static	49·0	43·9	100
1IF816	Internal	4·2	8	6·42	12·8	69·9	173
2IF816	Internal	4·2	8	8·00	28·3	46·9	150
3IF816	Internal	4·4	8	9·37	44·5	42·9	138
4IF816	Internal	4·1	8	10·54	50·8	55·3	299
5IF816	Internal	4·2	8	11·69	82·8	—	—
6IF816	Internal	4·0	8	static	26·0	51·5	110
1IF1216	Internal	4·1	12	6·37	8·2	105·4	158
2IF1216	Internal	4·4	12	7·89	17·5	69·0	178
3IF1216	Internal	4·0	12	9·27	38·1	50·0	159
4IF1216	Internal	4·0	12	static	29·5	56·8	112
5IF1216	Internal	4·1	12	10·57	43·1	61·3	177
6IF1216	Internal	4·4	12	11·56	61·8	55·2	183

Tensile test results for tube material: yield stress = 263 MN/m^2, UTS = 306 MN/m^2, modulus = 211 GN/m^2.

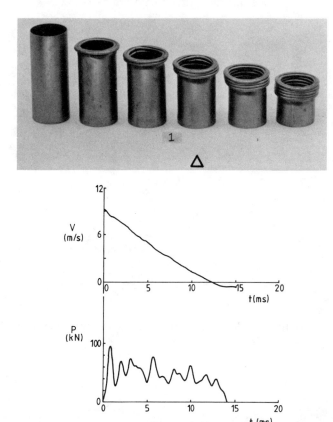

Fig. 4. Effect of dynamic loading on NF00 series unstiffened tubes. The velocity and load–time histories are presented for the specimen indicated by the symbol △.

than the corresponding unstiffened tubes, giving rise to a smaller additional potential energy due to the axial crushing of the tube. The complexity of the failure modes in Fig. 5 made the precise measurement of a mode length difficult. However, it appears that the mode lengths for both the plain and stiffened tubes were similar.

Static loading of the specimen with $T/D = 0.07$ produced a completely different mode of failure, as illustrated in Fig. 16(c). The static mode shows little sign of overall buckling and the load–deformation curve has only two adjacent peaks which are associated with the initial failure. As the static load reached this peak, several buckles appeared simultaneously along the tube length, some of which continued to fold over with further axial deformation. The smooth shape of the load-deformation curve in Fig. 16(c) confirms that all the folds were initiated early in the crushing process. This contrasts with the dynamic case in Fig. 5 where several

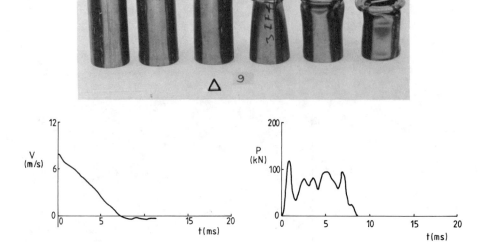

Fig. 5. Effect of dynamic loading on IF416 series tubes with four internal stringers having $T/D = 0.07$.

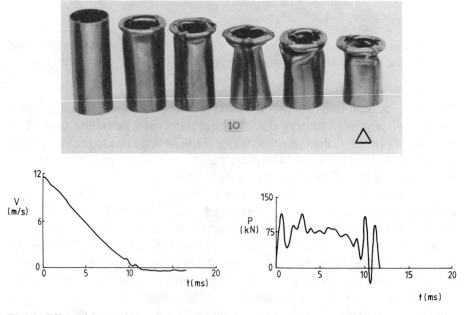

Fig. 6. Effect of dynamic loading on IF49 series tubes with four internal stringers having $T/D = 0.12$.

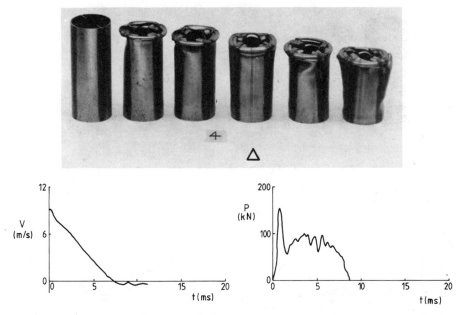

Fig. 7. Effect of dynamic loading on IF44 series tubes with four internal stringers having $T/D = 0.23$.

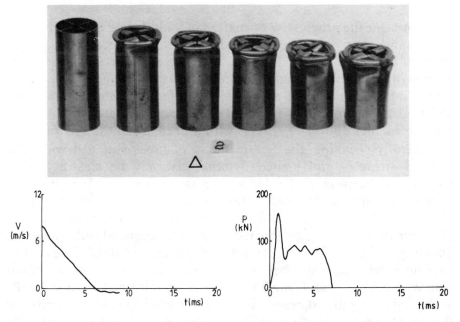

Fig. 8. Effect of dynamic loading on IF42 series tubes with four internal stringers having $T/D = 0.37$.

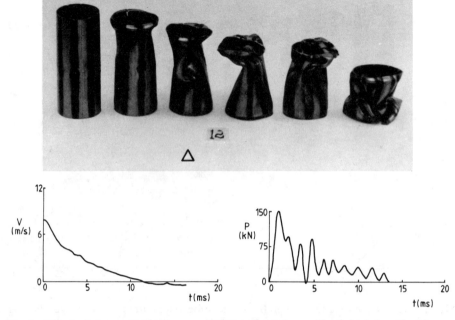

Fig. 9. Effect of dynamic loading on IF816 series tubes with eight internal stringers having $T/D = 0.07$.

peaks indicate the progressive formation of folds during axial collapse.

The same observations can be made for stiffened specimens with T/D ratios of 0·12, 0·23 and 0·37. Again, under dynamic loading, the tubes deform in a controlled progressive manner, as illustrated in Figs 6 to 8, while under static loading, a completely different mode of failure was observed, as shown in Figs 16(d) to 17(b). Large lobes are formed which become smaller and more regular with a decrease of the T/D ratio.

Generally speaking, the failure mode of tubes stiffened with four internal stringers and loaded dynamically may be classified as a modified concertina mode 1a, as shown in Fig. 18. This mode is progressive, with all the deformation occurring at the impacted end of the tube and with each fold forming outwards between the stringers. However, the results suggest that the mode may degenerate into an overall buckling failure mode with increased impact energy. In all the dynamic loading cases, the first lobes are formed dynamically with a regular bellows-type shape, while the final lobe, which is formed quasi-statically as the tup comes to rest, resembles the static loading case. It is apparent that as dynamic crushing progresses it will switch from a regular to an irregular progressive failure mode due to the differences observed

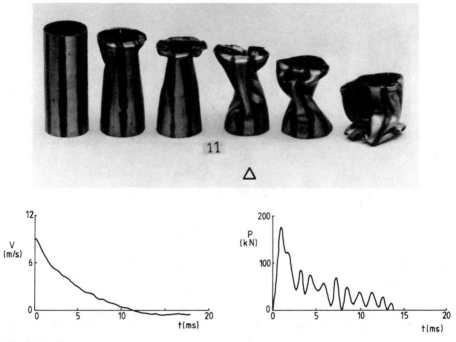

Fig. 10. Effect of dynamic loading on IF89 series tubes with eight internal stringers having $T/D = 0.12$.

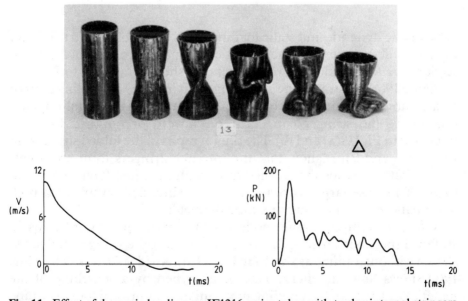

Fig. 11. Effect of dynamic loading on IF1216 series tubes with twelve internal stringers having $T/D = 0.07$.

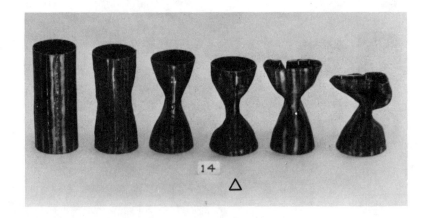

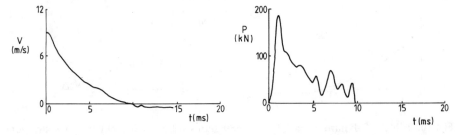

Fig. 12. Effect of dynamic loading on IF129 series tubes with twelve internal stringers having $T/D = 0.12$.

between the dynamic and static loading cases. This could lead to overall instability despite the increase in the second moment of area of the cross-section due to the addition of stringers, as shown in Figs 5 to 8.

Figure 19(a) illustrates how the stringers fit into this crumpling pattern by a combined folding and rotation about a root axis. This folding and rotation of the stringer can occur on inward or outward folds, as indicated in Fig. 19(a) and (b). The photographs of the folded stringers in Figs 20(a) and 21(a) show that the internal stringers form an almost regular pattern inside the crushed tubes with little interference between them. This regularity appears to be maintained even with high deformations approaching one tube diameter.

A second stringer failure mode was observed on outward folds in stiffened specimens with $T/D = 0.12$. In this case, the stringers tended to stretch without folding, as shown in Fig. 21(b). An idealised sketch in Fig. 19(c) shows how the energy may be absorbed by a stretching of the material rather than by a folding mechanism. For inward folds, the tube wall folds down onto the stringer and the mode is again shown in Figs 19(a) and 21(a). Therefore, for the smaller T/D ratios, two types of stringer

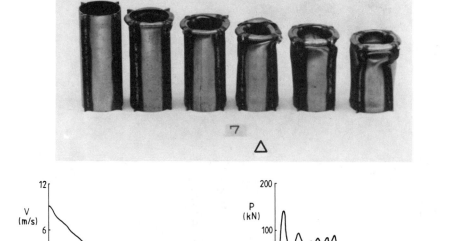

Fig. 13. Effect of dynamic loading on EF49 series tubes with four external stringers having $T/D = 0.12$.

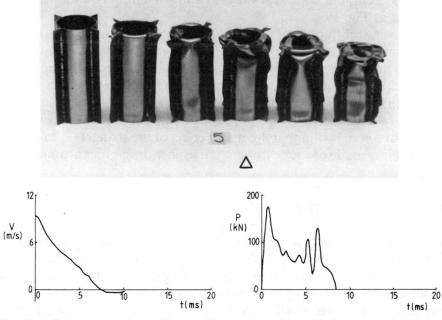

Fig. 14. Effect of dynamic loading on EF44 series tubes with four external stringers having $T/D = 0.23$.

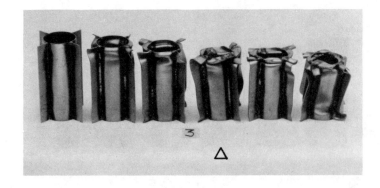

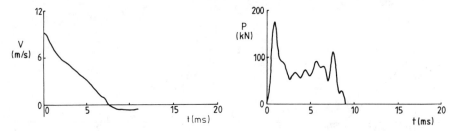

Fig. 15. Effect of dynamic loading on EF42 series tubes with four external stringers having $T/D = 0.37$.

crushing occur, buckling types A or B and stretching type C, which are sketched in Fig. 19.

The overall influence of the stringers can be seen in Fig. 22(a) for a given initial kinetic energy of 1·32 kJ, approximately. A comparison between the permanent deformations of a plain tube and stiffened tubes having four T/D ratios shows that by adding four stringers with a small T/D ratio there is a large reduction in deformation. However, increasing the T/D ratio beyond 0·12 produces only a marginal improvement. This leads to the conclusion that the major effect of the stringers is to modify the buckling mode of a tube rather than to absorb significant amounts of energy.

4.3 Eight internal stringers

By doubling the number of stiffeners from four to eight, a major change in the mode of failure occurs when $T/D = 0.07$ and $T/D = 0.12$, as shown in Figs 9 and 10. At the lower impact energies, a modified concertina mode develops which is characterised as type 3c in Fig. 18. This appears to change into a large lobe failure (modes 4 and 5 in Fig. 18) as the impact energy increases. Some of these tests have larger permanent deformations than the corresponding cases with four stringers, which indicates that this mode is less efficient in absorbing energy.

Static loading tests for stiffened cylinders with $T/D = 0.07$ and $T/D = 0.12$ are illustrated in Figs 17(c1) and 17(d1), respectively. Both these specimens exhibit similar modes with a closing up of the tubes at both ends. In contrast to the static tests on tubes with four stringers, it can be seen that the overall buckling shapes of the specimens with eight stringers have certain similarities to the dynamic case.

4.4 Twelve internal stringers

It is evident from Figs 11 and 12 that an overall buckling mode develops for stiffened tubes with $T/D = 0.07$ and $T/D = 0.12$. Two modes may be identified. A double concave mode, type 5 in Fig. 18, is the predominant mode for the tubes with $T/D = 0.12$. This mode and a modified diamond mode, type 4 in Fig. 18, also developed in the specimens with $T/D = 0.07$.

Under static loading, the specimens had a similar mode to that found in the tubes with eight stringers. Again the ends tend to fold inwards, as shown in Figs 17(c2) and 17(d2).

4.5 Four external stringers

In the case of externally stiffened tubes with $T/D = 0.12$, the mode appears to be progressive with little overall buckling. The failure shape is the modified concertina mode type 1a, which was observed previously for internally stiffened tubes. The folds are always formed outwards between the stringers, and the stringers fail by either buckling or stretching of the material (see Figs 13, 19 and 20) depending upon the T/D ratio.

Figures 14 and 15 show that the buckling mode for the stiffened tubes with $T/D = 0.23$ and $T/D = 0.37$ is not a controlled progressive type, which was found for the internally stiffened specimens. As the impact energy increases, the specimen is prone to overall failure. Again lobes are developed between the stringers, except now the diametrically opposed lobes are formed inwards and outwards. For the lower impact energies, this mode is fairly regular and is classified as another modified concertina mode of type 2b in Fig. 18. The stringers fail, as before, by combined buckling and rotation (see Fig. 19(a) and (b)), as indicated in Fig. 20(b).

R. S. Birch, Norman Jones

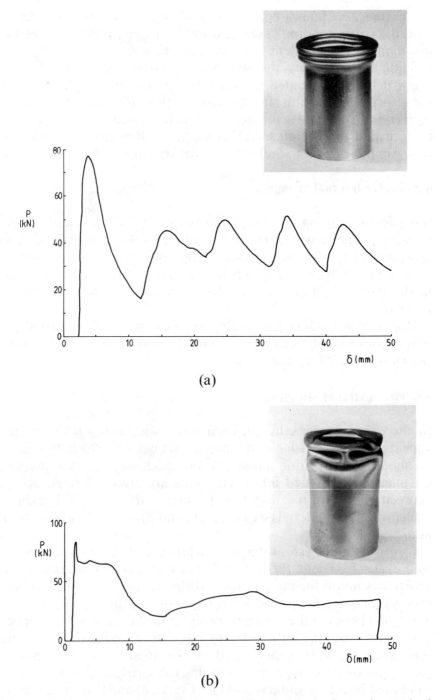

(a)

(b)

Fig. 16. Effect of static loading on NF00 series unstiffened tubes. (a) Concertina mode of failure. (b) Diamond mode of failure.

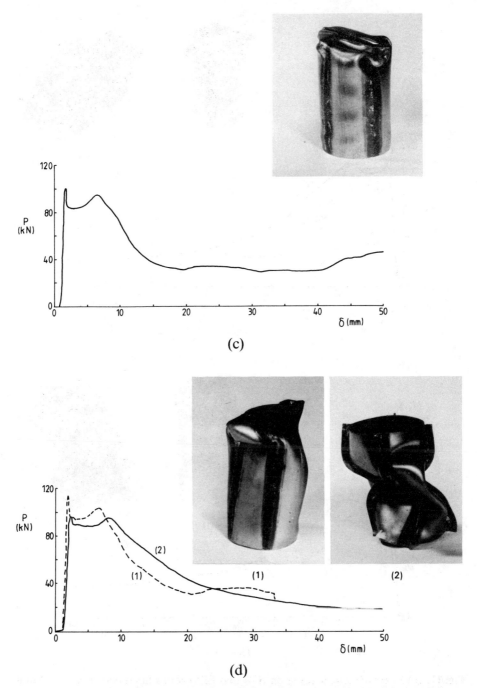

(c)

(d)

Fig. 16.—*contd.* (c) Effect of static loading on IF416 series tubes with $T/D = 0.07$ and 4 internal stringers. (d) Effect of static loading on IF49 and EF49 series tubes with $T/D = 0.12$ and with (1) 4 internal and (2) 4 external stringers, respectively.

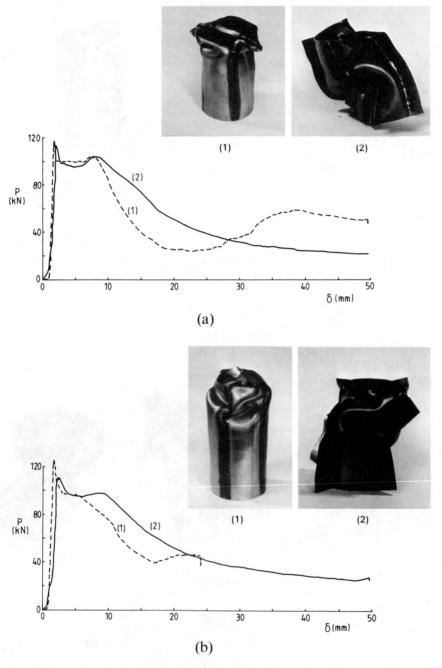

Fig. 17. (a) Effect of static loading on IF44 and EF44 series tubes with $T/D = 0.23$ and with (1) 4 internal and (2) 4 external stringers, respectively. (b) Effect of static loading on IF42 and EF42 series tubes with $T/D = 0.37$ and with (1) 4 internal and (2) 4 external stringers, respectively.

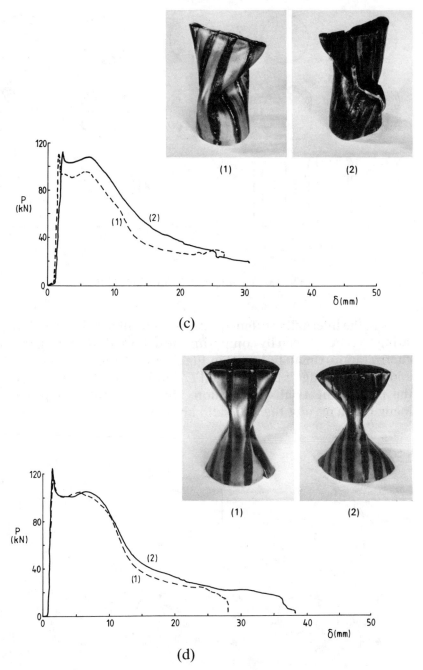

(c)

(d)

Fig. 17.—*contd.* (c) Effect of static loading on IF816 and IF1216 series tubes with $T/D = 0.07$ and with (1) 8 and (2) 12 internal stringers, respectively. (d) Effect of static loading on IF89 and IF129 series tubes with $T/D = 0.12$ and (1) 8 and (2) 12 internal stringers, respectively.

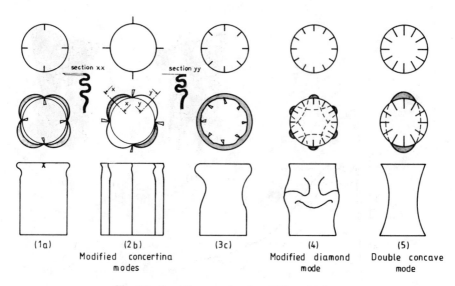

Fig. 18. Buckling modes for stiffened tubes.

As in the internally stiffened case, the overall influence of the external stringers is better seen by comparing the deformations for a given impact energy (approximately 1·3 kJ) in Fig. 22(b). Again, it is observed that by adding four stringers having small T/D ratios there is a large reduction in the permanent axial deformation. Only a marginal improvement is made by increasing the T/D ratio above 0·12.

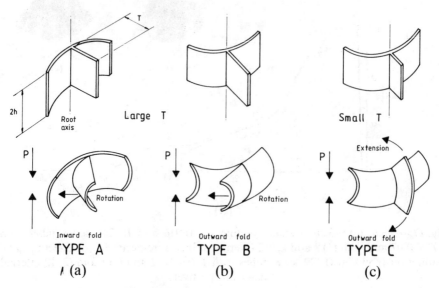

Fig. 19. Buckling modes of stringers.

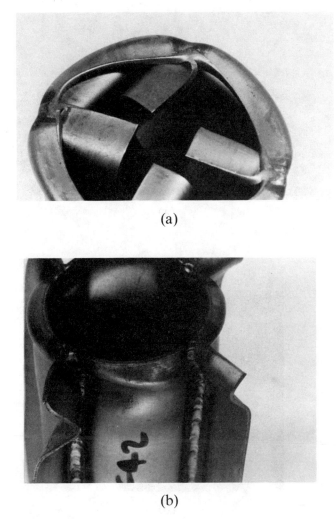

(a)

(b)

Fig. 20. Buckling modes of (a) internal and (b) external stringers having $T/D = 0.37$.

The static loading of these specimens produced a significantly different failure mode from that found in the corresponding dynamic tests. An overall buckling type of behaviour was observed for all the T/D ratios and had an instability which was far more pronounced than in any of the dynamic tests, as shown in Figs 16(d2), 17(a2) and 17(b2).

4.6 Influence of the stringers

It has been demonstrated that the dynamic progressive buckling of circular tubes is modified by the presence of stringers. The relationship

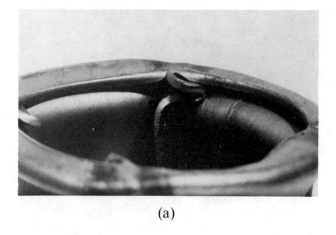

(a)

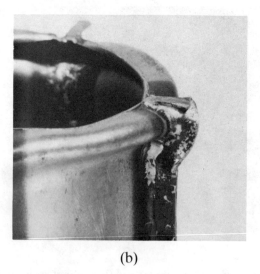

(b)

Fig. 21. Buckling modes of (a) internal and (b) external stringers having $T/D = 0 \cdot 12$.

between the deformation δ and the T/D ratio is presented in Fig. 23 for each impact velocity. These graphs show the same trend as found for external stiffeners.[7] However, insufficient experimental results are available to establish whether or not an optimum T/D ratio exists as predicted[7] for internal stiffeners. The effect of increasing the number of internal stringers can be seen in Fig. 22(c). For a given impact energy (approximately 1·3 kJ), the mode changes significantly from a modified concertina to a double concave mode.

(a)

(b)

(c)

Fig. 22. (a) Internal stringers with increasing T/D ratio; (b) external stringers with increasing T/D ratio; (c) internal stringers with $T/D = 0.12$ and an increasing number of stringers.

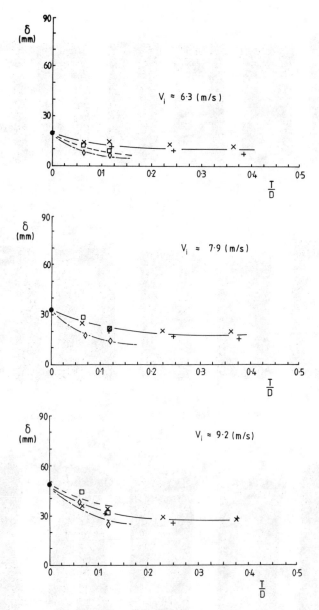

Fig. 23. Deformation–*T/D* relations for various impact velocities: ●, no stringers; +, 4 external stringers; ×, 4 internal stringers; □, 8 internal stringers; ◊, 12 internal stringers.

4.7 Static and impact loads

During the crushing process, the formation of the buckles is related to the cyclic variation of the load–deformation curve, as shown in Fig. 16a for

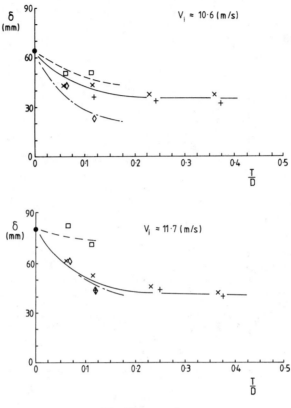

Fig. 23.—*contd.*

the static loading of a plain tube which developed a concertina mode. A second static test carried out on a plain tube produced a diamond failure mode with the rather flat load–deformation characteristics shown in Fig. 16b. These differences reflect the change in mode length for this type of failure.

Dynamic load recordings derived from the laser Doppler velocimeter signals show a similar pattern of peaks and troughs. A comparison with the static load–deformation trace is meaningful even though it is not directly related to time. Static loading of the stiffened tubes was characterised by an initial high load peak followed by an almost smooth decay (e.g. Fig. 16c). This pattern is also evident in the dynamic tests, but instead of a smooth decay a number of oscillations are present (e.g. Fig. 9). This may be attributed to the process of initiating buckles in a dynamic test. Under static loading, the buckles were initiated simultaneously after the peak load. However, it should be noted that the dynamic recordings also include the natural vibrations of the tup, specimen and anvil system.

The mean crushing load increases with the *T/D* ratio for four external

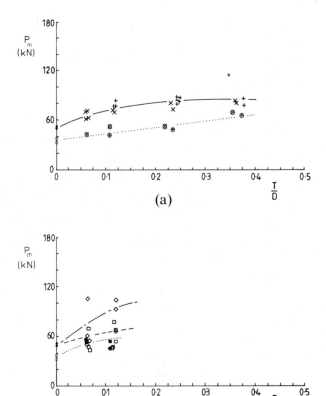

Fig. 24. Mean load–*T/D* relation: ●, no stringers (○, static loading); +, 4 external stringers (⊕, static loading); ×, 4 internal stringers (⊗, static loading); □, 8 internal stringers (■, static loading); ◇, 12 internal stringers (♦, static loading); ————, 4 stringers under dynamic loading; – – – – – –, 8 stringers under dynamic loading; –·––·––·–, 12 stringers under dynamic loading; ...., static loading case.

stringers, as shown in Fig. 24(a) where static and dynamic mean loads are presented on the same graph. The results show that increasing the *T/D* ratio beyond 0·23 gives little increase in the mean load, which suggests that an optimum *T/D* ratio may exist. The experimental result for specimen 1EF42 lies well above the other results because the mean load is associated with a single peak of the axial load–displacement curve. Figure 24(b) shows the results for specimens with eight and twelve stringers. These results are sensitive to the impact energy which is responsible for the scatter.

Figure 25(a) shows the relationship between the peak load and the *T/D* ratio for specimens with four stringers. As in the case of the mean load,

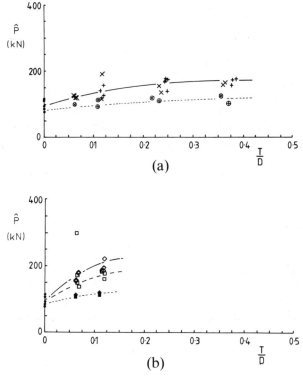

Fig. 25. Peak load–*T/D* relation (notation as defined in Fig. 24).

the peak load increases with the *T/D* ratio until *T/D* = 0·23. More experimental data are required for specimens with eight and twelve stringers in Fig. 25(b).

The mean load is subject to error if the axial deformations are small, because the initial peak load then becomes a significant contribution to the calculation of a mean. Under these circumstances, the concept of a mean load needs to be reconsidered and it is possible that a weighting factor could be used to offset this effect.

4.8 Deformation and impact energy

For the tests reported here, an almost linear relationship exists between the permanent axial deformation and the impact energy, as shown in Fig. 26. The only exception to this occurs for the specimens with eight and twelve stringers having *T/D* = 0·12 (and to some extent *T/D* ratios of 0·07) which have a parabolic deformation–impact energy relationship. These specimens failed by overall buckling rather than progressive buckling.

R. S. Birch, Norman Jones

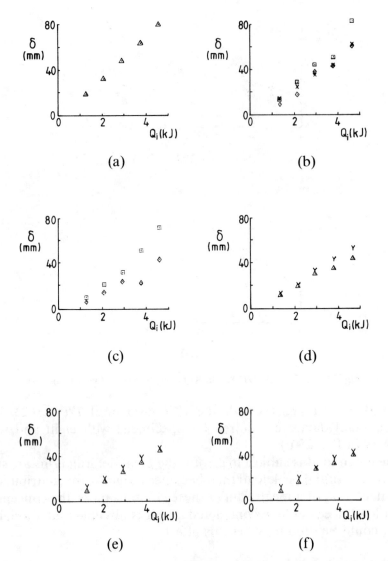

Fig. 26. Deformation–impact energy characteristics for (a) NF00 series of unstiffened tubes; (b) IF416, IF816 and IF1216 series tubes with $T/D = 0.07$ and $4\,(\times)$, $8\,(\square)$ and $12\,(\lozenge)$ internal stringers, respectively; (c) IF89 and IF129 series tubes with $T/D = 0.12$ and $8\,(\square)$ and $12\,(\lozenge)$ internal stringers, respectively; (d) IF49 and EF49 series tubes with $T/D = 0.12$ and internal (Y) and external ($\triangle$) stringers, respectively; (e) IF44 and EF44 series tubes with $T/D = 0.23$ and internal (Y) and external ($\triangle$) stringers, respectively; (f) IF42 and EF42 series tubes with $T/D = 0.37$ and internal (Y) and external ($\triangle$) stringers, respectively.

For any given energy, the tubular specimens with internal stiffeners crushed further than tubes with similar externally mounted stringers. The extra material included in the external fillet welds may play some part in this effect. Also, in a number of tests, some of the welds fractured. This was observed mostly for the higher impact energies and occurred only for the internally stiffened tubes. These failures were present in areas of high plastic strain at the stringer/tube wall interface. However, the results appear not to be seriously affected by this problem.

5 CONCLUSIONS

Some 83 axial impact and static crushing tests were carried out on stiffened and unstiffened circular mild steel tubes. The major effect of placing axial stiffeners on the inside or outside of the tubes is to modify the overall axial plastic collapse mode. The experimental results indicate that there is a stiffener T/D ratio beyond which there is no further improvement in the energy absorption capacity for a thin-walled tube. This, to some extent, confirms the theoretical findings[7] for the dynamic plastic buckling of thin-walled tubes with internal stiffeners.

The static and dynamic collapse modes are similar for plain unstiffened tubes. However, there are considerable differences between the static and dynamic collapse modes for the axially stiffened tubes which were even more pronounced in tubes with four axial stringers.

The static collapse of tubes stiffened with four external stringers occurs in an unstable overall buckling mode with peak collapse loads lower than those found in the specimens with four internal stringers. The dynamic collapse mode of the tubes stiffened with four internal stringers is generally a stable regular progressive type, while the dynamic collapse mode when the tubes are stiffened with four external stringers is an irregular progressive type, with some stability. Therefore, it would appear that it is advantageous to place the stringers on the inside of a tube.

ACKNOWLEDGEMENTS

The authors wish to thank the Science and Engineering Research Council for their support of this study through SERC Grant GR/D46748. The authors are indebted to the late Mr J. B. Cheetham at the University of Liverpool for his assistance with the preparation of the test specimens, and to Mrs A. Green and Mr F. Cummins for their preparation of the drawings.

REFERENCES

1. Alexander, J. M., An approximate analysis of the collapse of thin cylindrical shells under axial loading, *Qt. J. Mech. Appl. Math.*, **13** (1960) 1–9.
2. Pugsley, A. G. & Macaulay, M., The large scale crumpling of thin cylindrical columns, *Qt. J. Mech. Appl. Math.*, **13** (1960) 10–15.
3. Abramowicz, W. & Jones, N., Dynamic axial crushing of circular tubes, *Int. J. Impact Engng*, **2**(3) (1984) 263–81.
4. Abramowicz, W. & Jones, N., Dynamic progressive buckling of circular and square tubes, *Int. J. Impact Engng*, **4**(4) (1986) 243–70.
5. Fisher, C. A. & Bert, C. W., Dynamic buckling of an axially compressed cylindrical shell with discrete rings and stringers, *J. Appl. Mech.*, **40** (1973) 736–40. Also see errata, *J. Appl. Mech.*, **42** (1975) 249.
6. Simitses, G. J. & Sheinman, I., Static and dynamic buckling of pressure-loaded, ring-stiffened cylindrical shells, *J. Ship Res.*, **27**(2) (June) (1983) 113–20.
7. Jones, N. & Papageorgiou, E. A., Dynamic axial plastic buckling of stringer stiffened cylindrical shells, *Int. J. Mech. Sci.*, **24**(1) (1982) 1–20.
8. Pugsley, A. G., The crumpling of tubular structures under impact conditions, *Proc. Symp. on the Use of Aluminium in Railway Rolling Stock*, Institution of Locomotive Engineers, London, 1960, 33–41.
9. Macaulay, M. A. & Redwood, R. G., Small scale model railway coaches under impact, *The Engineer* (Dec.) (1964) 1041–6.
10. Lowe, W. T., Al-Hassani, S. T. S. & Johnson, W., Impact behaviour of small scale model motor coaches, *Proc. Inst. Mech. Eng., Auto Div.*, **186** (1972) 409–19.
11. Birch, R. S. & Jones, N., Measurement of impact loads using a laser doppler velocimeter, *Proc. Inst Mech. Engrs*, **204** (C1) 1990.

Thin-Walled Structures 9 (1990) 61–89

An Alternative Method for Determining the Behaviour of Round Stocky Tubes Subjected to an Axial Crush Load

R. H. Grzebieta

Department of Civil Engineering, Monash University, Clayton, Victoria 3168, Australia

ABSTRACT

An approximate method for determining the range of load oscillations and load–deflection behaviour of axially crushed round stocky tubes which deform in an axisymmetric mode is developed. Theoretical estimates based on different kinematic models are compared with each other and with experimental observations. Results indicate that the effects of axial and hoop stresses, imperfection sensitivity, strain-hardening and hinge curvature, should be considered in the analysis if the tube's behaviour is to be predicted accurately.

NOTATION

dW_b Increment of work due to bending
dW_E Increment of external work due to load
dW_h Increment of work due to hoop strains
$d\varepsilon_\theta$ Increment of hoop strain
H_f^s Axial length of crushed fold
L Length of one arm of plastic fold
L_C^α Shortest length between hinge points A and B
M_p Maximum bending moment per unit length
M_p' Reduced bending moment capacity per unit length
P Axial load
$\bar{P}$ Ratio of axial load to squash load (P/P_y)
P_L Lower load oscillation limit

Thin-Walled Structures 0263-8231/90/$03·50 © 1990 Elsevier Science Publishers Ltd, England. Printed in Great Britain

P_{max} Maximum possible failure load $(2P_y/\sqrt{3})$
P_U Upper load oscillation limit
P_y Squash load
r Coordinate in radial direction
R Radius of middle surface
t Wall thickness
z Coordinate in axial direction

α Angular displacement of fold due to $d\delta/2$
β Angular displacement as defined in Fig. 7 or Fig. 9
δ Axial deformation of tube
δ_C Total axial crush deformation
δ_{LC} Equivalent axial deformation during loading phase
δ^P Maximum axial rigid-plastic deformation (post peak)
δ^T Total axial deformation for one load cycle (elastic and plastic)
θ Coordinate in hoop direction
ρ_α Radius of curvature of plastic hinge
σ_u Ultimate tensile stress
σ_y Static yield stress
σ_θ Hoop stress
ψ Angular displacement equal to $\pi - \alpha$

1 INTRODUCTION

The theoretical methods for predicting how short stocky $(R/t < 30)$ cylindrical tubes deform in an axisymmetric mode (Fig. 1) when subjected to an axial crush load were reviewed recently.[1] Researchers who have analysed these structures have been able to derive an equation for the mean compressive load.[1-5] Nevertheless, it is well known that when these structures are crushed, the load oscillates between a peak (P_U) and residual (P_L) value, and the magnitude of these oscillations can be as large as two-thirds of the average crush load, as shown in Fig. 2.

In a design situation, if such a structure is used to absorb energy, or to resist a minimum load over a large range of deformation, it may be necessary to estimate these values and check that they are within certain design limits. For example, the designer may want to know if the superstructure to which these devices are attached could be damaged by an excessive peak load or by a much too small residual load. However, no-one has tried to define the range of load oscillations, or derive an expression for the load–deflection curve for one entire crush cycle. Therefore, it would seem worthwhile to develop a method which can determine these limits.

Fig. 1. Axisymmetric collapse mode for a tube with $R/t = 15\cdot4$.

In this paper the different kinematic models[1,2,5] sketched in Fig. 3 are assessed. Equations based on the Alexander[2] model are quoted from Ref. 1, whereas those based on the Abramowicz and Jones[5] model (Fig. 3(b)) and the modified model (Fig. 3(c)) are derived in the following sections. Using the results of this assessment and analysing in greater detail the crushing process of tubes with different R/t ratios, it was possible to formulate a simplified method for determining the axial load–deflection curve for the entire crushing process.

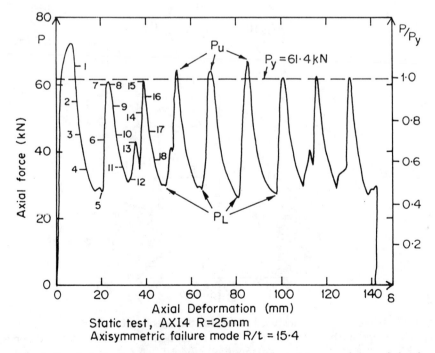

Fig. 2. Load–deflection plot of a round tube subjected to an axial crush load.

2 THE COLLAPSE CURVE

To predict how the tube shown in Fig. 1 behaves, the way in which an axisymmetric bulge forms and develops during collapse was analysed carefully. This was done by studying experiments carried out on stocky tubes with two different R/t ratios. The tubes were fixed at both ends and compressed in an axial direction. Further details of how the specimens were prepared and tested are available.[1,6]

When a typical load cycle starts at P_L (Fig. 2), a fold similar to ABC in Fig. 3 would have almost collapsed flat at this stage, and the next

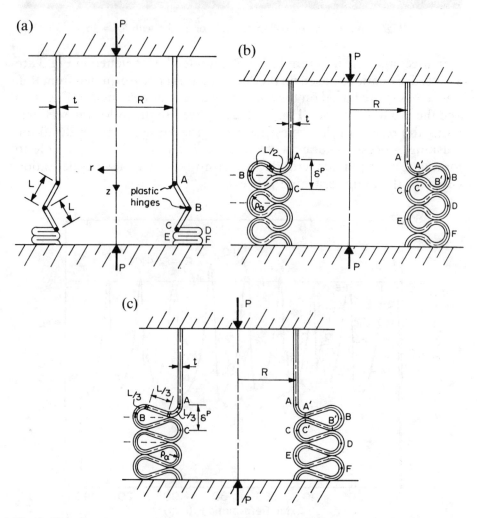

Fig. 3. Cross-sectional profiles used to model the axisymmetric failure mechanism: (a) model proposed by Alexander;[2] (b) model proposed by Abramowicz and Jones;[5] (c) modified model.

waveform would not be visible. Once the load starts to rise to a value of P_U, axial deformation will be non-linear and caused by a combination of different possible modes of elastic and plastic behaviour. For example, frames 6, 7, 14 and 15 in Fig. 4 show that the tube already has an imperfection in its profile prior to achieving a load of P_U. This occurs because final crushing or flattening of the previous fold occurs only when the load rises from P_L to P_U, and when this happens, the tube wall tends to move slightly inwards at point C. Thus, axial deformation during the loading phase can be attributed to plastic crushing of semi-closed folds, and to non-linear elastic and elasto-plastic outward buckling accentuated by an imperfection caused by the previous fold.

As deformations increase and load P_U is reached, plastic yield lines

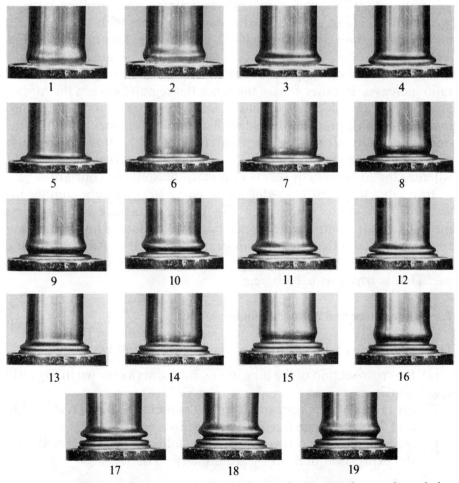

Fig. 4. Crush mechanism. Numbers indicate when each photograph was taken relative to the axial load–deflection plot shown in Fig. 2.

form at levels A and B in the hoop direction. The mechanism having formed then starts to collapse and the load steadily decreases. Crushing of the cylinder continues until the fold almost closes and the load has dropped again to a value P_L. Once the end of the collapse phase is reached a new cycle begins.

Assuming that the load cycle from P_L to P_U and back to P_L repeats itself, it is only necessary to evaluate one of these cycles to predict how the structure behaves when crushed. Moreover, only the collapse phase between loads P_U to P_L is analysed in this section. To calculate axial deformations during the loading phase is in itself a difficult task and will not be attempted here but left for further discussion later in the paper. It should also be mentioned that some of the assumptions made in this paper have already been assessed in a previous publication by the author.[1]

Two models will be considered in the analysis about to follow. It seems the first model (Fig. 3(b)) is most suitable for tubes with a very low R/t ratio, i.e. less than approximately 20, whereas the second model (Fig. 3(c)) can be used for thinner tubes. This was done because Figs 5 and 6 show how the plastic hinges tend to become more concentrated as the R/t ratio increases. In other words, there is a flat region between the hinges, and the curvature does not extend as far as the Abramowicz and Jones[5] model (Fig. 3(b)) predicts. Thus the mechanism becomes more like the one proposed by Alexander[2] (Fig. 3(a)) for larger R/t ratios. Figure 4 also shows that hinge curvature tends to vary throughout the collapse cycle, whereas the hinge length seems to remain reasonably constant.

To predict the axial load–deflection curve of these tubes, either the static[7] or kinematic[2,8] approach can be used because both of these methods result in the same upper bound solution.[1] However, it was suggested in Ref. 1 that the solution strategy adopted by Andronicou and Walker,[9] which is a kinematic approach, is probably the best method to use. That is why it is used here.

2.1 Abramowicz and Jones kinematic model

The assumptions adopted for the analysis are as follows:

(1) the cross-section of the tube in Fig. 1 deforms as shown in Figs 3(b) and 7;
(2) the radius of curvature of the hinges at points A, B and C (Figs 3(b) and 7) can change during deformation;
(3) the length L of one arm of the plastic fold can be determined from the expression derived by Alexander,[1,2] viz.

$$L = 1.347\sqrt{Rt} \tag{1}$$

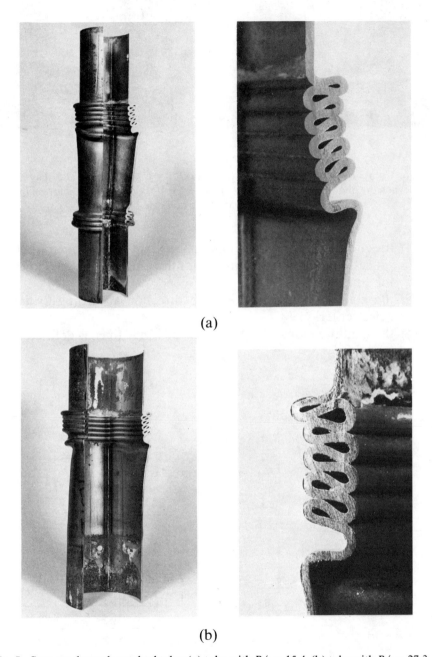

(a)

(b)

Fig. 5. Saw-cut through crushed tube: (a) tube with $R/t = 15\cdot4$; (b) tube with $R/t = 27\cdot3$.

(a)   (b)

Fig. 6. Comparison of failure mechanisms: (a) $R/t = 15\cdot4$; (b) $R/t = 27\cdot3$. The point in time when the photograph was taken is equivalent to position 11 in Fig. 2 for each test, i.e. towards the end of the collapse phase.

(4) the effective hinge length remains constant throughout the collapse process and in this case it is $L/2$ for the hinges at A and C and L for the hinge at B;

(5) the material yields in the hoop direction according to the von Mises criterion;

(6) the bending moment capacity of the hinge lines is defined by the equation[1]

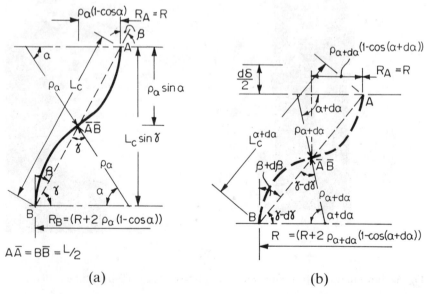

(a)   (b)

Fig. 7. Assumed movement of portion AB in Fig. 3(b) during an incremental displacement of $d\alpha$.

$$M'_p = \frac{2M_p}{\sqrt{3}}\left[1 - \frac{3}{4}\left(\frac{P_y}{P}\right)^2\right] \tag{2}$$

(7) because deformations are large, contraction in the axial direction of the region between the hinges caused by hoop strains is ignored. It was found that the contribution of energy due to this deformation is negligible.[6]

Using Fig. 7, the increment of work done to bend the three hinges at points A, B and C by a value of $d\delta$ can be determined approximately as

$$dW_b = 4\pi(R_A + R_B)M'_p \, d\alpha \tag{3}$$

where M'_p is the plastic bending resistance of the hinges per unit length.

Naturally R_A and R_B vary over the length of the hinge. However, to introduce the radii as variables of the distance at any point along the hinge would complicate the analysis. By choosing the smallest and largest radius for the hinges at A and B respectively, an average value of the work done by bending the hinges can be determined. Therefore, using eqn (2) and calculating values of the radii from Fig. 7, eqn (3) becomes

$$dW_b = \frac{8\pi M_p}{\sqrt{3}}\left[1 - \frac{3}{4}\bar{P}^2\right]\left[R + \left(R + 2\{1 - \cos(\alpha + d\alpha)\}\rho_{\alpha + d\alpha}\right)\right]d\alpha \tag{4}$$

which for small increments of $d\alpha$ can be approximated to

$$dW_b = \frac{8\pi M_p}{\sqrt{3}}\left[1 - \frac{3}{4}\bar{P}^2\right]\left[2R + 2(1 - \cos\alpha)\rho_{\alpha + d\alpha}\right]d\alpha \tag{5}$$

where $\bar{P} = P/P_y$.

The radius of curvature of the hinges after a deformation of $d\alpha$ can be related to the hinge length as

$$\frac{L}{2} = \rho_\alpha \alpha = \rho_{\alpha + d\alpha}(\alpha + d\alpha) \tag{6}$$

Substituting eqn (6) into eqn (5) gives for small increments of $d\alpha$ approximately

$$dW_b = \frac{8\pi M_p}{\sqrt{3}}\left[1 - \frac{3}{4}\bar{P}^2\right]\left[2R + \frac{L(1 - \cos\alpha)}{\alpha}\right]d\alpha \tag{7}$$

Alexander[2] determined the increment of virtual work carried out by the hoop strains for the model shown in Fig. 3(a) as approximately

$$dW_h = 2\pi\sigma_\theta tL^2 \cos\alpha \, d\alpha \tag{8}$$

By replacing α and L by $(\beta + d\beta)$ and $L_C^{\alpha + d\alpha}$ as shown in Fig. 7, and assuming $d\beta$ is small, an average value for the increment of work carried out by the hoop strains can be calculated as

$$dW_h = 2\pi\sigma_\theta t(L_C^{\alpha + d\alpha})^2 \cos\beta \, d\beta \tag{9}$$

To account for yielding of the material between the plastic hinges,[1,9] the principal stresses, $\sigma_1 = -\sigma$, $\sigma_2 = \sigma_\theta$ and $\sigma_3 = 0$, can be substituted into the von Mises yield criterion,

$$2\sigma_y^2 = (\sigma_1 - \sigma_2)^2 + (\sigma_1 - \sigma_3)^2 + (\sigma_2 - \sigma_3)^2 \tag{10}$$

Solving for σ_θ and knowing that $\sigma/\sigma_y = P\cos\alpha/P_y$ for large deformations,

$$\sigma_\theta = \sigma_y\left[-\bar{P}\cos\alpha + \sqrt{4 - 3\bar{P}^2\cos^2\alpha}\right] \tag{11}$$

Figure 7(a) shows that the relationship between α and β is

$$\beta = \frac{\alpha}{2} \tag{12}$$

which gives

$$d\beta = \frac{d\alpha}{2} \tag{13}$$

$L_C^{\alpha + d\alpha}$ can also be determined from Fig. 7 such that

$$\sin\left(\frac{\alpha + d\alpha}{2}\right) = \frac{L_C^{\alpha + d\alpha}}{4\rho_{\alpha + d\alpha}} \tag{14}$$

and using eqn (6), the expression

$$L_C^{\alpha + d\alpha} = \frac{2L \sin\left(\dfrac{\alpha + d\alpha}{2}\right)}{\alpha + d\alpha} \tag{15}$$

can be obtained. Expanding and simplifying this expression for a small increment of $d\alpha$ gives

$$L_C^{\alpha + d\alpha} = \frac{2L\left[\sin\left(\dfrac{\alpha}{2}\right) + \cos\left(\dfrac{\alpha}{2}\right)\dfrac{d\alpha}{2}\right]}{\alpha + d\alpha} \tag{16}$$

By substituting eqns (13) and (16) into eqn (9) a formula which accounts for the curvature of the fold can be derived.

Finally, adding eqns (7) and (9), and substituting for β, $d\beta$ and $L^{\alpha + d\alpha}$, the total increment of work done by the model shown in Fig. 3(b) for an increment of $d\alpha$ can be expressed as

$$
dW_T = \left\{ \frac{8\pi M_p}{\sqrt{3}} \left[1 - \frac{3}{4}\bar{P}^2 \right] \left[2R + \frac{L(1 - \cos\alpha)}{\alpha} \right] \right.
$$

$$
+ \frac{2\pi\sigma_y t L^2 \sin^2\left(\dfrac{\alpha}{2}\right) \cos\left(\dfrac{\alpha}{2}\right)}{\alpha^2}
$$

$$
\left. \left[-\bar{P}\cos\alpha + \sqrt{4 - 3\bar{P}^2\cos^2\alpha} \right] \right\} d\alpha \tag{17}
$$

Using Fig. 7(a),

$$
\delta = 2L\left(1 - \frac{\sin\alpha}{\alpha} \right) \tag{18}
$$

and after differentiating with respect to α and multiplying by the external load P, the increment of external work is

$$
dW_E = Pd\delta = \left[\frac{2PL}{\alpha^2}(\sin\alpha - \alpha\cos\alpha) \right] d\alpha \tag{19}
$$

Equating the external work to the internal work, simplifying for $d\alpha$, and replacing M_p by $\sigma_y t^2/4$, the equilibrium equation can be derived as[1]

$$
\frac{t\left(1 - \frac{3}{4}\bar{P}^2\right)}{\sqrt{3}} \left[2R + \frac{L(1 - \cos\alpha)}{\alpha} \right] + \frac{L^2 \sin^2\left(\dfrac{\alpha}{2}\right)\cos\left(\dfrac{\alpha}{2}\right)}{\alpha^2}
$$

$$
\left[-\bar{P}\cos\alpha + \sqrt{4 - 3\bar{P}^2\cos^2\alpha} \right] - \frac{2\bar{P}LR}{\alpha^2}(\sin\alpha - \alpha\cos\alpha) = 0 \tag{20}
$$

Because α cannot be solved explicitly from eqn (18), the load P was found for a certain angle α and then δ was calculated using eqn (18).

The maximum crushing distance[5] between points A and C of the profile shown in Fig. 3(b) is $(2L - t - 2\rho_{\alpha + d\alpha})$. Equating this value to eqn (18) and using eqn (6) gives

$$
2\sin\alpha - \frac{\alpha t}{L} - 1 = 0 \tag{21}
$$

Solving this equation for α for the tube shown in Fig. 1 gives approximate values of $\alpha = 140°$ and $\delta^P = 12\cdot9$ mm.

Equation (20) is compared to the experimental curve in Fig. 8. In this graph three cycles are shown from Fig. 2. The theoretical curve is positioned in the plot such that the calculated squash load (at $\delta = 0$) occurs at the same position along the axial deformation axis as the peak load P_U. A curve (eqn (37) in Ref. 1) which represents the Alexander model[2] (Fig. 3(a)) was also drawn in Fig. 8. In all cases L was determined from eqn (1).

For some of the curves plotted in Fig. 8, the yield stress σ_y was replaced by the ultimate tensile stress σ_u of the material. In Ref. 1 it was shown that for the tubes considered here, the ultimate capacity of the material is reached when the fold deforms to an angle α of approximately $40°$. This is equivalent in time to when frames 2, 9 and 16 in Fig. 4 were

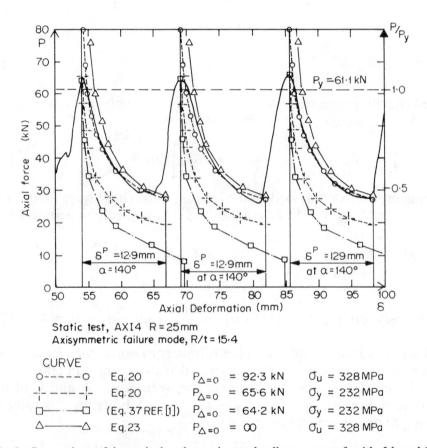

Static test, AXI4 R = 25 mm
Axisymmetric failure mode, R/t = 15·4

CURVE

o-----o	Eq. 20	$P_{\Delta=0}$ = 92·3 kN	σ_u = 328 MPa
-----	Eq. 20	$P_{\Delta=0}$ = 65·6 kN	σ_y = 232 MPa
□——□	(Eq. 37 REF. [1])	$P_{\Delta=0}$ = 64·2 kN	σ_y = 232 MPa
△———△	Eq. 23	$P_{\Delta=0}$ = ∞	σ_u = 328 MPa

Fig. 8. Comparison of theoretical and experimental collapse curves for 4th, 5th and 6th load cycles in Fig. 2.

photographed, in other words, in the initial stages of collapse when P is equal to approximately $0.85P_y$ (Fig. 2).

Figure 8 shows that there is a definite improvement in the solution when the curvature of the mechanism is modelled, and the yield stress σ_y is replaced by the ultimate tensile stress σ_u.[1,4,5] In fact eqn (20) predicts the general behaviour of the collapse mechanism reasonably well once the axial load P drops below P_y.

An equation which is based on assumptions made by Abramowicz and Jones[4,5] can also be obtained from eqn (20). They assume the axial stress is negligible in comparison to unity and the hoop stress σ_θ is directly equated to σ_y. Thus

$$\frac{t}{\sqrt{3}}\left[2R + \frac{L(1 - \cos\alpha)}{\alpha}\right] + \frac{2L^2\sin^2\left(\frac{\alpha}{2}\right)\cos\left(\frac{\alpha}{2}\right)}{\alpha^2}$$

$$-\frac{2\overline{P}LR}{\alpha^2}(\sin\alpha - \alpha\cos\alpha) = 0 \qquad (22)$$

Knowing that $P_y = 2\pi Rt\sigma_y$, this equation can be reduced to

$$P = \left\{\frac{2t}{\sqrt{3}}\left[2R + \frac{L(1 - \cos\alpha)}{\alpha}\right] + \frac{4L^2\sin^2\left(\frac{\alpha}{2}\right)\cos\left(\frac{\alpha}{2}\right)}{\alpha^2}\right\}$$

$$\times \frac{\pi t\alpha^2\sigma_y}{2L(\sin\alpha - \alpha\cos\alpha)} \qquad (23)$$

Figure 8 shows that the curve representing eqn (23) tends to overestimate the residual load during collapse.

2.2 Modified model

When eqn (20) was used to predict the collapse behaviour of a tube with an R/t ratio of 27·3 (Figs 5(b) and 6(b)), it overestimated the residual load. This was especially evident towards the end of the collapse phase. Therefore the model proposed in Fig. 3(b) was changed.

The profile shown in Figs 3(c) and 9 seems visually to be more representative of the cross-section shown in Fig. 5(b) than the Abramowicz and Jones[5] model. Once again, L is defined by eqn (1), eqn (2) is used to model the bending moment capacity of each hinge, eqn (11) is used for the hoop stress, and the effective length of the plastic hinges is assumed constant throughout the load cycle. Their lengths are $L/3$ for the hinges at A and C, and $2L/3$ for the hinge at B as shown in Figs 3(c) and 9. The

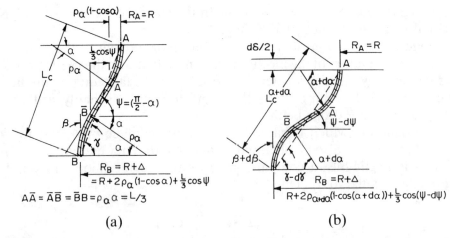

Fig. 9. Assumed movement of portion AB in Fig. 3(c) during an incremental displacement of $d\alpha$.

trigonometric relationships for the model can also be determined from Fig. 9.

The solution strategy adopted is the same as that used for eqn (20). Therefore, the amount of work it takes to bend the hinges at A, B and C by a small increment of $d\alpha$ can also be defined by eqn (3). However, this time Fig. 9 is used to determine the lateral deflection. Therefore substituting for Δ, eqn (3) can be expressed as

$$dW_b = \frac{8\pi M_p}{\sqrt{3}}\left[1 - \frac{3}{4}\bar{P}^2\right]\left[2R + 2[1 - \cos(\alpha + d\alpha)]\rho_{\alpha + d\alpha}\right.$$
$$\left. + \frac{L\cos(\psi - d\psi)}{3}\right]d\alpha \tag{24}$$

Knowing that $\psi = \pi - \alpha$ and $\rho_{\alpha + d\alpha} \approx L/3\alpha$, this expression becomes

$$dW_b = \frac{8\pi M_p}{\sqrt{3}}\left[1 - \frac{3}{4}\bar{P}^2\right]\left[2R + \frac{2L(1 - \cos\alpha)}{3\alpha} + \frac{L\sin\alpha}{3}\right]d\alpha \tag{25}$$

Similarly, an average value for the increment of energy absorbed by the hoop strain can be determined using eqn (9). However, in this case $L_C^{\alpha + d\alpha}$, β, and $d\beta$ are determined from Fig. 9(b). Therefore,

$$L_C^{\alpha + d\alpha} = \sqrt{\left[\left(L - \frac{\delta}{2}\right)^2 + \Delta^2\right]} \tag{26}$$

which becomes

$$L_C^{a+d\alpha} = \sqrt{\left[\left\{\sin(\alpha + d\alpha)\rho_{a+d\alpha} + \frac{L\cos(\alpha + d\alpha)}{3}\right\}^2\right.}$$

$$\left. + \left\{\left(1 - \cos(\alpha + d\alpha) + \frac{L\sin(\alpha + d\alpha)}{3}\right)\rho_{a+d\alpha}\right\}^2\right] \tag{27}$$

and can be approximated to

$$L_C^{a+d\alpha} = \sqrt{\left[\left(\frac{2L\sin\alpha}{3\alpha} + \frac{L\cos\alpha}{3}\right)^2 + \left(\frac{2L(1-\cos\alpha)}{3\alpha} + \frac{L\sin\alpha}{3}\right)^2\right]} \tag{28}$$

and

$$\beta = \cos^{-1}\left(\frac{L - \dfrac{\delta}{2}}{L_C}\right) \tag{29}$$

which can be expressed as

$$\beta = \cos^{-1}\left\{\frac{\dfrac{2\sin\alpha}{\alpha} + \cos\alpha}{\sqrt{\left[\dfrac{4}{3}\left(\dfrac{2(1-\cos\alpha)}{\alpha} + \sin\alpha\right) + 1\right]}}\right\} \tag{30}$$

Differentiating β with respect to α gives

$$\frac{d\beta}{d\alpha} = \frac{JK - 2MN}{2M\sqrt{(M - J^2)}} \tag{31}$$

where

$$J = \frac{2\sin\alpha}{\alpha} + \cos\alpha$$

$$K = \frac{16(\cos\alpha - 1)}{\alpha^3} + \frac{4\sin\alpha}{\alpha^2} + \frac{4\cos\alpha}{\alpha}$$

$$M = \frac{8(1 - \cos\alpha)}{\alpha^2} + \frac{4\sin\alpha}{\alpha} + 1$$

$$N = \frac{2(\alpha\cos\alpha - \sin\alpha)}{\alpha^2} - \sin\alpha$$

To obtain the total amount of work dissipated by the mechanism for an increment of $d\alpha$, eqn (25) is added to eqn (9) to give

$$dW_T = \left\{ \frac{8\pi M_p}{\sqrt{3}} \left(1 - \frac{3}{4}\bar{P}^2 \right) \left(2R + \frac{2L(1 - \cos\alpha)}{3\alpha} + \frac{L\sin\alpha}{3} \right) \right.$$

$$\left. + 2\pi\sigma_\theta t \left(L_C^{\alpha + d\alpha} \right)^2 \cos\beta \frac{d\beta}{d\alpha} \right\} d\alpha \tag{32}$$

This increment of virtual work is equated to the amount of work done by the applied load P through an increment of $d\delta$. Thus from Fig. 9(b).

$$\frac{\delta}{2} = L - \frac{2L\sin\alpha}{3\alpha} - \frac{L\cos\alpha}{3} \tag{33}$$

therefore

$$d\delta = \left\{ \frac{2L(3\sin\alpha - 2\cos\alpha)}{3\alpha} \right\} d\alpha \tag{34}$$

Multiplying $d\delta$ by the load P, substituting the result into the left-hand side of eqn (32), substituting for $M_p = \sigma_y t^2/4$, replacing σ_θ by eqn (11), and simplifying the expression, the equilibrium equation for the mechanism shown in Fig. 3(c) is derived as

$$\frac{t}{\sqrt{3}} \left(1 - \frac{3}{4}\bar{P}^2 \right) \left(2R + \frac{2L(1 - \cos\alpha)}{3\alpha} + \frac{L\sin\alpha}{3} \right)$$

$$+ (-\bar{P}\cos\alpha + \sqrt{4 - 3\bar{P}^2\cos^2\alpha}) \left(\frac{2L\sin\alpha}{3\alpha} + \frac{L\cos\alpha}{3} \right) L_C^{\alpha + d\alpha} \frac{d\beta}{d\alpha}$$

$$- \frac{2\bar{P}LR}{3\alpha} \left(\frac{2\sin\alpha}{\alpha} - 2\cos\alpha + \alpha\sin\alpha \right) = 0 \tag{35}$$

where $L_C^{\alpha + d\alpha}$ and $d\beta/d\alpha$ are defined by eqns (28) and (31) respectively. Once again eqn (35) can only be solved iteratively. After determining α for a given load P, eqn (33) can be used to determine the vertical deformation.

The maximum crushing distance can also be found by adopting the same procedure used for eqn (21). Thus for the fold shown in Fig. 3(c), knowing $\delta^P = 2L - t - 2\rho_\alpha$, using eqn (33) and substituting for $\rho_\alpha = L/3\alpha$, the result

$$L - 2L\sin\alpha - L\alpha\cos\alpha + \frac{3\alpha t}{2} = 0 \tag{36}$$

is obtained. This expression can be solved for α and substituted back into eqn (33) to determine the maximum deflection.

Equations (20) and (35) are compared with experimental results in Fig.

10 for the tube shown in Fig. 5(b). The entire test is plotted, and a theoretical curve representing each kinematic model in Fig. 3 is compared in each load cycle. To account for strain hardening of the material, the ultimate stress was again used instead of the yield stress[1,4,5] to calculate the collapse loads.

Figure 10 gives an overall impression of how the curvature of the plastic hinges at points A, B and C can affect the theoretical analysis. Already it can be seen from this plot that towards the end of the plastic collapse cycle, the experimental curve is lower than the curve predicted by eqn (20) in all of the cycles. Equation (35) seems to give a slightly better indication of the value of the residual load at this stage of collapse. Moreover, it can be seen that the curve representing the Alexander model[1] predicts an even lower value. It seems that equation is more suitable for cylinders with a higher R/t ratio where the mechanism is more like the model shown in Fig. 3(a). This also could be the reason why Andronicou and Walker[9] obtained such good correlation between their theoretical results and experimental observations. They used the Alexander model to analyse tubes with an R/t ratio of 150. Figure 11 shows the displacement profile of the finite element model developed by them.[9] Clearly the hinges are more concentrated during large displacements in their numerical results than the models shown in Fig. 3(b) and (c).

3 THEORETICAL CRUSH BEHAVIOUR

So far the analysis has dealt only with the calculation of the collapse curve. Calculating the upper and lower load limits of the crushing process shown in Figs 2 and 10 can be achieved by analysing one complete load cycle. Because the deformation in these graphs is regular, the entire axial load–deflection curve for the tube can be modelled by repeating this cycle a certain number of times. It should be stated at this point that the problem presented here is complex, whereas the solution proposed tends to simplify this complexity. However, it could possibly form the basis of future research work in this area.

For example, depending on the R/t ratio, either eqn (20) or eqn (35) can be used to plot the collapse curve as shown in Fig. 12. Because this equation is incorrect for very small values of δ, a horizontal line representing the structure's maximum axial compressive load could be drawn intersecting the load axis and the collapse curve. Again Fig. 12 shows how this is done. Thus the actual rigid-plastic collapse behaviour would be similar to curve efg, and horizontal lines can be drawn through

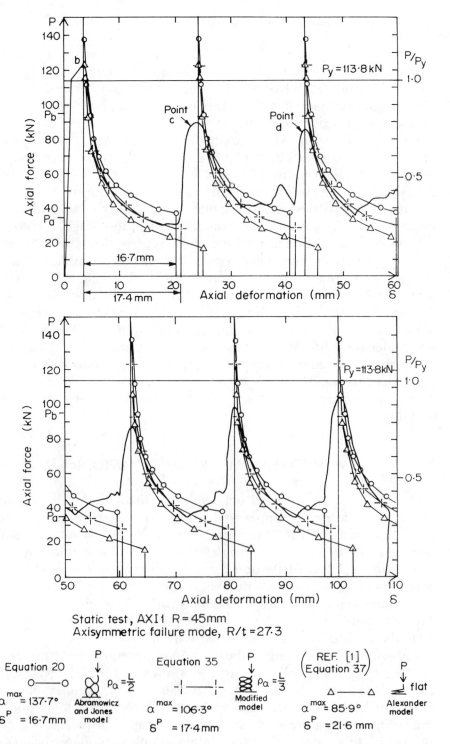

Fig. 10. Comparison of theoretical and experimental collapse curves. All equations make use of eqn (1) to determine L and $\sigma_u = 328$ MPa.

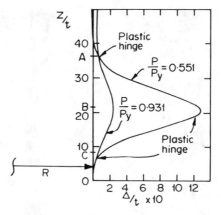

Fig. 11. Deformation profile of axisymmetric fold (after Andronicou and Walker[9]).

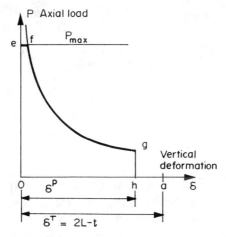

Fig. 12. Predicted rigid-plastic collapse curve of one crush cycle.

points f and g, each representing the upper (P_U) and lower (P_L) load oscillation limit.

Unfortunately, Fig. 10 shows that for tubes with larger R/t ratios, the above procedure would either underestimate the failure load, or overestimate the peak load of subsequent load cycles. Figures 2 and 10 clearly show that the first load cycle is different from the rest of the deformation process and peaks at a higher value. Moreover, it was shown in Ref. 1 that the magnitude of this load should be approximately $P = 2P_y/\sqrt{3}$. Obviously the structure behaves differently once it has failed. Once again, an understanding of why the peak loads are less than the first failure load can be obtained from experimental observations.

Figure 13 shows two photographs of the cylinder with the R/t ratio of

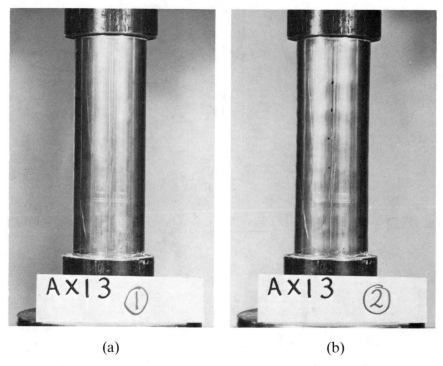

(a)   (b)

Fig. 13. Static test of cylinder (R/t = 27·3) subjected to axial load: (a) prior to loading;
(b) point b in Fig. 10.

27·3. The first photograph was taken prior to load application, whereas
the second one was taken immediately before the structure failed. When
the load was at the value indicated by point b (peak of first load cycle) in
Fig. 10, buckles could be felt by running one's hand along the cylinder.
They are quite noticeable in Fig. 13(b). It was interesting to note that
these buckles remained after the tubes were unloaded. This indicates that
plastic deformation occurred when they formed. Therefore, once the first
load cycle was complete, subsequent load cycles started on a portion of
the tube which already had an initial imperfection. The shape of these
imperfections was similar to the sketch of the exaggerated profile shown
in Fig. 14. These axisymmetric elasto–plastic buckles also occurred in the
stockier tubes (R/t < 20) but they were of a much smaller magnitude.
Nevertheless, they could still be felt by running one's hand along the tube
immediately before the failure load was reached.

Another peculiar phenomenon which occurs just prior to failure, and
may be the reason why the upper load limit for the thinner tube is lower
than the first peak load, can be noticed in Fig. 15. All of these

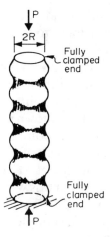

Fig. 14. Sketch showing how the tube buckles just prior to failure (deformation is exaggerated).

Point 7 in Fig. 2   Point 14 in Fig. 2

(a)

Point c in Fig. 10   Point d in Fig. 10

(b)

Fig. 15. Photographs of tubes taken immediately before a peak load in a load cycle: (a) static test for tube with $R/t = 15\cdot4$; (b) static test for tube with $R/t = 27\cdot3$.

photographs show that the tube's radius becomes slightly smaller at a position where the bottom plastic hinge of the next fold is about to form. One explanation why this happens could be as follows.

When a fold forms and collapses its profile is somewhat similar to the sketches shown in Fig. 16. Once the mechanism is initialised there are essentially two ways in which it can deform. The first way is for point B' to come into contact with the fold or the restraint below it, as shown in Fig. 16(v). The load starts to increase and then decrease until point A' finally touches point C' (Fig. 16(vi)). This then causes the gradient of the loading curve to rise sharply until the next mechanism forms (Fig. 16(vii), then 16(i), and so on). Usually when the fold collapses in this way, the axial load–deflection plot shows a second, much smaller, load cycle forming just before the peak load in the cycle is reached. An example of this can be seen in Fig. 2 where the 3rd, 4th, 8th and 9th load cycles are preceded by a small peak. It can also be seen in all cycles except the first two in Fig. 10. This form of loading and collapse was labelled as a type II load oscillation.

The second way in which the fold can deform is when points A' and C' in Fig. 16 come into contact with each other at the same time that point B' contacts the restraint or the fold below it. When this happens there is no smaller load peak evident before the peak load P_U is reached. Load cycles 1, 2, 5, 6 and 7 in Fig. 2 and the 1st and 2nd load cycle in Fig. 10 are typical of such a situation. These cycles were labelled as type I load oscillations as shown in Fig. 16.

Irrespective of the way the mechanism progresses, when all three points A', B' and C' finally come into contact with another fold or restraint (Fig. 16(vi)), all folds are compressed even further. In other words, the radii at B' and C' are reduced such that H_f^7 in Fig. 16(vii) is smaller than H_f^5 in Fig. 16(v). With increased load the curvature between points A and A' in Fig. 16(vi) changes, causing point A to be pushed slightly inwards (Fig. 16(vii)). This movement reduces the cylinder's radius at point A, thus making the tube imperfect in the axial direction and initiating the next fold at a lower peak load. The cycle then repeats itself.

Experimental evidence of the fact that the next fold starts with such an initial imperfection can be seen in frames 7 and 14 of Fig. 4 and in Figs 5 and 6(b). Thus to calculate the peak load for a thinner tube it is only necessary to estimate the magnitude of this imperfection and determine the equivalent collapse load at which it occurs. All of these photographs show that the value of this imperfection is approximately equal to the wall thickness t of the tube with $R/t = 15\cdot4$, and equal to about $1\cdot5t$ for the tube with $R/t = 27\cdot3$.

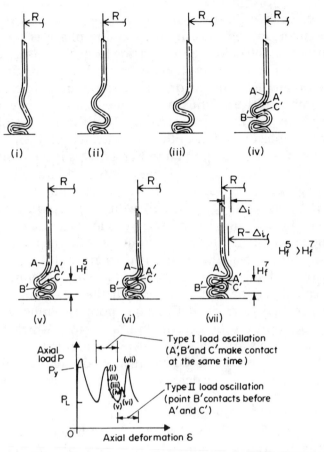

Fig. 16. Sketch showing how the cross-section of an axisymmetric fold for a stocky tube forms and collapses.

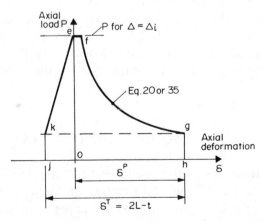

Fig. 17. Predicted axial load–deflection curve for one crush cycle.

From the above brief discussion it becomes evident that the load–deflection curve observed during the loading phase is the result of a complex process. The deformations arising from elastic deflections, fold compaction and elasto–plastic changes in hinge curvature are all superimposed on each other to form the loading curve. To calculate each of these components and thus predict the loading curve is difficult. Therefore it was felt that the procedure about to be described would provide the simplest solution to this complicated problem.

The first step is to define point h in Fig. 17. This is the position on the deformation axis when the material at points A', B' and C' in Fig. 16 is assumed to come into contact with another fold. Point h can be determined by using either eqn (20) with (21) or eqn (35) with (36) depending on the R/t ratio, assuming a type I load cycle, and by using the method shown in Fig. 12. It is worth noting that for the models shown in Fig. 3(b) and (c), δ^P is smaller than the total crushable amount of axial deflection for one load cycle, i.e. $\delta^T = 2L - t$ where L is defined by eqn (1).

Having calculated the position of point h, the maximum deflection δ^T can be marked back from it to define a new point j as indicated in Fig. 17. This is the position on the deformation axis from which the loading curve is assumed to start. The region between points j and o represents the sum of displacements caused by crushing of the previous fold, and the elastic and elasto–plastic deformation of the current fold during the loading phase.

The next step is to define the maximum load. This can be done by using once again either eqn (20) or (35) depending on the R/t ratio. By assuming that the fold is initialised by an imperfection Δ_i approximately equal to the wall thickness t for $R/t < 20$ and to $1.5t$ for $R/t > 20$, the value of the collapse load for the structure which causes this lateral deflection can be found. For example, for $R/t < 20$, $\Delta_i = t$ and a new radius $R_i = R - t$ can be substituted into eqn (20) and solved for P. Having calculated this value, a horizontal line is drawn intersecting the vertical load axis and the rigid plastic curve as shown in Fig. 17. Finally a straight line is drawn from point k to point e. This line then becomes the predicted loading curve.

4 COMPARISON OF RESULTS

In order to see how this method predicts the behaviour of the cylinders tested, the above procedure was carried out for the two types of tubes. The plots shown in Fig. 18 can be compared to experimental observations in Figs 2 and 10. The comparison shows that the actual amount of energy

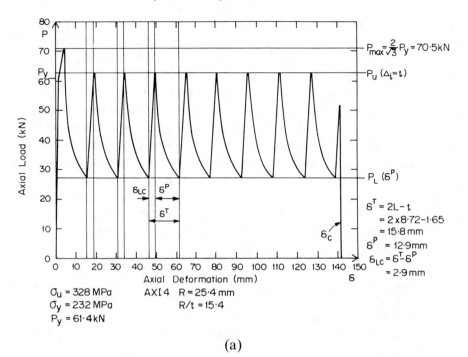

(a)

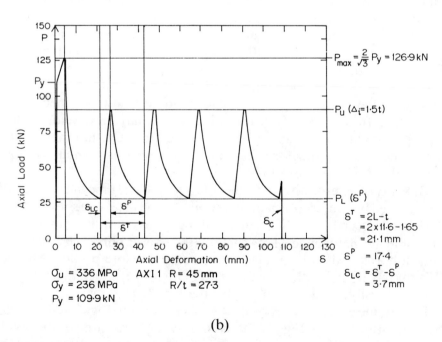

(b)

Fig. 18. Theoretical axial load–deflection curves: (a) prediction of AXI4 deformation using eqn (20); (b) prediction of AXI1 deformation using eqn (35).

absorbed by the tubes is underestimated slightly. Nevertheless, considering the complexity of the problem and the number of approximations made to obtain a solution, it is possible to obtain reasonable results and gain an overall impression of how the cylinder will deform.

The first cycle was also predicted using this method. In this case it is assumed there are no initial imperfections. The cycle is still δ^T long and the collapse curve is predicted as shown in Fig. 17. However, the peak load[1] is now $P_{max} = 2P_y/\sqrt{3}$. Thus elastic deformation is assumed until the squash load is reached, and then a straight line is drawn from this point to P_{max} at the intersection point equivalent to e in Fig. 17.

To predict the crush behaviour of simply supported cylinders would also be straightforward. In this case the rigid-plastic model needs to be changed to a two-hinge mechanism rather than a three-hinge one for the first fold. However, once the first fold has closed, the boundary conditions and mechanism for the remaining folds are the same as those for a clamped cylinder.

Figure 19 shows how the predicted range of load oscillations compares with experimental observations. Because both tubes initially fail by yielding rather than buckling, the maximum possible load sustainable[1] by the structure is $2P_y/\sqrt{3}$. However, once the first fold has collapsed the tube becomes imperfect in its shape (Fig. 15). Thus failure of the next fold occurs somewhere between a load of P_{max} and P_U depending on the magnitude of imperfection. Calculating an accurate value of the lower limit P_L can also be just as difficult as predicting the upper load limit. Figures 10 and 16 show that not only does P_L depend on how concentrated the hinge points are within the mechanism, which in turn is related to the R/t ratio, but it also depends on how the mechanism progresses. In other words, if the collapse mechanism develops into a type I load oscillation, P_L in Fig. 18 is the lower limit. On the other hand, if the structure tends to deform into a type II mechanism, the lower load limit will be a little above this value.

One way of determining the value of P_L for a type II mechanism could be achieved by considering a model similar to the ideal one shown in Fig. 20. It can be seen in this diagram that if there was an initial imperfection of Δ_i, the mechanism develops such that the lower portion BC becomes almost horizontal and contacts other material before portion AB does (Fig. 20(iv)). By estimating the angle (α_i in Fig. 20) at which this occurs, it may be possible to determine P_L for the type II load cycle.

Finally, the energy absorbed by the tubes shown in Figs 1 and 6(b) can be determined from Fig. 18. It is simply the area under the load–deflection curve. An approximate value can also be determined by multiplying the average crush load $P_{av} = (P_U + P_L)/2$, by the total crush distance δ_C.

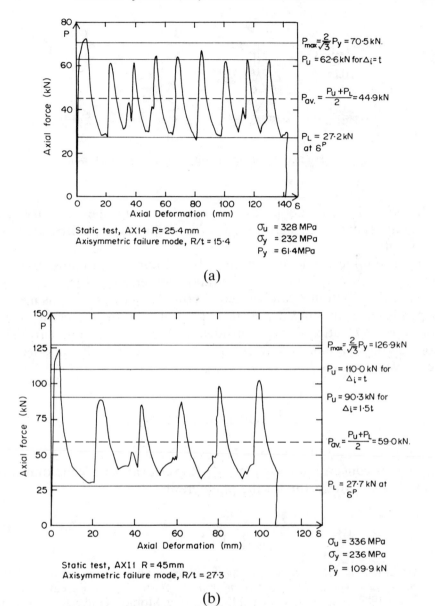

Fig. 19. Predicted range of load oscillations: (a) prediction of load oscillation limits using eqn (20); (b) prediction of load oscillation limits using eqn (36).

5 CONCLUSIONS

The axisymmetric collapse behaviour of stocky thin-walled tubes subjected to an axial crush load can be modelled using a plastic mechanism approach. However, in order to obtain a reasonably accurate

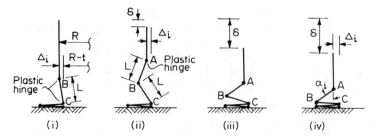

Fig. 20. Assumed plastic mechanism for type II crush mode.

solution, axial and hoop stresses, effective hinge length, curvature, material strain hardening, and yield criteria should be incorporated into the solution.

To determine the load–deflection behaviour of the entire crushing process of tubes which have an R/t ratio between 30 and 15, the method presented in Section 3 can be used. Again, the accuracy of this method depends on estimating the correct value of tube imperfection for the range of R/t ratios being considered. This fact is not surprising considering that axially loaded cylinders are notoriously imperfection-sensitive structures.[10]

ACKNOWLEDGEMENTS

The author would like to thank Professor Noel Murray for his valuable comments concerning the paper, Mr Rob Alexander for the drawings, and Mr Don McCarthy for the photographs.

REFERENCES

1. Grzebieta, R. H., *A review of methods for determining the rigid-plastic collapse curve of axisymmetrically deforming round mild-steel tubes,* Research Report No. 4/1988, Department of Civil Engineering, Monash University, Australia.
2. Alexander, J. M., An approximate analysis of the collapse of thin cylindrical shells under axial loading, *Qt. J. Mech. Appl. Math.,* **13** (1960) 11–15.
3. Johnson, W., *Impact Strength of Materials,* Edward Arnold, London; Crane Russak, New York, 1972.
4. Abramowicz, W. & Jones, N., Dynamic axial crushing of circular tubes, *Int. J. Impact Engng,* **2**(3) (1984) 263–81.
5. Abramowicz, W. & Jones, N., Dynamic progressive buckling of circular and square tubes, *Int. J. Impact Engng,* **4**(4) (1986) 243–70.
6. Grzebieta, R. H., The equilibrium approach for predicting the axial crush

behaviour of round thin-walled tubes. PhD Thesis, Department of Civil Engineering, Monash University, Australia (to be submitted).

7. Murray, N. W., The static approach to energy dissipation in some thin-walled structures, in *Structural Crashworthiness*, ed. N. Jones and T. Wierzbicki, Butterworths, London, 1983, 44–65.

8. Jones, N. & Wierzbicki, T., Preface, *Structural Crashworthiness*, Butterworths, London, 1983.

9. Andronicou, A. & Walker, A. C., A plastic collapse mechanism for cylinders under axial end compression, *J. Constr. Steel Res.*, **1**(4) (1981) 23–34.

10. Donnell, L. H. & Wan, C. C., Effects of imperfections on buckling of thin cylinders and columns under axial compression, *J. Appl. Mech.*, **17** (1950) 73–83.

Thin-Walled Structures **9** (1990) 91–120

Ultimate Load Behaviour of Box-Columns under Combined Loading of Axial Compression and Torsion

M. Mahendran & N. W. Murray*

Department of Civil Engineering, Monash University, Clayton, Victoria 3168, Australia

ABSTRACT

This paper describes a study of the theoretical and experimental behaviour of box-columns of varying b/t ratios under loadings of axial compression and torsion and their combinations. Details of the testing rigs and the testing methods, the results obtained such as the load–deflection curves and the interaction diagrams, and experimental observations regarding the behaviour of box-models and the types of local plastic mechanisms associated with each type of loading are presented. A simplified rigid–plastic analysis is carried out to study the collapse behaviour of box-columns under these loadings, based on the observed plastic mechanisms, and the results are compared with those of experiments.

1 INTRODUCTION

The box-section is one of the commonest thin-walled structures and has been utilized widely in large columns and bridges and for members in stationary and moving industrial structures. When box-sections are used as parts of the structure, they are not always subjected to axial compression only, but to combined loading of axial compression, torsion and bending. The behaviour of box-sections under axial compression is fairly well understood, but this is not so when they are subjected to loadings accompanied by torsion. The ultimate load of box-sections, even when they carry only torsional loading, cannot be

*To whom correspondence should be addressed.

91

Thin-Walled Structures 0263-8231/90/$03·50 © 1990 Elsevier Science Publishers Ltd, England. Printed in Great Britain

predicted. Scheer and Nölke[1] have shown that it would be extremely dangerous to use plate girder theories for box-sections. However, their test results revealed that it is satisfactory to design box-sections using the German code specifications[2] which are based on linear theories. However, reliance on an elastic analysis and first yield as the limiting criterion could result in an unnecessarily conservative design. The investigation described here has therefore been carried out to find how box-sections respond to axial, torsional and combined axial–torsional loading.

2 EXPERIMENTAL ANALYSIS

2.1 General

Fifty-four small-scale steel square box-specimens of width/thickness ratios (b/t) of 60, 78, 100 and 158 were tested with various combinations of axial compression and torsion. The tests with single loadings were completed first and these were followed by those with combined loading. Some box-specimens of high b/t ratios of 200 and 300 were also tested in single loadings in order to obtain a complete ultimate-strength diagram. In order to fabricate box-specimens of different b/t ratios, only the thickness (t) was changed. Except for five longer box-specimens (length/ width L/b = 9), all had a constant L/b ratio of 4·3. The specimen length, chosen to represent the part between two adjacent rigid diaphragms, ensured that the central regions of the box-specimen would deform without any restraint from the loaded edges which had complete rotational fixity. The ends of all the test specimens were strengthened by means of a layer of plaster in order to prevent any premature localized buckling.

Figure 1 shows the cross-sectional dimensions of a typical specimen and the method of fabrication. A simpler method of seam-welding was chosen in order to minimize the initial imperfections and residual stresses. This method of fabrication was the same as that used by Scheer and Nölke,[1] Scheer et al.,[3] and Lacher and Böhm.[4] There would be some effects on the behaviour due to the projections in the specimen, but Scheer and Nölke's[1] experiments on torsion confirmed that the type of joints used in fabricating the box-specimens did not have much influence on the collapse loads or the behaviour. Theoretical considerations showed that in the present programme the small projections would have had only a small influence upon either the torsional or axial properties of the specimens. The yield and ultimate stresses of steel were in the range

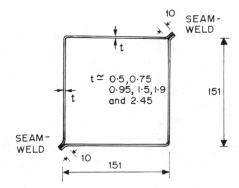

Fig. 1. Cross-sectional dimensions of a typical box-specimen.

of 195–245 MPa and 310–340 MPa, respectively, for thicker sheets (1·90 and 2·45 mm), and 260–310 MPa and 340–375 MPa, respectively, for thinner sheets.

2.2 Tests with axial compression

Altogether nine axial compression tests were performed in an ordinary testing machine. The Moiré fringe technique was used to obtain contour maps of the out-of-plane deflection in all categories of testing.

2.3 Tests with torsion

Altogether 16 tests were carried out with pure torsion. An isometric view of the rotating component of the testing rig and an aerial view of the entire testing rig are given in Figs 2 and 3 respectively. An important component of the testing rig was the rotating channel A which was a 254 × 89 × 36 section of length 3500 mm and was hung from the cross-beams by means of a spherical bearing. Another cylindrical type of bearing was also installed to stabilize the rotating component. The height of channel A could be changed easily by readjusting the spherical bearing if it was required to accommodate shorter or longer specimens. The box-specimen with cover plates at the top and bottom was placed within the space between the channel A and the fixed channel B. Channel A was rotated by pulling the cables, each of 12 mm diameter, at the ends in opposite directions around two small curved channels C at a distance of 1525 mm from the axis of the shaft. The radii of the curved channels C were also set equal to the distance of 1525 mm. Figure 4 shows the special arrangement by which channel A was pulled by means

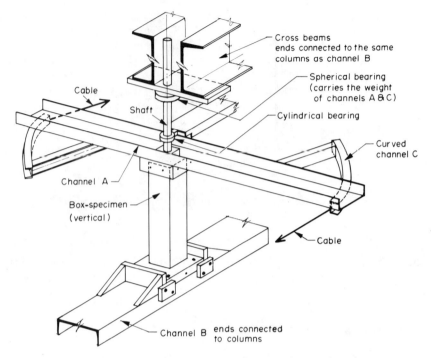

Fig. 2. A simple isometric view of the torsion testing rig.

Fig. 3. An aerial view of the torsion testing rig.

Fig. 4. Components of the torsion testing rig: hydraulic jack–pulley arrangement.

of hydraulic jacks via the cables. Altogether four universal columns were used in the testing rig, two of which were used in the above hydraulic jack–pulley arrangement and the other two were used for fixing the bottom channel B and the cross-beams.

The tensile force in each of the two cables was measured by a tension load cell which was fixed to the cable midway between the pulley and channel C. The tensile forces in the cables were maintained equal by monitoring through the display on the exciter connected to each load cell, and the rotation of the specimen was measured at the ends of two sets of long bars fixed around the plastered parts of the specimens via displacement transducers. All displacement transducers and load cells were connected to a datalogger which printed out the readings.

2.4 Tests with combined axial compression and torsion

Altogether 29 tests were carried out with combined loading. Five longer specimens were used in the case of loadings with a small axial load component in order to accommodate the steeply-spiralling mechanisms on all four sides. The specimen was loaded first with an axial compression force up to a predetermined value between zero and the ultimate capacity of the specimen in pure axial compression, and then loaded with torsion to failure while maintaining the constant axial compression force. In practice, this loading sequence is more likely than that in the reverse order because, for example, a loaded crane would have axial compression in one of its members and, during slewing operations or during a wind gust, torsion could be introduced.

The torsion testing rig was modified in order to load the specimen with combined axial compression and torsion, each of which could be carried out independently. Figure 5 shows the details of the modified components of the testing rig. Additional components, namely a hydraulic jack, a load cell and a loading plate, were accommodated in the space between the bottom channel B and the strong floor. A hole was cut through the channel B to allow axial loading of the specimen. The bottom cover plate of the specimen was no longer bolted to the channel B, but it was free to move vertically. The top-end of the shaft was prevented from moving by means of a very heavy plate of thickness 100 mm clamped to the cross-beams.

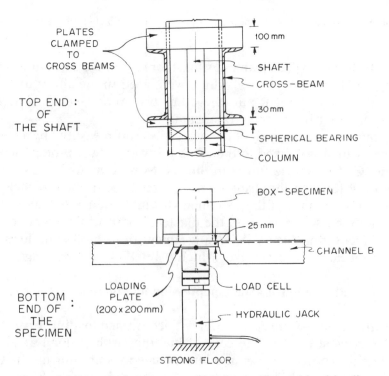

Fig. 5. Additional components used in tests with combined loading.

3 EXPERIMENTAL RESULTS

3.1 Tests with axial compression

The box-specimens of low b/t ratios (60 and 78) developed roof-shaped mechanisms (Fig. 6) and those of high b/t ratios developed the so-called flip-disc mechanisms (Fig. 7) at the same level on all four sides with

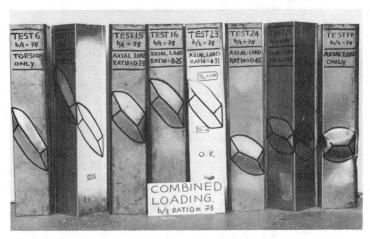

Fig. 6. Box-specimens of b/t ratio = 78 after failure in combined loading of axial compression and torsion — roof mechanism.

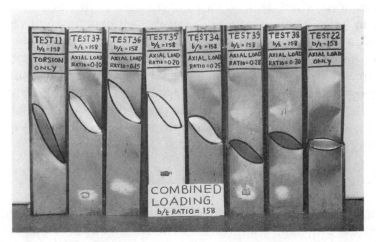

Fig. 7. Box-specimens of b/t ratio = 158 after failure in combined loading of axial compression and torsion — flip-disc mechanism.

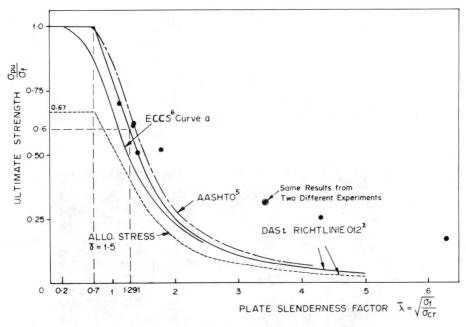

Fig. 8. Curves of ultimate strength in axial compression together with experimental results (●).

alternating concavity and convexity. In general, the behaviour of box-specimens fell into two groups depending on these types of mechanism. Figure 8 presents the curve of ultimate strength in axial compression σ_{pu} versus plate slenderness factor $\bar{\lambda}$ $(= \sqrt{\sigma_f/\sigma_{cr}})$ recommended by some code specifications, where σ_f and σ_{cr} are the yield stress and the plate buckling stress in axial compression, respectively. All experimental results are plotted in the same figure and they exhibit a sufficient margin of safety when compared with the curve of allowable stress (safety factor $\gamma = 1 \cdot 5$) recommended by the German code.[2] However, experimental results belonging to thinner box-columns appeared to have a greater margin of safety than those of thicker box-columns, due to the available post-buckling strength of thinner box-columns which is ignored by the linear buckling theory adopted by the codes.

3.2 Tests with torsion

In general, the behaviour of box-specimens again fell into two groups as in the tests with axial compression. The specimens developed similarly shaped mechanisms, but they were inclined at approximately 30° to the axis of the box-specimen and not at a right angle as in the tests with axial compression (Figs 6 and 7). Tests showed that the presence of a spiralling mechanism in only two sides was sufficient to fail the box-specimen in pure torsion. This result is similar to that found by Murray and Lau[7] in their tests on channel cantilevers. Figure 9 compares the experimental results with the curves of ultimate strength in shear (τ_{pu}) versus plate slenderness factor $\bar{\lambda}$ ($= \sqrt{\tau_f/\tau_{cr}}$) according to plate girder theories developed by Basler,[8] Höglund[9] and Herzog,[10] and those recommended by some code specifications, where τ_f and τ_{cr} are the shear yield stress equal to $\sigma_f/\sqrt{3}$ and the plate shear buckling stress, respectively. The experimental ultimate strength values obtained here appear to agree with those obtained from Scheer and Nölke's[1] experiments (Fig. 9). As observed by Scheer and Nölke,[1] plate girder theories were found to overestimate the ultimate strength of box-columns in torsion in the present case also. However, Basler's[8] theory is safer to use for box-columns of high *b/t* ratios ($\bar{\lambda} > 1.5$, see Fig. 9). The German code[2] recommends the same curve for shear and axial compressive loadings in this non-dimensionalized format, but with a smaller safety factor γ of 1·32 for the former. Comparison of experimental results with this curve leads to the same comments as those made in the case of axial compression.

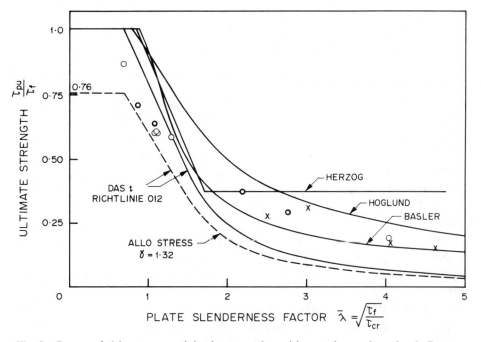

Fig. 9. Curves of ultimate strength in shear together with experimental results. ○, Present experiments; ×, Scheer and Nölkes' experiments.

The presence of initial imperfections and residual stresses did not seem to have a significant effect on box-columns in torsion. A different method of fabrication, such as arc-welding along four corners of the box-section, which would have increased the magnitude of such imperfections, was used in some box-specimens, but the decrease in the ultimate strength of the specimens was insignificant. This observation is similar to those made in the past about the shear behaviour of plates by Harding *et al.*,[11] Dowling *et al.*[12] and Massonnet and Janss,[13] and about the torsional behaviour of box-sections by Scheer and Nölke.[1]

3.3 Tests with combined loading

The behaviour of box-specimens under combined loading was again of two types. They still developed similarly-shaped plastic mechanisms as before. The mechanism which formed perpendicular to the axis of the specimen under pure axial compression and at approximately 30° under pure torsion was inclined at angles between these two values when the specimen was tested with combined axial compression and torsion. Figures 6 and 7 show that as the applied axial compression component in combined loading was decreased and the torque increased, the axis of the mechanisms became more elongated. The same effects are also indicated by the corresponding Moiré fringe photographs of the two types of mechanisms obtained during the tests (Figs 10 and 11). The mechanisms spiralled around the specimen as in the tests with torsion, but all four sides failed in this case.

The ultimate torsional moment, the ductility and the post-collapse strength of the specimen decreased as the axial compression component in combined loading was increased. In the tests conducted with large axial compression closer to the ultimate capacity of the specimen in pure axial compression, the specimen collapsed rapidly from its ultimate torsional moment and pre-set axial compression. Longer specimens behaved in a similar manner to shorter ones tested with the same loading and were able to accommodate the long spiralling mechanisms on all four sides.

Some specimens developed a combined elastic buckling mode under the action of torsion and axial compression. This buckling mode appeared to fall between those in pure axial compression and in pure torsion (Fig. 12(b)) and are in agreement with the plots obtained using a finite strip buckling analysis.[14]

In all categories of test, thicker specimens which developed roof mechanisms collapsed in a ductile manner compared with thinner specimens which developed flip-disc mechanisms. This is because in the

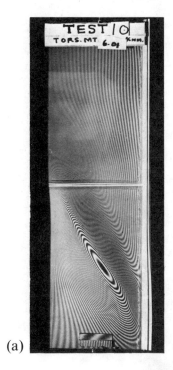

(a)

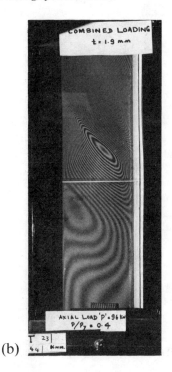

(b)

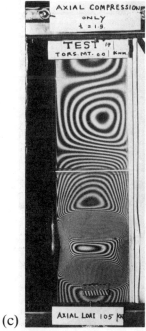

(c)

Fig. 10. Moiré fringe patterns of roof mechanisms — box-specimens of *b/t* ratio = 78: (a) torsion only; (b) combined loading; (c) axial compression only.

M. Mahendran, N. W. Murray

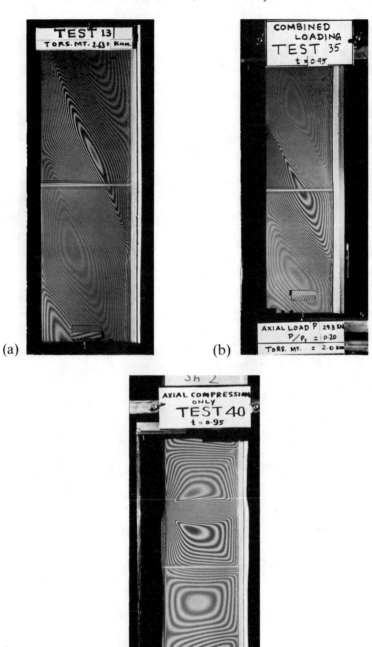

Fig. 11. Moiré fringe patterns of flip-disc mechanisms — box-specimens of *b/t* ratio = 158: (a) torsion only; (b) combined loading; (c) axial compression only.

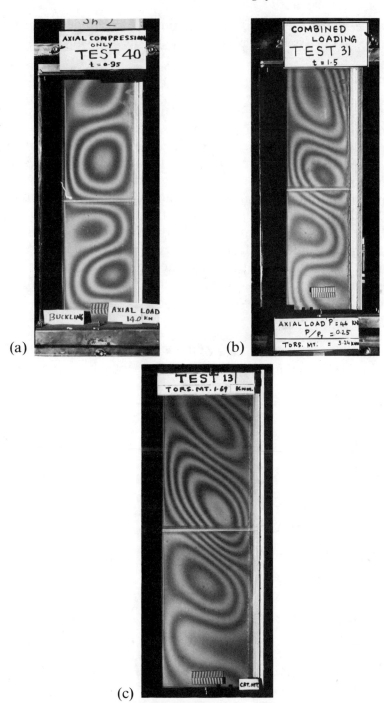

Fig. 12. Various buckling modes observed in the tests: (a) axial compression only;
(b) combined axial compression and torsion; (c) shear only.

former case there are significant regions which undergo in-plane yielding, i.e., failure is by developing a quasi-mechanism.[15]

3.4 Interaction diagrams

Figure 13 is an interaction diagram of ultimate shear stress (τ_u/τ_f) versus maximum (applied) axial compressive stress (σ_a/σ_f) in a non-dimensionalized form. The interaction diagrams of box-columns with b/t ratios of 60 and 78 appear to be similar to each other and the same is true with b/t ratios of 100 and 158. In the case of thicker box-columns, the increasing magnitude of axial compression component in combined loading gradually reduced the carrying capacity of the box-column in torsion (Fig. 13); whereas in the case of thinner box-columns, the torsional strength suddenly decreased to zero as the axial compression approached the ultimate capacity of the box-column in pure axial compression. When the interaction diagrams are presented in a different format (Fig. 14), the graph represented by the equation

$$(\sigma_a/\sigma_{pu}) + (\tau_u/\tau_{pu})^2 = 1 \tag{1}$$

is the best-plot suitable in the case of thicker box-columns ($b/t = 60$ and 78). For thinner box-columns, the graphs represented by the equations

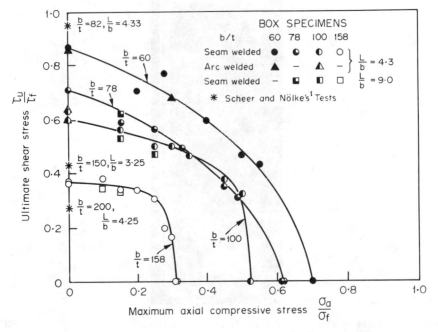

Fig. 13. Experimental interaction diagrams for box-columns.

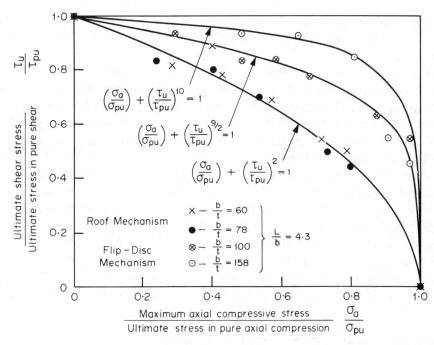

Fig. 14. Experimental interaction diagrams for box-columns of b/t ratios = 60, 78, 100 and 158.

$$(\sigma_a/\sigma_{pu}) + (\tau_u/\tau_{pu})^{9/2} = 1 \tag{2a}$$

$$(\sigma_a/\sigma_{pu}) + (\tau_u/\tau_{pu})^{10} = 1 \tag{2b}$$

prove to be the best-plots for b/t ratios of 100 and 158, respectively.

4 RIGID–PLASTIC ANALYSIS

4.1 General

When subjected to increasing loads of any type, a thin-walled structure will go through three different phases, namely the elastic, the elasto-plastic and the plastic phase. The elastic theory can only predict the behaviour until one of the fibres of the structure begins to yield. In the present case, elastic theory is quite simple, that is, for axial compressive loading Hooke's law is used and for torsional loading the following formula is used:

$$\tau = \frac{T}{2At} \tag{3}$$

where τ is the constant shear stress across the profile of constant thickness t due to a torque T, and A is the area $(=b^2)$ enclosed by the profile.

A non-linear elasto–plastic analysis can be used for the second phase, but it is complicated and expensive in computer time. The final post-collapse behaviour can be analysed using the rigid–plastic theory. This simple but approximate analysis is used to ascertain the suddenness of collapse of structures. Basic concepts of rigid–plastic analysis of thin-walled structures and many examples of applications are given by Murray.[15] Rigid–plastic analysis of thin-walled structures is based upon the type and sizes of some local plastic mechanisms observed in the laboratory tests. In the present experiments, different types of complicated local plastic mechanisms were observed (Section 3), but the rigid–plastic analysis is based on the simplified geometry of such mechanisms. The sides of the box-column are considered to deform with identical mechanisms of a constant idealized geometry and therefore only one plate element of the square box-column is considered in the analysis.

4.2 Reduced plastic moment capacity of hinges

The complicated spatial mechanisms are, in fact, formed by means of a consistent arrangement of many straight or curved line hinges (yield lines). In order to analyse the spatial mechanism, one should know the plastic moment capacity of the line hinges. In the case of a simple line hinge with only the axial load acting perpendicular to the hinge, the plastic moment capacity M'_p per unit length is given by[16]

$$M'_p = M_p \left[1 - \left(\frac{\sigma}{\sigma_f} \right)^2 \right] \tag{4}$$

where σ/σ_f is the ratio of average axial stress to yield stress, and M_p is the full plastic moment capacity in pure bending per unit width of plate $(=\sigma_f t^2/4)$.

When the line hinge is inclined to the axial load and the rigid–plastic analysis is carried out using an equilibrium method, Murray[17,18] has shown that it requires a new moment capacity M''_p per unit width of plate, which is given by

$$M''_p = M'_p \sec^2 (90 - \alpha) \tag{5}$$

where α is the angle of inclination of line hinge with the axial load. However, when the structure is subjected to combined loads and the hinge is not perpendicular to the line of action of the axial load, no such simple formula is available. In this section the reduced plastic moment capacity of such a hinge is derived by using a von Mises criterion.

Figure 15 shows the plate which carries an average compressive stress σ and an average shear stress τ. The plastic hinge is inclined at an angle α to the line of action of σ. The average compressive stress σ_1 acting normal to the plane of the hinge, the average compressive stress σ_2 acting in the direction of the hinge, and the average shear stress τ_{12} associated with them may be found by using Mohr's circle. Thus,

$$\sigma_1 = \frac{\sigma}{2} - \sqrt{\left(\frac{\sigma}{2}\right)^2 + \tau^2} \cos(2\alpha + \beta) \tag{6}$$

$$\sigma_2 = \frac{\sigma}{2} + \sqrt{\left(\frac{\sigma}{2}\right)^2 + \tau^2} \cos(2\alpha + \beta) \tag{7}$$

$$\tau_{12} = \sqrt{\left(\frac{\sigma}{2}\right)^2 + \tau^2} \sin(2\alpha + \beta) \tag{8}$$

$$\beta = \tan^{-1}\left(\frac{2\tau}{\sigma}\right) \tag{9}$$

It must be emphasized that σ_1 is an average compressive stress at the hinge, but there will be a tension yield zone of depth $\frac{1}{2}t - d$ and a compression yield zone of depth $\frac{1}{2}t + d$ (Fig. 16) in which the stresses

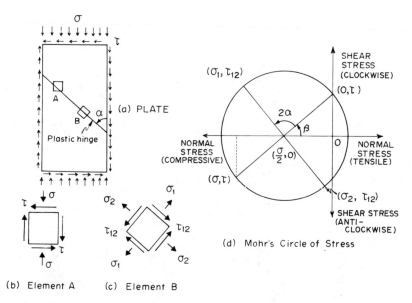

Fig. 15. Mohr's circle of stress to determine σ_1, σ_2 and τ_{12}.

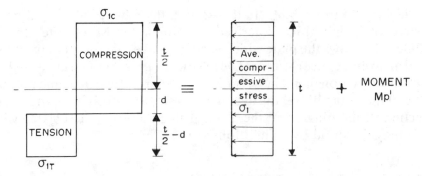

Fig. 16. Assumed stress distribution of σ_1.

normal to the hinge plane are σ_{1T} and σ_{1C}, respectively. As in an earlier analysis by Murray,[18] it is assumed that the other stresses, viz. σ_2 and τ_{12}, are uniformly distributed through the thickness and are therefore given by eqns (7) and (8).

Figure 17 shows the distribution of stresses on elements in the compression and tension zones at the hinge face. The von Mises criterion for yielding in these zones gives the following relationships:

(a) for element C

$$\sigma_f^2 = \sigma_{1C}^2 + \sigma_2^2 - \sigma_{1C}\sigma_2 + 3\tau_{12}^2 \tag{10}$$

(b) for element T

$$\sigma_f^2 = \sigma_{1T}^2 + \sigma_2^2 + \sigma_{1T}\sigma_2 + 3\tau_{12}^2 \tag{11}$$

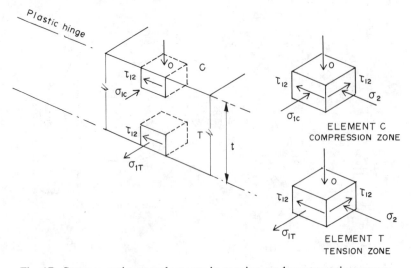

Fig. 17. Stresses acting on elements in tension and compression zones.

Solving these quadratic equations and letting

$$\sigma_{1C} = k_{1C}\sigma_f \quad \text{and} \quad \sigma_{1T} = k_{1T}\sigma_f \tag{12}$$

we obtain

$$k_{1C} = R + \frac{\sigma_2}{2\sigma_f} \quad \text{and} \quad k_{1T} = R - \frac{\sigma_2}{2\sigma_f} \tag{13}$$

where

$$R = \sqrt{\left[1 - \frac{3}{4}\left(\frac{\sigma_2}{\sigma_f}\right)^2 - 3\left(\frac{\tau_{12}}{\sigma_f}\right)^2\right]} \tag{14}$$

In order to locate the dividing line between the tensile and compressive yield zones, an equilibrium analysis can be carried out using Fig. 16. Thus,

$$\sigma_1 t = \sigma_{1C}\left(\frac{t}{2} + d\right) - \sigma_{1T}\left(\frac{t}{2} - d\right) \tag{15}$$

From eqns (6) and (7) and solving.

$$\frac{d}{t} = \frac{1}{2R}\left(\frac{\sigma}{\sigma_f} - \frac{3\sigma_2}{2\sigma_f}\right) \tag{16}$$

Finally, the plastic moment capacity per unit length of hinge is

$$\begin{aligned}
M'_p &= \sigma_{1C}\left(\frac{t}{2} + d\right)\left(\frac{t}{4} - \frac{d}{2}\right) + \sigma_{1T}\left(\frac{t}{2} - d\right)\left(\frac{t}{4} + \frac{d}{2}\right) \\
&= \frac{\sigma_{1C} + \sigma_{1T}}{2}\left[\left(\frac{t}{2}\right)^2 - d^2\right] \\
&= M_p R\left[1 - \left(\frac{2d}{t}\right)^2\right]
\end{aligned} \tag{17}$$

This result has been compared with a similar analysis based on the Tresca yield criterion by Mahendran.[19]

4.3 Rigid–plastic analysis of plastic mechanisms observed in tests with axial compression on box-columns

A number of researchers (e.g. Murray[20] and Walker and Murray[21]) have observed and analysed the roof mechanism for plates of low *b/t* ratio. However, there were differences in the way they idealized the geometry of the mechanism. Figure 18 shows the idealized roof mechanism in this analysis. Present experiments revealed that the angle α and the ratio

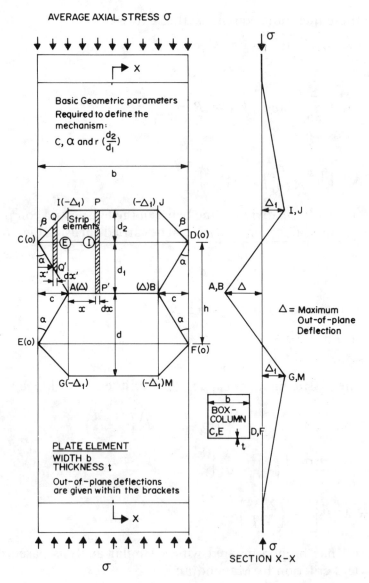

Fig. 18. Idealized roof mechanism for pure axial compression.

$r(= d_2/d_1)$ are about 30° and 0·6, respectively, which are different from those assumed by Murray.[20] As pointed out by Murray,[15] any complicated plastic mechanism can be analysed by subdividing it into many so-called basic mechanisms. In the present case the mechanism can be considered in two parts, the inner region of width $b - 2c$ and the two identical edge regions each of width c, by analysing the equilibrium of a strip element from each region.

For small deflections, this mechanism behaves like a true mechanism since the regions adjoining the mechanism can undergo elastic deformations. Beyond small deflections, the edge regions EAC and FBD will be yielding to maintain a kinematically admissible mechanism. Therefore at large deflections, the mechanism behaves like a quasi-mechanism [15] formed when a true mechanism (inner region) is combined with yielding regions (edge regions). In this section the large-deflection theory is used to derive the unloading curves.

For the inner region, the hinges are perpendicular to the axial load and thus the M'_p expressions given by eqns (4) and (17) are identical. Using the expression for M'_p given by eqn (4) for the equilibrium of the strip element in a similar way to Murray,[20] the total force carried by the inner region is obtained:

$$F_{inner} = \sigma_f (b - 2c)t \left[\sqrt{(1 + r)^2 \left(\frac{\Delta}{t}\right)^2 + 1} - (1 + r)\frac{\Delta}{t} \right] \tag{18}$$

For the edge regions in large deflections, the force carried by the edge regions is given by

$$F_{edge} = 2\sigma_f ct \tag{19}$$

From eqns (18) and (19), the average axial stress σ across the box-column is obtained:

$$\frac{\sigma}{\sigma_f} = \frac{b - 2c}{b} \left[\sqrt{(1 + r)^2 \left(\frac{\Delta}{t}\right)^2 + 1} - (1 + r)\frac{\Delta}{t} \right] + \frac{2c}{b} \tag{20}$$

Figure 19 compares the theoretical large deflection unloading curves with those of experiments. During testing with all cases of loading, it was observed that the outer hinges tended to move towards the central hinge during large deflections, i.e. r tended to zero. Hence the unloading curve for the geometry of mechanism with r equal to zero, as assumed by Walker and Murray,[21] is also plotted in the same figure. Thus the theoretical and experimental results for the roof mechanisms appear to agree reasonably well. The flip-disc mechanism (Fig. 20) has also been analysed [19] using four assumed shapes. The analysis is complicated by the presence of kinks at the corners. These kinks allow axial shortening of the specimens to occur.

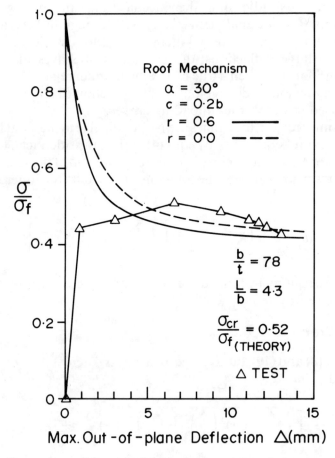

Fig. 19. Comparison of theoretical rigid–plastic curves and experimental results.

4.4 Rigid–plastic analysis of plastic mechanisms observed in tests with loads associated with torsion

Figure 21 shows the idealized roof mechanism in this case. The stresses due to these loadings are the torsional shear stress τ and an average axial compressive stress σ_a as shown in the same figure. Each plate element undergoes a shear-type deformation and shortening in its own plane and a twisting-type deformation. The twisting-type deformation of plate elements is considered not to affect the out-of-plane deflection. In fact, such twisting-type deformations of plate elements tend to change the

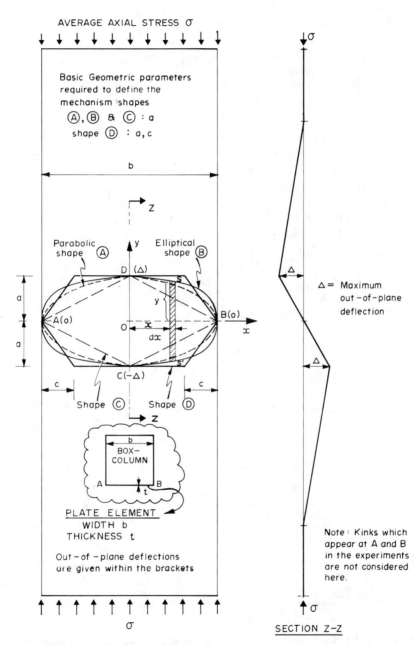

Fig. 20. Idealized flip-disc mechanism for pure axial compression.

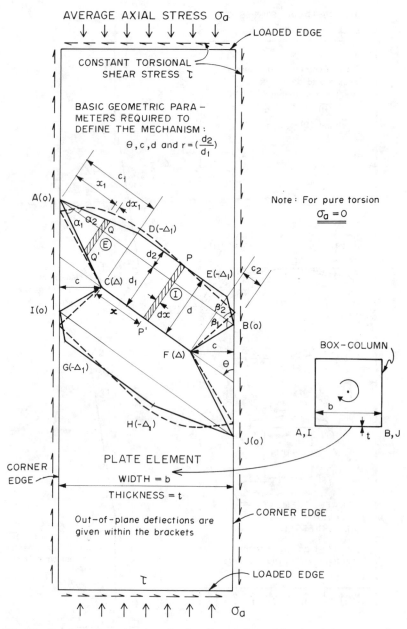

Fig. 21. Idealized roof mechanism for loadings of combined axial compression and torsion and pure torsion.

shape of the mechanism to that shown by dotted lines in Fig. 21. The change of shape of the mechanism becomes less noticeable as the axial compression component in combined loading is increased. For the sake of simplicity, the changes to the shape of the mechanism are ignored in the analysis. Hence the mechanism can be considered to consist of the inner region with parallel hinges and the two edge regions with inclined hinges and again these regions are analysed separately using a large-deflection theory.

We consider a strip element in the inner region with the forces acting on it as shown in Fig. 22. As the hinges are inclined at an angle θ to the plate edge parallel to the box-column axis, the stresses are provided with a subscript θ. The shear stress τ acting on a plane parallel to the loaded edge of the plate is assumed to be constant across the box-column at any stage of the loading. It can be shown by considering longitudinal equilibrium of elements around the profile that this assumption will not lead to significant errors. But the associated normal stress σ varies across the width of each plate element with an average axial stress equal to the applied axial stress σ_a, that is,

$$\frac{\sigma_a}{\sigma_f} = \left(1 - \frac{2c}{b}\right)\frac{(\sigma)_{in}}{\sigma_f} + \frac{2c}{b}\frac{(\sigma)_{edge}}{\sigma_f} \tag{21}$$

where appropriate additional subscripts are provided to separate the stresses across the regions. It is to be noted that $(\sigma)_{edge}$ is an average stress across the edge regions whereas $(\sigma)_{in}$ is constant across the inner region.

For rotational equilibrium of the strip element,

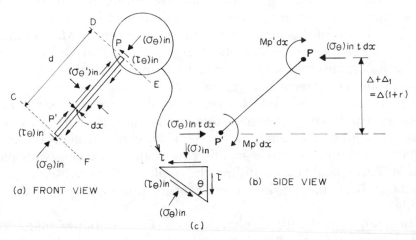

(a) FRONT VIEW   (b) SIDE VIEW   (c)

Fig. 22. A strip element in the inner region of roof mechanism — torsional loadings.

$$(\sigma_\theta)_{in} \, t \, dx \, (1 + r) \, \Delta \; = \; 2 M'_p \, dx \tag{22}$$

where M'_p is a function of $(\sigma)_{in}$, τ and θ, and is given by eqn (17). Letting $M'_p = R_m M_p$, we obtain

$$\frac{(\sigma_\theta)_{in}}{\sigma_f} \; = \; \frac{0 \cdot 5 \, R_m}{(1 + r) \, \Delta / t} \tag{23}$$

The relationship between $(\sigma)_{in}$, τ and $(\sigma_\theta)_{in}$ is given by eqns (6) to (9) written in another form, i.e.

$$(\sigma_\theta)_{in} \; = \; (\sigma)_{in} \sin^2\theta + \tau \sin 2\theta \tag{24}$$

For large deflections, the edge regions ACI and BFJ are assumed to be yielding under the combined action of shear and axial compression to maintain a kinematically admissible mechanism. Under such conditions, the average stress $(\sigma)_{edge}$ acting on a plane parallel to the loaded edge within the edge regions is given by the following equation:

$$\frac{(\sigma)_{edge}}{\sigma_f} \; = \; \sqrt{1 - \left(\frac{\tau}{\tau_f}\right)^2} \tag{25}$$

The main aim of this analysis is to obtain values of Δ for various load levels of τ and a constant σ_a. Hence for values of τ / τ_f ranging from 0 to 1, $(\sigma)_{edge}$, $(\sigma)_{in}$ and $(\sigma_\theta)_{in}$ are calculated first using eqns (25), (21) and (24), respectively, and thus Δ is determined finally from eqn (23). This process is repeated for all combinations of torsion and axial compression by using the geometrical parameters of the observed mechanism in each case.

For small deflections, equations similar to (23) are obtained for each edge region by considering the rotational equilibrium of a strip element. These equilibrium equations have to be solved iteratively to satisfy eqn (21). The details of this iterative procedure are given by Mahendran.[19]

Figure 23 compares the theoretical large-deflection unloading curves derived for the observed value of r and also for $r = 0$ as in the case of axial compression. The agreement is generally good considering the complexity of the mechanism, and it improves as the axial compression component in combined loading increases due to the fact that the idealized mechanism used in the analysis represents the experimentally observed mechanism more accurately in this case than in the case with pure torsion. Theoretical curves confirm the sudden collapse observed for a very large axial compression component in combined loading during testing.

The analysis of the flip-disc mechanism (Fig. 24) follows that of the roof mechanism for small deflections. Since the effect of kinking during

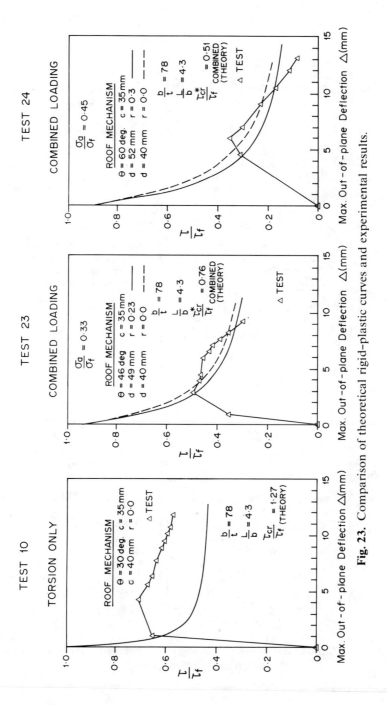

Fig. 23. Comparison of theoretical rigid-plastic curves and experimental results.

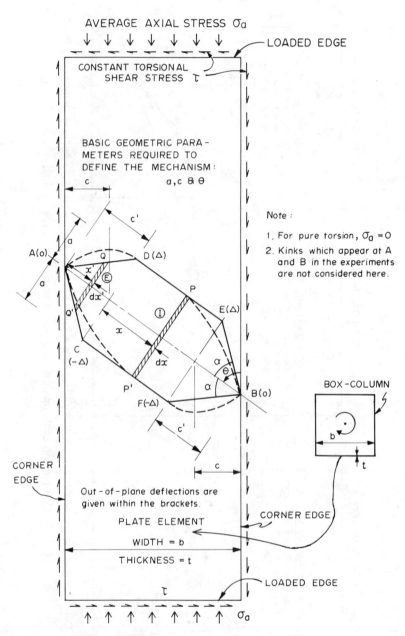

Fig. 24. Idealized flip-disc mechanism for loadings of combined axial compression and torsion and pure torsion.

large deflections is not accounted for, theoretical curves are found to be underestimates.[19] However, these curves predict the general trend of collapse as the interaction of torsion and axial compression takes place.

5 CONCLUSIONS

This paper presents the details of an experimental programme studying the behaviour of box-columns under various combinations of torsion and axial compression. Experimental interaction diagrams obtained thus can be used in the design of box-columns under these loadings. The use of plate girder theories in estimating the ultimate strength of box-columns in torsion is mostly found to be unsafe, as observed by Scheer and Nölke.[1] Two types of local plastic mechanisms, namely the roof and flip-disc mechanisms, were observed in all cases of loading. Collapse behaviour of these box-columns was studied by means of a simplified rigid–plastic analysis of the observed complicated plastic mechanisms and the results are compared with those of experiments. Large-deflection theoretical curves derived in the case of roof mechanisms agree reasonably well with experimental curves for all cases of loading.

ACKNOWLEDGEMENT

One of the authors (M.M.) would like to thank Monash University for making available the Monash Graduate Scholarship during this research work.

REFERENCES

1. Scheer, J. & Nölke, H., Traglastversuche an torsionsbelasteten, dunnwandigen Kastentragermodellen, *Bauingenieur,* **51** (1976) 381–6.
2. DASt Richtlinic 012 — Beulsicherheitsnachweise für platten, *Deutscher Ausschuss für Stahlbau,* Oct. 1978.
3. Scheer, J., Nölke, H. & Böhm, M., Traglastversuche an dunnwandigen Kastentragermodellen mit Biegemomentenbeanspruchung, *Bauingenieur,* **53** (1978) 379–86.
4. Lacher, G. & Böhm, M., Traglastversuche an dunnwandigen Kastentrager-modellen mit kombinierter Biegemomenten- und Torsionsbeanspruchung, *Bauingenieur,* **56** (1981) 45–54.
5. AASHTO, *Standard Specifications for Highway Bridges,* 11th Edition, Washington, DC, 1977.

6. ECCS, *European Recommendations for Steel Construction,* The Construction Press, UK, 1981.
7. Murray, N. W. & Lau, Y. C., The behaviour of a channel cantilever under combined bending and torsional loads, *Thin-Walled Structures,* **1** (1983) 55–74.
8. Basler, K., Strength of plate girders in shear, *J. Struct. Div., Proc. ASCE,* No. ST7 (Oct. 1961) 151–97.
9. Höglund, T., Livets Verkningssatt och Barformaga Hos Tunnavaggig I-Balk, Div. Building Statics and Structural Engineering, Royal Inst. Tech., *Bulletin No. 93* (1971), Stockholm.
10. Herzog, M., Die Traglast unversteifter und versteifter, dunnwandiger Blechtrager unter reinem Schub und Schub mit Biegung nach Versuchen, *Bauingenieur,* **49** (1974) 382–9.
11. Harding, J. E., Hobbs, R. E. & Neal, B. G., Ultimate load behaviour of plates under combined direct and shear in-plane loading, in *Steel Plated Structures,* ed. P. J. Dowling *et al.,* Crosby Lockwood Staples, London, 1977, 369–403.
12. Dowling, P. J., Frieze, P. A. & Harding, J. E., Imperfection sensitivity of steel plates under complex edge loading, *ECCS–IABSE Colloquium on Stability of Steel Structures,* Prelim. Report, Liège, Belgium, April 1977, 305–14.
13. Massonnet, Ch. & Janss, J., A state of art report on tolerances in steel plated structures, in *The Design of Steel Bridges,* ed. K. C. Rockey and H. R. Evans, Granada, London, 1981, 83–118.
14. Mahendran, M. & Murray, N. W., Elastic buckling analysis of ideal thin-walled structures under combined loading using a finite strip method, *Thin-Walled Structures,* **4** (1986) 329–62.
15. Murray, N. W., *Introduction to the Theory of Thin-Walled Structures,* Oxford Press, London, May 1984.
16. Matheson, J. A. L., *Hyperstatic Structures,* Vol. 1, Butterworths, London, 1959.
17. Murray, N. W., Das aufnehmbare Moment in einem zur Richtung der Normalkraft schrag liegenden plastischen Gelenk, *Bautechnik,* **50**(2) (1973) 57–8.
18. Murray, N. W., The effect of shear and normal stresses on the plastic moment capacity of inclined hinges in thin-walled steel structures, *Festschrift Roik,* Inst. für Konstruktiven Ingenieurbau, Rhur Uni Bochum, Mitt. Nr 84–3 (Sept. 1984) 237–48.
19. Mahendran, M., *Box-columns with combined axial compressive and torsional loading,* PhD Thesis, Monash University, Australia, June 1985.
20. Murray, N. W., Buckling of stiffened panels loaded axially and in bending, *Structural Engineer,* **51**(8) (Aug. 1973) 285–301.
21. Walker, A. C. & Murray, N. W., A plastic collapse mechanism for compressed plates, *Publ. IABSE,* **35-I** (1975) 217–36.

SESSION 2

Thin-Walled Structures **9** (1990) 121–134

The Treatment of Shear Lag in Design

B. A. Burgan

Sir Frederick Snow (International) Ltd, PO Box 9806, Amman, Jordan

&

P. J. Dowling

Department of Civil Engineering, Imperial College of Science and Technology,
London SW7 2BU, UK

ABSTRACT

*This paper presents a comprehensive guide to designers for dealing with the
shear lag problem in structural design. First, the effect of shear lag on the
elastic behaviour of box girders is addressed and simple design rules for
estimating its influence are described. The second part of the paper describes
design methods for assessing the effect of shear lag at the ultimate limit state.
These are derived from the results of recent research and their impact on the
new generation of limit state codes is examined. The paper provides a compact
reference of practical design methods and a bibliography of the associated
research. It also forms the background to the design rules in EC3 Part 2
(Bridges).*

NOTATION

A Total cross-sectional area of the flange plate and associated stiffeners

A_f Total cross-sectional area of the flange plate

A_s Total cross-sectional area of the flange stiffeners

A_w Total cross-sectional area of the web plates

b Plate panel width

Thin-Walled Structures 0263-8231/90/$03·50 © 1990 Elsevier Science Publishers Ltd,
England. Printed in Great Britain.

B	Flange breadth
B_e	Shear lag effective breadth of the flange
d_s	Stiffener depth
E	Young's modulus
l	Length of stiffened panel between cross girders
l/r	Strut slenderness
L	Span between supports
M_i	Bending moment at cross-section considered due to load $i(i = 1, \ldots n)$
t	Flange plate thickness
t_s	Stiffener thickness
t_w	Web plate thickness
α	Ratio of the cross-sectional area of the flange stiffeners to the cross-sectional area of the flange plate
β	Plate panel slenderness $= (b/t)\sqrt{(\sigma_0/E)}$
σ_0	Yield stress
σ_m	Longitudinal flange stress at a web–flange junction
σ_x	Longitudinal flange stress at a distance x from the mid-point between two webs
ψ_e	Elastic shear lag effective breadth ratio
ψ_i	Effective breadth ratio appropriate to load $i(i = 1, \ldots, n)$
ψ_{max}	Ratio of the ultimate strength of the compression flange in the presence of shear lag to the yield stress
ψ_u	Ratio of the ultimate strength of the compression flange in pure bending to the yield stress
ψ_x	Effective breadth under the point of application of the load
ψ^p_{2x}	Effective breadth ratio for a point load at mid-span of a girder with length $2x$
ψ^p_{2y}	Effective breadth ratio for a point load at mid-span of a girder with length $2(L - x)$

1 INTRODUCTION

In the derivation of the elementary theory of bending, it is assumed that the cross-sections of a girder which were plane before bending remain plane after bending. However, for a girder with wide flanges, deviations from this assumption occur; owing to the action of in-plane shear strain in the flanges, the longitudinal displacements in the parts of the flange remote from the webs lag behind those nearer the webs. This phenomenon, termed shear lag, was first recognized in aircraft design by the advent of metal sheets to replace the fabric covers in wing structures. The same problem was also encountered by ship designers, particularly in consideration of the overall bending behaviour of a ship.

The development in bridge design and construction methods during this century has resulted in bridge structures (of both steel and composite steel/concrete) in which the proportions are such that the shear lag phenomenon is of significance and requires consideration in design. Consequently, considerable research effort was directed towards the development of design rules that would enable the designer to account for shear lag in practical design situations.

The evolution of various generations of design codes and the development in methods of construction have played a significant role in the way in which shear lag design rules have developed. In broad terms, the research effort can be divided into the study of the effect of shear lag on the elastic behaviour and subsequently on the nonlinear behaviour of the structure. This reflects the shift from allowable stress to limit state design.

The consequence of shear lag in the elastic range is that deflections and longitudinal stresses at the web–flange intersections of a girder increase above those predicted by the elementary theory of bending. The longitudinal elastic stress distribution in the flange of a girder caused by shear lag, due to shear deformations in the flange, takes a nonlinear form as illustrated in Fig. 1.

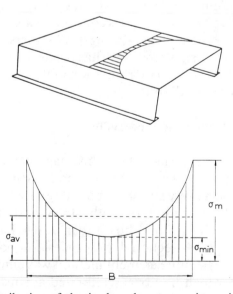

Fig. 1. Distribution of elastic shear lag stresses in a wide flange.

The effect of shear lag on girder behaviour in the presence of material and geometric nonlinearities is more complex and depends largely on the ability (or otherwise) of the structure to deform without significant load shedding. Since the advent of limit state codes, it became necessary to consider the effect of shear lag both at the serviceability limit state (when the structure is assumed to behave elastically) and at the ultimate limit state (when geometric and/or material nonlinearities affect the structural behaviour).

The aim of this paper is to describe simple design methods for dealing with the shear lag problem at both the serviceability and the ultimate limit states and to give the designer an insight into these design methods which constitute the background to EC3 Part 2 (Bridges).

2 SHEAR LAG IN THE ELASTIC RANGE

The effect of shear lag on a girder with wide flanges is manifested by an increase in the overall deflection of the girder, an increase in longitudinal stresses at the web–flange intersection and a decrease in the longitudinal stresses at the centre of the flange. For design purposes, it is often convenient when calculating the deflections or stresses of a wide-flanged girder to replace the actual breadth B of each flange by a certain reduced breadth B_e, such that the application of the elementary theory of bending to the transformed girder cross-section gives the correct value of maximum deflection or longitudinal stress. The reduced breadth B_e is termed the effective breadth and this concept for accounting for shear lag has found wide acceptance amongst designers. The appeal and simplicity of such a design procedure has produced the need for a simple and reliable method for the determination of the effective breadth under any set of practical conditions.

2.1 Background to the design procedure

The first comprehensive study of the shear lag phenomenon in steel box girders to be undertaken was by Moffatt and Dowling.[1,2] The study led to a complete, comparatively simple, set of design rules which can be used for estimating the variation of both stress and deflection effective breadths along the length of a box girder bridge having any practical plan dimensions, cross-sectional properties, support conditions and load distribution. The finite element method was employed in the study, using a program which had been calibrated against experimental and analytical data. The results of the study formed the basis of the shear lag rules in the steel bridge design code BS 5400 (Part 3).[3]

The study showed that shear lag was most significantly dependent on the plan dimensions of the flange, expressed as *B/L*. The dramatic effect of this parameter is clearly illustrated by Fig. 2 which shows the variation of the effective breadth ratio with *B/L* for a simply supported girder under point loading and uniformly distributed loading.

The flange orthotropy, expressed in terms of the ratio of the flange stiffener area (A_s) to the flange plate area (A_f) showed an approximately linear effect on the effective breadth ratio which decreased as the stiffening ratio increased because there is proportionally more extensional stiffness to be mobilized by the same shear stiffness. (This observation is also of practical significance in composite steel–concrete and reinforced concrete girders where, after cracking, the concrete contributes only to the shear stiffness while extensional rigidity is provided solely by the steel. In that case there is an excess of shear stiffness compared to the extensional stiffness of the equivalent steel flange obtained by smearing the area of reinforcing bars.) The design rules give values of the effective breadth ratio for values of the stiffening ratio equal to 0 and 1 respectively. As the relationship between the effective breadth ratio and the stiffening ratio is linear, the effective breadth for intermediate degrees of stiffening can be determined by linear interpolation.

The cross-sectional dimensions, expressed in terms of the ratio of the flange area (A) to the associated web area (A_w), was found to have little influence, except in the case of stress effective breadth at a cross-section under a point load. In such cases, a multiplication factor given by $(1 \cdot 08 - 0 \cdot 04 \, A/A_w)$ was proposed to account for this effect.

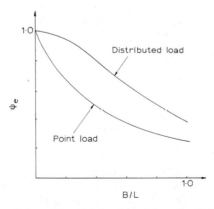

Fig. 2. Variation of shear lag effective breadth ratio with flange aspect ratio.

The position and type of the applied loads, the support conditions and the position in the span at which the effective breadth is calculated were all significant parameters and were accounted for in tabular form and through the use of simple design expressions.[1,2] Furthermore, it was found that the effective breadth of the flange of a continuous girder can be conveniently estimated by treating each portion of the girder between points of contraflexure as an equivalent simply supported span.

On the basis of the above observations an analytical model was proposed whereby any girder is considered to consist of an assemblage of simply supported L-girders each comprising a flange plate and an associated web plate. The effective breadths of the individual L-girders are determined from a set of tables which have as parameters the type of load (point, uniform), the breadth to length ratio of the flange, the stiffener to plate area ratio of the flange and the position along the span where the effective breadth is required (mid span, quarter span, support). An example of one such table for a girder carrying a uniformly distributed load is shown in Table 1. The parameters in each table are

TABLE 1
Effective Breadth Ratios for Simply Supported Box Girders
(Uniform load over length of each web)

α	$\dfrac{B}{L}$	Stress effective breadth			Deflection effective breadth		
		Mid-span	Quarter-span	Support	Mid-span	Quarter-span	Support
0·0	0	1·00	1·00	1·00	1·00	1·00	1·00
	0·05	0·98	0·98	0·84	0·98	0·98	0·98
	0·10	0·95	0·93	0·70	0·94	0·94	0·93
	0·20	0·81	0·77	0·52	0·79	0·79	0·77
	0·40	0·50	0·46	0·32	0·48	0·47	0·47
	0·60	0·29	0·28	0·22	0·31	0·30	0·30
	0·80	0·20	0·19	0·16	0·21	0·20	0·20
	1·00	0·16	0·15	0·12	0·17	0·16	0·16
1·0	0	1·00	1·00	1·00	1·00	1·00	1·00
	0·05	0·97	0·96	0·77	0·93	0·92	0·92
	0·10	0·89	0·86	0·60	0·84	0·84	0·83
	0·20	0·67	0·62	0·38	0·62	0·62	0·60
	0·40	0·35	0·32	0·22	0·33	0·33	0·32
	0·60	0·22	0·20	0·15	0·21	0·20	0·20
	0·80	0·16	0·15	0·11	0·16	0·16	0·16
	1·00	0·12	0·11	0·09	0·12	0·12	0·12

such that values of the effective breadth for intermediate values of B/L, the stiffening ratio and the position in the span could be obtained by linear interpolation between the values in the tables.

In addition to the above parameters, an expression was given to account for the variation in the position of a point load within the span. This is based on the effective breadth ratio of an equivalent span and is given by

$$\psi_x = \tfrac{1}{3}(2\psi_{2x}^{\text{p}} + \psi_{2y}^{\text{p}})$$ (1)

For a point loaded girder, the effective breadth ratio of the flange increases with increasing distance from the point of application of the point load. A method, based on linear interpolation, for estimating the effective breadth variation along the span in such cases was given. An expression for estimating the effective breadth ratio under any load combination was also given by utilizing the effective breadth ratios for the individual constituent load conditions. In such cases the effective breadth ratio is given by

$$\psi = \frac{M_1 + M_2 + \ldots + M_n}{\dfrac{M_1}{\psi_1} + \dfrac{M_2}{\psi_2} + \ldots + \dfrac{M_n}{\psi_n}}$$ (2)

The availability of effective breadth ratios enables the peak stresses at the web–flange junction to be calculated by application of simple bending theory. However, in the design of a bridge flange, it may often be necessary to have an estimate of the longitudinal stresses in parts of the flange remote from the web–flange junction. The following simple expression which describes the stress distribution across the flange plate by a quartic polynomial was derived by Moffatt and Dowling[1,2] and later incorporated into BS 5400:[3]

$$\sigma_x = \sigma_{\text{m}} \left[\left(\frac{2x}{B}\right)^4 + \frac{5\psi_{\text{e}} - 1}{4} \left\{ 1 - \left(\frac{2x}{B}\right)^4 \right\} \right]$$ (3)

In the codification of BS 5400, the above design rules were presented in two parts: a simple set covering commonly occurring cases (simply supported, cantilevered, propped cantilevered and fixed-ended girders under uniform loads), and a comprehensive set covering cases in which a special study is warranted such as a point load of significant magnitude acting either in isolation or in combination with other loads or where there is a single span with a cantilevered projection continuous over the support.

3 SHEAR LAG AT THE ULTIMATE LIMIT STATE

With the introduction of limit state design in the last decade, it became pertinent to enquire as to the significance of shear lag with reference to the different limit states, and particularly, the serviceability and the ultimate limit states. Despite this, however, most design codes until this date deal with the shear lag problem in a linear elastic fashion. The only exception to this is the bridge code BS 5400 which addresses the problem at the ultimate load within the limits of certain geometric restraints.

The effect of shear lag at the ultimate load depends (in addition to the parameters of significance in the elastic range) on the flange slenderness and its material properties, since geometric and material nonlinearities come into play at such load levels. Consequently, the effect of the shear lag on a tension flange can be significantly different from its effect on a compression flange.

Clearly, if the flange was in tension and made of ductile steel, any non-uniform distribution of direct stress predicted by elastic theory would have little influence on the ultimate load. Once yielding has commenced in the more highly stressed edge zones, further loading would produce a redistribution of forces to the central region. With sufficient ductility, this process would continue until either the entire flange width had yielded or the full length of the flange longitudinal edges, through which the load is transmitted to the flange, had failed.

A compression flange might also have the capacity to redistribute forces across its width. In addition to the factors governing the redistribution capacity of a tension flange, however, the flange slenderness becomes of prime importance in regulating the redistribution process. This combination of shear lag and flange buckling is much more difficult to handle analytically than the isolated effect of either shear lag or buckling. This is due to the interaction between the two phenomena, both of which reduce the flange efficiency. Whereas well-established design methods are available for dealing with the isolated effects of shear lag and buckling, the combined effect, due to its complexity, received less attention until recently.

In this connection, Dowling *et al.*[4] carried out a series of tests on six box girders. These were divided into three pairs in each of which the girders had the same geometry and material properties. The first girder in each pair was tested under combined shear and bending and the second under pure bending, hence providing a datum to assess the effect of shear lag. Based on a detailed analysis of the experimental results, the authors showed that for the effect of shear lag to be ignored in an ultimate limit state design of steel box girders, it would be necessary to satisfy at least two criteria. Firstly, the components near the web–flange junction must have sufficient strain capacity to allow complete redistribution of the flange forces to occur without significantly unloading. Secondly, the process of redistribution must not advance to such a stage at service loading as to cause unacceptable permanent deformation in the components near the web–flange junction. Thus, slenderness requirements were imposed to ensure the stability of edge stiffeners and panels and were quantified by the following simple expressions limiting the plate and stiffener slenderness:

$$\frac{b}{t} < 2.77 \sqrt{\frac{E}{\sigma_0}} \tag{4a}$$

$$\frac{d_s}{t_s} < 0.4 \sqrt{\frac{E}{\sigma_0}} \tag{4b}$$

The above geometric limitations ensure that shear lag has no detrimental effect at ultimate load nor does it cause any permanent yielding under service loading provided the degree of shear lag itself is limited such that the maximum to minimum longitudinal flange stress ratio as predicted by elastic theory does not exceed 2; i.e.

$$\frac{\sigma_m}{\sigma_{min}} < 2 \tag{5}$$

Lamas and Dowling[5] carried out a study of the effect of shear lag on the collapse of simply supported box girders carrying symmetric point loads. The authors presented three upper bound expressions which reflected the limitations placed on flange strength by web and flange shear capacity and by the flange compressive strength. In the first instance, the appropriate effective width for calculating the ultimate load capacity of the flange would be that which exhausts the shear capacity of its edges or the edges of the webs. The expressions were derived by considering the overall equilibrium of the structure and can therefore be used to obtain an upper bound to the flange ultimate strength as follows:

$$\psi_{max} < \frac{1}{(1+\alpha)\sqrt{3}} \frac{L}{B} \tag{6a}$$

$$\psi_{max} < \frac{1}{(1+\alpha)\sqrt{3}} \frac{t_w}{t} \frac{L}{B} \tag{6b}$$

A further upper bound to the flange ultimate strength is its compressive strength. This becomes the governing condition where the B/L ratio is low and/or the flange slenderness is high.

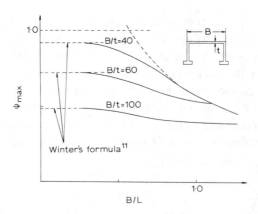

Fig. 3. Convergence of numerical results to upper bound solution.

Lamas and Dowling[5] carried out numerical analysis of a number of girders with different flange slenderness and aspect ratio. Two distinct modes of failure were identified: for long narrow flanges the full compressive strength was reached at the centre; for short wide flanges, the flange strength was limited by the shear capacity of the web–flange junction. Over a range of medium flange aspect ratios interaction of the two collapse modes was observed. The convergence of the numerical results towards the upper bound solutions is reproduced in Fig. 3.

3.1 Background to the design procedure

The extent of the above studies was inhibited by two factors. In the case of experimental work, the large expense associated with tests of this nature limited such work to the most commonly encountered geometries. In the case of analytical work, the complex nature of the problem forced researchers to adopt numerous simplifying assumptions to enable a solution which can be tempered for design purposes to be derived.

The more recent introduction of powerful and highly versatile numerical tools based on the finite element method has enabled researchers to tackle more thoroughly those problems that were hitherto not amenable to accurate quantitative analysis. Some such programs[6,7] have become sufficiently advanced to enable the modelling of combined geometric and material nonlinearities of plate assemblages.

A numerical study of the effect of shear lag on the collapse behaviour of box girders covering a wider range of geometries than that examined in earlier work[4,5] was undertaken by Burgan[8] and Burgan and Dowling[9] using the finite element program FINAS. To provide a reliable measure of the effect of shear lag on the behaviour, two types of analysis were performed on each geometry: central point load analysis on simply

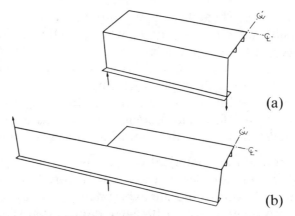

Fig. 4. Simple cases modelled in numerical parametric study: (a) central point loading;
(b) two-point loading.

supported models, and two-point loading analysis producing pure
bending over the central region of the models. In each case the numerical
model consisted of one quarter of a symmetric open-section girder as
illustrated in Fig. 4. The size of the model was reduced by assuming the
flange to be stiffened by a total of four flat bar stiffeners, and by assuming
symmetry on the longitudinal and transverse centrelines.

The main geometric parameters investigated were divided into two
categories. The first, which governs shear lag, included the flange
breadth to length ratio (B/L) and the stiffening ratio (A_s/A_f). The second,
which governs buckling, included plate panel slenderness (b/t) and strut
slenderness (l/r). Of these, the former controls plate panel buckling
whilst the latter controls overall buckling of the stiffened flange plate.
Combinations of each of these ratios between 60 and 80 were studied.
The B/L ratio in each case was varied from 0·2 to 1·0 and the stiffening
ratio from 0·25 to 1·0.

The results of the numerical study were examined in great detail and
the effect of shear lag on the behaviour was assessed by dividing the load
history into four stages, as follows.

(a) In the elastic range, the effect of shear lag was to reduce the flange
     efficiency and consequently the overall stiffness of the girder. The
     effect was accurately predicted by the design rules[1,2] described in
     the previous section.

(b) In the post-elastic range the effect of shear lag was to produce
     premature buckling and/or yielding which progressed from the
     web–flange junction across the width, leading to gradual
     reduction in the overall stiffness. This stage in behaviour
     commenced at smaller loads for larger degrees of shear lag.

(c) The effect of shear lag on the ultimate load was found to be negligible for B/L values of 0·2 while significant reductions were observed as this parameter was increased. For $B/L = 1·0$, the knock-down factor due to shear lag was found to be in excess of 50% of the strength in pure bending.

(d) In the post-ultimate regime of the load history, the rate of unloading was found to decrease with increasing B/L, showing a high level of ductility for conditions of severe shear lag.

Consideration of the numerical results for $B/L = 0·2$ at the ultimate load showed that the nonlinear stress distribution due to shear lag was fully redistributed, confirming the experimental findings of Dowling *et al.*[4] and the recommendation of BS 5400, namely that shear lag has no weakening effect on the ultimate strength of girders satisfying the geometric limitations recommended by these authors.

For design purposes, it was necessary to put the results of the study into a simple format which accurately described the effect of shear lag on the ultimate load for any flange geometry. The authors recommended the following expression:[8, 9]

$$\psi_{max} = \psi_u \psi_e^{(B/2L)} \tag{7}$$

For a flange which is just within the limitations of BS 5400, the above expression predicts a reduction in the ultimate strength of about 1%. As B/L increases, the effect of shear lag on ultimate load predicted by the above expression also increases and is found to accurately represent the strength reduction modelled numerically. A comparison between the ultimate loads obtained numerically and those predicted by the above

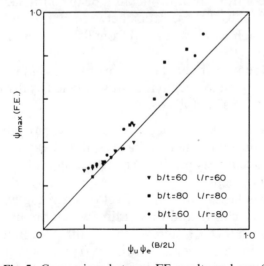

Fig. 5. Comparison between FE results and eqn (7).

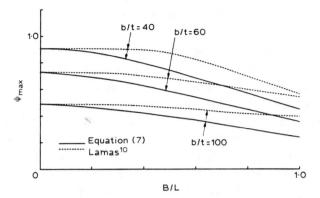

Fig. 6. Interaction of shear lag and inelastic buckling in stiffened flanges.

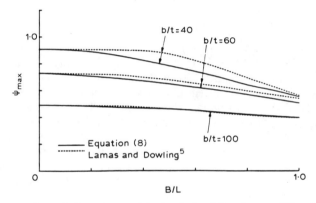

Fig. 7. Interaction of shear lag and inelastic buckling in unstiffened flanges.

expression is shown in Fig. 5, which clearly demonstrates the adequacy of the design expression.

A comparison of the predictions of the proposed expression with the results of an earlier study by Lamas[10] and Lamas and Dowling[5] is shown in Fig. 6. This further confirms the accuracy and validity of the expression.

The authors also proposed a design expression for evaluating the effect of shear lag on the ultimate strength of unstiffened compression flanges. This takes the same format as the expression for stiffened compression flanges but relates the effect of shear lag in the plate slenderness. This is given by

$$\psi_{max} = \psi_u \psi_e^{(B/2L\beta)} \tag{8}$$

The accuracy of the above expression in predicting the ultimate strength of unstiffened compression flanges is illustrated in Fig. 7 which shows a comparison with the results of numerical analysis obtained by Lamas and Dowling.[5]

4 CONCLUSIONS

This paper has presented the background to a comprehensive set of design rules for dealing with shear lag at both the serviceability and the ultimate limit states. In each case, the method has been based on parametric studies using finite element programs which had been validated against experimental results. A number of simple expressions which form part of these design techniques have also been given. The accuracy of the proposed approach to shear lag design at the ultimate limit state was demonstrated through comparisons with well-established results. The design methods described in the paper are proposed as the basis of the design rules in EC3 Part 2 (Bridges).

REFERENCES

1. Moffatt, K. R. & Dowling, P. J., *Parametric study on the shear lag phenomenon in steel box girder bridges*, CESLIC Report BG17, Engineering Structures Laboratories, Imperial College of Science and Technology, London, 1972.
2. Moffatt, K. R. & Dowling, P. J., Shear lag phenomenon in steel box girder bridges, *Structural Engineer*, **53**(10) (October 1975) 439–48.
3. *BS 5400, Steel, Concrete and Composite Bridges, Part 3: Code of Practice for Design of Steel Bridges*, British Standards Institution, London, 1982.
4. Dowling, P. J., Moolani, F. M. & Frieze, P. A., The effect of shear lag on the ultimate strength of box girders, in *Steel Plated Structures*, ed. P. J. Dowling *et al.*, Crosby Lockwood Staples, London, 1977.
5. Lamas, A. R. G. & Dowling, P. J., Effect of shear lag on the elastic buckling behaviour of thin-walled structures, *Proc. Int. Conf. on Thin-Walled Structures*, University of Strathclyde, Glasgow, UK, April 1979.
6. Trueb, U., Stability problems of elasto–plastic plates and shells by finite elements, PhD Thesis, University of London, September 1983.
7. Bates, D. N., Nonlinear elasto–plastic analysis of stiffened plates and shells by finite elements, PhD Thesis, University of London, 1987.
8. Burgan, B. A., Special problems in wide and narrow stiffened compression flanges, PhD Thesis, University of London, January 1987.
9. Burgan, B. A. & Dowling, P. J., Effect of shear lag on the collapse of stiffened compression flanges, *Proc. ECCS Colloquium on Stability of Plate and Shell Structures*, Ghent, Belgium, April 1987, 163–71.
10. Lamas, A. R. G., Influence of shear lag on the collapse of wide-flange girders, PhD Thesis, University of London, June 1979.
11. Winter, G., Strength of thin steel compression flanges. *Preliminary Publications*, IABSE 4th Congress, Cambridge and London, 1952.

Thin-Walled Structures **9** (1990) 135–149

Prestressed Membrane Structures — The Ultimate Thin-Walled Structure

P. W. Kneen

Department of Structural Engineering, University of New South Wales, Kensington, New South Wales 2033, Australia

ABSTRACT

Whilst for normal thin-gauge materials such as steel and aluminium, buckling is a problem when the ratio of unsupported width to thickness is perhaps in the order of 200 or so, membrane roof structures may behave satisfactorily with ratios of up to 50 000 and thus might be termed the 'ultimate thin-walled structure'. All modern architectural membrane structures are prestressed to maintain a tensile state and to reduce deflections under applied loadings such as from wind. These forms of 'soft shells' are in two broad categories — the air-supported type and the tension type. This paper discusses the general design principles which are used to achieve exciting, visual and technologically intriguing forms with such high slenderness ratios.

1 INTRODUCTION

Membrane structures in the forms of tents have existed since ancient times, but with the advent of high technology materials and computer-assisted design and stress analysis techniques, membrane structures are becoming increasingly popular as an economical means of enclosing large spans. They also provide the designer with a chance to make an architectural statement not possible with conventional rigid forms of construction.

This paper discusses the two main forms of modern membrane structures — the air-supported and tensioned membrane structures.

Thin-Walled Structures 0263-8231/90/$03·50 © 1990 Elsevier Science Publishers Ltd, England. Printed in Great Britain

Modern architectural fabric structures are all prestressed either by deliberately making them smaller than the intended final shape and stretching the membrane by jacking of masts, tightening of edge cables, expanding of support arches, etc., or alternatively, for totally enclosed structures, by using an artificial, sustained preload condition such as internal air pressure.

Before discussing the two forms, a short discussion of the general properties of the fabrics used is required.

2 FABRIC MATERIAL PROPERTIES

There is insufficient space to examine all aspects of fabric properties in this general paper. Nevertheless, what is important is to note that the fabrics currently used are available in only a *limited range of strengths*. The majority of the surface area of a fabric structure uses only one layer of fabric for the structural load carrying component. There is a limit to the thickness and spacing of the yarns used in the manufacture of architectural fabrics which in turn limits the available strengths.

Generally, there are two common types of fabric used in these structures. One is polyester based cloths coated with PVC, perhaps combined with Tedlar or acrylic finishes to enhance appearance. Additives are present in the coatings to increase resistance to degradation from ultraviolet radiation as well as to act as fire retardants. The other form of fabric is fibreglass yarns coated with teflon. This is generally a more expensive fabric which is stiffer and is less prone to creep under sustained load. There is less deterioration of strength and optical properties, including general appearance. It has excellent fire resistance and long life expectancy.

The mechanical properties of the fabrics are described in terms of the following items:

(a)   type of material used for the yarns;
(b)   type of coating(s) used, noting that they may be different on the two sides;
(c)   type or pattern of weaving;
(d)   weight of the base cloth without any coatings;
(e)   final coated weight
(f)   uniaxial strip tensile strengths in the warp and weft directions;
(g)   some tear strength results in warp and weft direction;
(h)   an indication of the elongation at failure;
(i)   an indication of the adhesion of the coating to the base cloth; and rarely

(j) an indication of the load–deformation curves in a biaxial stress state.

Table 1 shows some mechanical properties for a range of polyester fabrics (PES) and fibreglass fabrics. Polyester fabrics are normally grouped in terms of weight (or strength) as Types I to VI. Type I is generally too light for outdoor structures whilst Types V and VI are rarely used.

It can be seen from the table that the tearing strength is considerably lower than the simple uniaxial tensile strength.

3 AIR SUPPORTED STRUCTURES

The prestress is introduced by means of internal air pressure which requires the constant operation of mechanical plant. For many structures, the same or similar equipment would be required for air conditioning. Extra fan capacity is needed only on relatively few occasions such as the initial inflation, during storms (wind or snow) and perhaps when many exits are being used constantly.

The geometric form is a synclastic surface with centres of curvature for two orthogonal directions on one side of the fabric or membrane — the side from which the additional preload pressure is applied. Tensions are developed in the fabric which depend on the overall geometric form (which influences the wind loading, for example) and the local radius of curvature.

For a local area which can be considered spherical, the tensions are equal in both directions and are given by

$$t = pr/2 \tag{1}$$

in which t is the fabric tension in kN/m, p is the resultant load or pressure in kPa, and r is the local radius of curvature in metres.

For a cylindrical form, with curvature in only one direction, the fabric tension in the curved direction will be twice that of a sphere. In the majority of cases, these simple approximations are adequate at least for a preliminary analysis provided a reasonable estimate of the local radius of curvature can be made.

3.1 Small air hall structures

For a cylindrical profile, which is typical of the majority of the smaller air bubbles over swimming pools or single tennis courts, the radius is known accurately in the pure prestress state. When wind loads are added, they

P. W. Kneen

TABLE 1
Typical Fabric Properties

Fabric spec.	Type	Total weight (g/m²)	Cloth weight (g/m²)	Tensile warp (kN/m)	Strength weft (kN/m)	Tongue warp (N)	Tear weft (N)
Polymar							
6505	PES Type I	850	—	60	60	300	350
6506	PES Type II	900	—	90	80	600	600
6601	PES Type III	1 050	—	120	110	1 000	1 200
6602	PES Type IV	1 400	—	150	130	1 200	1 200
6603	PES Type V	1 600	—	180	170	2 000	2 000
Shelter-rite							
8128	PES	1 175	225	70	62	1 000	1 000
8028	PES	1 205	255	90	90	1 200	1 200
9032	PES	1 430	340	110	110	1 300	1 300
Duraskin							
12923	PES Type I	800	210	60	55	310	350
12723	PES Type II	900	275	88	79	520	580
12323	PES Type III	1 050	370	115	102	800	950
12333	PES Type IV	1 300	490	149	128	1 100	1 400
12343	PES Type V	1 450	650	196	166	1 600	1 900
Chemfab							
Sheerfill I	Glass + PTFE	1 530	—	140	120	270	360
Sheerfill II	Glass + PTFE	1 270	—	90	75	160	170

are basically resisted by two mechanisms. Primarily, the structure changes shape and this is followed by changes in fabric tensions.

The change in shape is large compared to conventional rigid structures but may not appear to be important. The local radii of curvature, however, can change by as much as 50–200% with acceptably small deflections.

Normal internal pressures for air-supported structures are in the order of 0·2–0·3 kPa. If the available strength of a fabric is 110 kN/m, and a cylindrical form is required, then the maximum radius is given by

$$r_{max} = t_{max}/p \tag{2}$$

A factor of safety of 8–10 is often used as measured against the uniaxial tensile strengths to account for the reduced tearing resistance. This leads to $t_{max} = 110/10 = 11$ kN/m and the maximum radius $r_{max} = 11/0·3 = 36·7$ m.

This approximate analysis ignores the higher net pressures that occur under wind loading, which are detrimental, or the deformation of the structure which will decrease the local radius of curvature in regions of high pressure loads — a beneficial effect. Even with this crude analysis, considering that the nominal thickness is 1 mm, the slenderness ratio of the fabric is in excess of 100 000 for a half cylinder of this radius. More typically, practical spans have been in the order of 20–40 m for simple air hall type structures.

3.2 Large span air supported structures

Much larger air-supported roof structures have been built and these are possible by controlling the maximum *local* radius of curvature in the fabric. They utilize a network of crossing steel cables which subdivide the surface into panels which typically measure 9–18 m on edge. Each such panel has a geometry with small radii of curvature which limits the fabric stresses to acceptable levels. Each interior panel has a form approaching a spherical bubble and hence the resultant pressures are transferred in two directions.

For an interior 10 m square panel, considering only the central sections as being portions of spheres, then, for a rise of 2 m, the local radius is given by

$$r = \frac{(\text{span}/2)^2 + \text{rise}^2}{2 \times \text{rise}} \tag{3}$$

In this case, $r = 7·25$ m, a small value.

The crossing cables are used to carry most of the loads to the perimeter anchorage system. Since these cables can be selected from a large range of strengths (unlike the fabric panels), the overall curvatures can be comparatively low. The cable tensions for a spherical form can be approximated by the same simple equation (1) after making allowances for the contributing width of the panel w.

$$T_{\text{cable}} = (p_{\text{net}} \times \text{width} \times \text{radius})/2 \tag{4}$$

Thus, for example, if $w = 10$ m, $p_{\text{net}} = 1 \cdot 0$ kPa (making some allowance for wind suction in addition to the internal pressures), and for a span of 120 m and a cable rise of 15 m the radius becomes 127·5 m and the cable tension $T_{\text{cable}} = 637 \cdot 5$ kN. At a cable stress of 500 MPa, a cable diameter of approximately 40 mm is obtained. To allow for the strength of fittings, etc., a slightly larger diameter could be selected. This is not a large cable as such and indicates how structurally efficient these forms of structures are.

Considerable benefit is achieved for low profile structures under wind loads in that the entire roof is under a net uplift pressure which is reasonably uniform: this in turn keeps the fabric in tension. In cold climates, where snow loading is present, the internal pressure is increased to counteract the downward gravity loads. Hot air is normally directed upwards at the roof to assist in melting the snow.

Obviously the structural integrity depends on the continuous operation of the mechanical plant which is used for the air conditioning function as well as maintaining a pressure differential. A large pump capacity is required for initial inflation and to cope with peak demands such as crowd exits, storms, and maintenance of individual pumps.

For large stadium structures, a horizontal ring beam at the top of the spectator seating can be designed to incorporate the air ducts which cannot be attached to the flexible roof. The ring beam is made sufficiently wide to allow a working space for the erection of the roof panels and for possible storage of the fans, and to have adequate bending strength in the horizontal plane so that only vertical loads need be carried by columns or the seating support structure.

A problem with this form of crossed cable system is that the corners of a rectangular or square shape are extremely flat. This can be true for both the overall structure as well as the internal panels. For the overall structure, the corners are invariably truncated, or the horizontal ring beam is curved in some form of ellipse, circle or rectangle/square with generous corner radii. One example is shown in Fig. 1.

The corner flatness of the internal panels can be modified by the initial shape given to the panel by the patterning of the fabric. Water ponding at the cable intersections is a potential problem which, once

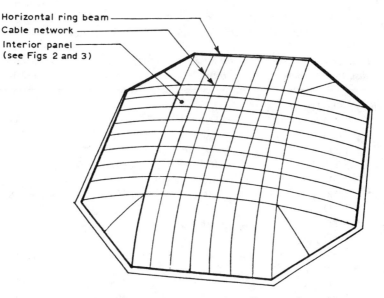

Horizontal ring beam ——————
Cable network ——————
Interior panel ——————
(see Figs 2 and 3)

Fig. 1. Typical air supported stadium roof.

started, can progress to a dangerous situation. Panels can be made steeper adjacent to the cables, hence avoiding corner ponding of water. Such panels are potentially more flexible, however, and may not behave as well if ponding has already started — perhaps initiated by a heavy snowfall.

Table 2 indicates the initial shapes of two internal panels with a 10 m square base (fixed in position) and a central nominal height of 2 m. Two initial shapes were considered, as can be gauged from the initial heights tabulated along the diagonal. A single concentrated load of 1 kN was applied at various points along the diagonal and the deflections under the load calculated with a non-linear program. An internal pressure of 0·3 kPa was taken and the load of 1 kN could represent a person or an initial amount of water.

The initial shape was generated using modified isoparametric shape functions with the initial height as 2000 in both cases. The fabric was 'set' in size accordingly (i.e. the patterns were not altered) and the panel pressurized and allowed to modify the profile to be in equilibrium under the internal pressure. For the parabolic shape the central portion came down, whilst for the circular shape it was raised. Initial surface areas were 110·9 m² for the parabolic profile and 120·1 m² for the circular profile.

From Table 2 it is seen that the 'parabolic' profile is much flatter in the corners, as indicated by the initial Z-coordinate, and, for a point load

TABLE 2
Behaviour of Two Internal 10 m Square Panels

Load position (x,y dist. from corner)	Initial Z (mm)	Final Z (mm)	Vertical displ. (mm)
'Parabolic' profile (Fig. 2)			
500	98	−45	−143
1 000	286	116	−170
1 500	542		
2 000	835	652	−183
2 500	1 133		
3 000	1 409	1 161	−248
3 500	1 642		
4 000	1 816	1 495	−321
4 500	1 923		
5 000	1 960	1 612	−348
'Circular' profile (Fig. 3)			
500	382	188	−194
1 000	753	407	−346
1 500	1 080		
2 000	1 370	1 054	−316
2 500	1 623		
3 000	1 839	1 555	−284
3 500	2 011		
4 000	2 139	1 869	−270
4 500	2 216		
5 000	2 243	1 976	−267

500 mm in from both adjacent edges, the fabric is actually depressed below the horizontal. The steeper 'circular' profile is sufficiently high near the corners to prevent undue deflections and is concluded to be less prone to ponding. The actual response in a corner will depend very much on the detailed patterning used.

3.3 Other structural factors

For medium-sized air-supported roofs, it has been common to utilize only one direction of cables. This eliminates many problems with waterproofing at the junction of crossing cables. The fabric, however, has a really large curvature only in one direction and hence acts as a one-way system. Most stadium structures have a single structural skin of fabric, but to improve acoustics and thermal insulation, a second liner of lighter weight is used to hang closely underneath the pressurized outer skin.

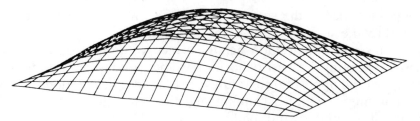

Fig. 2. Internal panel with parabolic profile.

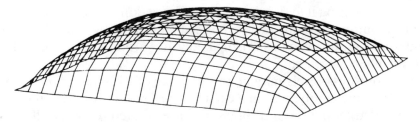

Fig. 3. Internal panel with circular profile.

For high rise structures (say a rise to span ratio of 0·3 or more) there is the possibility of wind pressures being positive on the windward side, causing the fabric to be pushed inwards. There is some short term additional resistance offered by the fact that the enclosed volume wants to remain constant but this should not be counted on for design purposes. If the fabric 'buckles' inwards from the pressure, the real danger comes after the gust passes when the structure will snap violently back and possibly tear to pieces rapidly. The internal pressure should be increased to help avoid this. Any sudden peak loading on a temporary anchorage system will weaken the system.

Under high winds, for portable structures, there is the chance of the air seals around the base being broken, placing the structure in danger. One form of seal is provided by fabric tubes filled with water. For sloping sites, such tubes should be in short independent lengths and of adequate volume and checked at frequent intervals.

4 TENSION STRUCTURES

These are typically more complex in their geometric form and are characterized by an anticlastic surface shape with a variety of internal and perimeter support conditions. The anticlastic or saddle shape has the centres of curvature for two lines at right angles on the surface located on opposite sides of the surface. The fabric stress in one direction is opposed by the stresses in the other direction.

Uneven stresses are found when the two curvatures are different, and generally speaking the 'best' behaviour will be found when conditions of near equal (and opposing) curvatures are present. The criterion for 'best' behaviour might be the least amount of deflection or the smallest change in fabric stress under wind load.

The initial prestress conditions are obtained by taking the shaped fabric skin which has been fabricated slightly smaller than the finished size, and stretching it to fit into the desired position of the supports. This usually requires boundary edge cables to be shortened, or the adjustment of internal supports such as raising bale rings around masts, or jacking arch members apart, etc.

Initial prestress levels may be in the range of 1 kN/m for small span structures using a polyester fabric to 6 kN/m for the stiffer teflon-coated fibreglass structures. Wind pressures are shared between the two directions with an increase in one and a decrease in the other. The prestress state should be such as to prevent the fabric from 'going into compression' under all loadings.

In Fig. 4, it is expected that R_1 would decrease and R_2 increase, which would mean that the applied load could be resisted even without major changes to the fabric stress. Quite significant changes in radii of curvature can take place with very little strain or stretching of the fabric material. For high loads, large movements will cause tensions to change as well as curvatures.

It can also be seen in Fig. 4 that if the fabric prestress levels (i.e. T_1 and

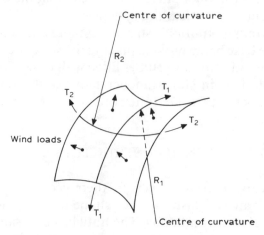

Fig. 4. Concepts for a tension fabric structure.

T_2) are higher then, to withstand an applied external load, the changes in R_1 and R_2 (i.e. the shape) are smaller. In other words, the higher the prestress the smaller the deflections. Again, as with air supported structures, the object is to prevent the fabric from becoming slack under applied loads, particularly wind. If areas become slack and are then subject to shock loading after a gust, damage from tearing could result.

Maintaining the level of prestress is no problem for air supported structures provided the mechanical plant continues to operate and no major tears develop. For tension structures it is found that for PVC coated polyester fabrics, the prestress decreases with time, due to creep of the fabric, and periodic adjustments to edge cables and guy cables or jacking of masts may be required. For fibreglass fabrics, the initial (higher) prestress is sufficient to overcome any setting in by the fabric yarns, and retensioning is rarely called for.

Limiting cases of the tension type structure are those which consist of panels which are planar, or nearly so. They rely on the elasticity of the fabric material which in turn enables the curvatures to develop under load. These curvatures would be of a synclastic form rather than anticlastic and hence both directions of the fabric would assist in carrying the load. Fortunately for polyester fabrics in particular, the fabric can elongate by as much as 15% before failure and thus enable the panel to work.

For large span structures of the tension type, it is often architecturally difficult to have high curvatures, and the use of a system of opposing high and low, adjacent, nearly parallel ridge and valley cables becomes attractive. In such a scheme, adopted for the large Sun Sails at Expo88 in Brisbane, the alternate ridge cables resist wind from one side of the surface whilst the intermediate valley cables resist wind from the other side and both define the overall shape. The ridge and valley cables can be arranged in a radial fashion around a central mast and a series of perimeter shorter masts and tie downs. The radial span can thus be quite large but the effective span of the fabric is cut down.

By considering the elongation of the fabric, planar panels acting in the one direction only (as indicated in Fig. 5) behave satisfactorily, even ignoring the flexibility of the mast/cable support system. Generally speaking, the structure resists loads by undergoing deformations, and measures taken to limit the flexibility can lead to localized high stresses.

4.1 Example geometric forms

The simplest example of a tension structure is the hypar or simple saddle shaped surface as shown in Figure 6(a). Almost all tension fabric

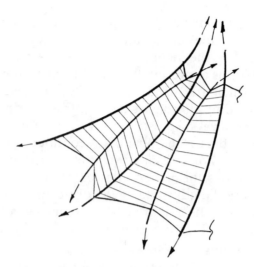

Fig. 5. Nearly planar panels formed between ridge and valley cables.

structures will have portions of the surface similar in shape to a hypar. If the four corners are based on a square plan layout, the curvature is introduced by having the adjacent corners alternating in height. Very effective structures are obtained by a repetition of these simple units. Typical edge dimensions are from 6 to 20 m.

Another common form is the conical arrangement in which a central mast supports an enlarged bale or tension ring, as shown in Fig. 6(b). The fabric is clamped to this ring which can be raised in height either by jacking the mast up or by shortening the suspension cables. The outer perimeter is normally clamped onto a rigid steel frame, or ends with a series of catenary edge cables anchored to a number of points around the base. In many structures, a series of light radial cables joins the central tension ring to the edge supports. These may be used to assist in defining the shape, to help resist wind loads and/or to act as a fail-safe guy system for the central mast in the event of fabric failure or panel re-erection.

Another common form, especially for longer narrow openings, is a series of intersecting crossed arches (Fig. 6(c)). These have been used for shopping malls. In cases where two arcades meet at right angles, a domed structure which interfaces with the crossed arch units is often provided as a focal point. Alternatively, a suspended mast and cone can be used for the same attraction.

Typical spans for fabric are 6–50 m depending on the geometric form, and with a fabric thickness of 1 mm this gives rise to incredible slenderness ratios of up to 50 000 and hence the notion that perhaps these structures can be viewed as the ultimate thin-walled structure.

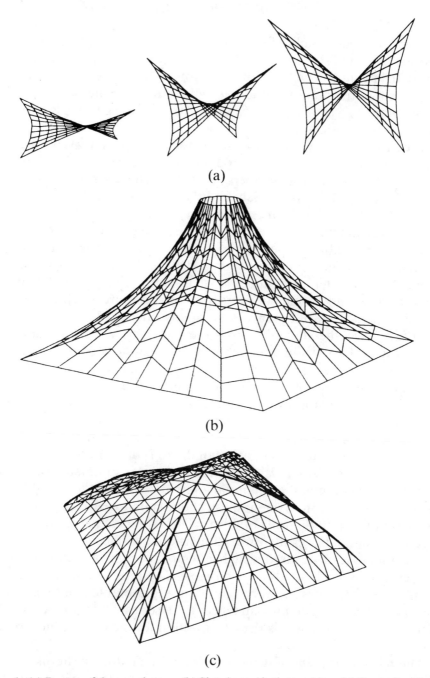

(a)

(b)

(c)

Fig. 6. (a) Range of hypar shapes. (b) Simple conical structure. (c) Crossed arched module.

5 COMPUTER ANALYSIS

Almost all larger membrane structures are now analysed by computer and some form of stiffness analysis is used which incorporates the non-linear behaviour.[1] The non-linearity comes from the large displacements (out of the plane) and to a lesser degree the material non-linear stress–strain curves. Account should be taken of the geometric stiffness terms for the fabric and cables.

The surface is represented by a set of nodes whose (x, y, z) coordinates are prescribed, and by a set of various elements which connect the nodes and model the structural members and fabric. The main initial problem is to arrive at a shape which is in equilibrium with the applied prestressing loads and is in tension everywhere.

A common method is to employ at least some fabric elements (and possibly some cable elements) which are free to change shape whilst maintaining a constant prestress force. If all surface elements are of this form, the computer can model a 'soap film'. The surface shape is modified until movements in successive iterations are acceptably small and there is no 'out of balance' load at any node.

At this stage, the shape becomes the starting point for the analysis under external applied loads such as wind, snow, etc. Any 'theoretical' materials such as soap film must be converted into 'real' materials and the initial mesh generation becomes irrelevant. Ideally, the program should model the fabric which cannot resist compressive forces and is generally made from two sets of interlocking yarns at right angles.

Quite often, at the analysis stage, the finite element mesh layout may not represent the actual final layout of the rolls of fabric. The warp and weft yarn directions could be unknown. Another problem connected with the modelling is that manufacturers do not want to waste fabric material and the finite element mesh should aim towards matching the maximum width of the rolls of fabric. This is not easy since the roll of fabric can wander over the three dimensional surface.

Techniques can be used which attempt to align a series of finite elements in as straight a line as possible. The most common is to add small 'geodesic strings', i.e. very lightly stressed cable elements which are free to change length but, attached to a series of fabric soap film elements, will tend towards the best position for the edge of the strip of fabric.

The related problem of determination of the cutting patterns can be done with a separate series of analyses in which more care is taken with the layout of the finite element mesh. In other words, a coarser model may be used for load analysis and a finer model for patterning.

This is important when one considers the unknown nature of the loads (wind and snow) on such complex geometric forms. On the other hand, very significant fabric stresses can be introduced into the surface by inaccurate modelling. These unwanted stresses can be much more severe than the additional stresses due to applied, distributed loadings.

Detailed discussion of the patterning is beyond the scope of this paper.

REFERENCE

1. Kneen, P. W., Computer aided design of tensioned fabric structures. In *Proc. First Int. Conf. on Lightweight Structures in Architecture,* 24–29 August, Sydney, Australia. Unisearch Limited, University of New South Wales, Australia, 1989, pp. 992–1009.

Thin-Walled Structures **9** (1990) 151–162

On the Natural Frequencies of Vibration of a Ring Surrounded by and/or Containing a Fluid

H. M. Irvine

School of Civil Engineering, The University of New South Wales, Kensington, New South Wales 2033, Australia

ABSTRACT

An energy approach is used to derive simple expressions for the effective modal mass and effective modal stiffness of a thin, uniform, circular ring when vibrating freely in an inextensional ring mode. These expressions include both the circumferential and radial inertia of the ring, and the additional mass of fluid both within and without the ring; they also allow for the destabilizing (or stiffening) effect of ring compression (or tension) due to pressure loading which is always normal to the surface. The natural frequencies of these inextensional modes of vibration of the ring, which are derived from the effective mass and effective stiffness, are exact to the first order of small quantities. Numerous special cases are contained within the general result, including all the classical results.

NOTATION

a	Ring radius
$A_n(t)$	Displacement coefficient
b	Radial length
$K_{e,n}$	Total effective stiffness in n^{th} vibration mode
E	Young's modulus
I	Second moment of area of ring
m	Mass per unit length of ring
$M_{e,n}$	Total effective mass in n^{th} vibration mode

151

Thin-Walled Structures 0263-8231/90/$03·50 © 1990 Elsevier Science Publishers Ltd, England. Printed in Great Britain.

P Ring tension force

$\left.\begin{array}{l} P_n \\ R_n \\ S_n \end{array}\right\}$ Lamb's constants

R Radial force

v, w Circumferential and radial displacements

ε Circumferential strain

θ Angle between radius and the horizontal

v Poisson's ratio

ρ Curvature

ρ_e, ρ_i External and internal fluid densities

ϕ Potential function

ψ Stream function

ω_n Natural frequency of nth vibration mode

1 INTRODUCTION

Scattered in the literature are the solutions to a number of ring vibration or ring stability problems. Most were originally solved more than 100 years ago and names like Bresse, Rayleigh, Love and Lamb, for example, are associated with the theoretical and, in some cases, additional experimental work done. Some problems that come to mind are as follows.

The problem of inextensional vibrations of a circular ring of given flexural rigidity was solved by Rayleigh (see Ref. 1). The adjective inextensional refers to modes of vibration in which there is no change in length of the centreline of the ring. It is this type of vibration which is almost invariably of most interest when ring vibration problems are encountered. Rayleigh introduced the concept of inextensional vibration.

In the case of a circular jet, a pattern of circumferential standing waves (in which surface tension counters the modulation set up by radial fluid motion) is often noticed in the region near the orifice. The theory for this was presented by Rayleigh (see Ref. 2).

The classical stability problem of a circular ring under uniform external pressure was solved by Bresse (see Ref. 3). In this problem, the analysis must account for the fact that the fluid loading remains normal to the buckled surface. Other loading cases in which, for example, the direction of loading remains fixed are given in the comprehensive work by Simitses.[4]

It is of interest to derive a general result for a ring of given flexural rigidity, the ring itself being in tension or compression depending on whether internal or external pressure exists, and for which the additional mass of the internal and/or external fluid is fully accounted for in the vibration problem. The scattered results alluded to in the preceding paragraphs constitute parts of the general result. The purpose of the present paper is to derive the general result and to show how specific solutions fit into it.

An energy approach is used for the present study, as it was for some of the original investigations of specific problems. This is considered more straightforward than forming the governing differential equations and then solving them. A full account of that approach to the buckling of thin rings and arches is given by Simitses.[4]

The present energy approach is considered capable of providing an expeditious, physically motivated solution to a complete vibration problem that is exact to the first order of small quantities, and is subject only to the constraints implied by linear elastic material properties and ideal fluid flow theory.

2 KINEMATICS OF INEXTENSIONAL VIBRATION

Consider a thin circular ring of radius a on which is superimposed, at any point, small radial and tangential displacements of w and v, respectively: see Fig. 1.

The element of the ring of length $a\,d\theta$ at P becomes of length $(a + w)\,d\theta + dv$ at P′, to first order. The circumferential strain arising from this set of displacements is thus

$$\varepsilon = \frac{(a + w)\,d\theta}{a\,d\theta} + \frac{dv}{a\,d\theta} - 1 = \frac{w}{a} + \frac{dv}{a\,d\theta} \tag{1}$$

The condition that the centreline of the ring does not extend or contract is, therefore, that the displacements w and v be linked by

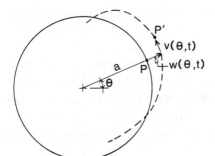

Fig. 1. Definition diagram for radial and tangential displacements.

$$w + \frac{dv}{d\theta} = 0 \tag{2}$$

This is Rayleigh's condition of inextensibility of the centreline of the ring. If we define the radial length b as

$$b = a + w \tag{3}$$

then the curvature of an element of the dotted line shown in Fig. 1 is given by the expression

$$\rho = \frac{1}{b} - \frac{1}{b^2} \frac{d^2 b}{d\theta^2} \tag{4}$$

provided the new profile is little different from the circle. The first term is expected since we are dealing with a problem in which little alteration from a circle of radius a is envisaged, and a circle of radius b has curvature $1/b$. On the other hand, the second term accounts for the possibility of circumferential variation in curvature. It is this term that is encountered in the mechanics of straight members. Both arise when the member is curved.

On substitution and rearrangement we have, for the change in curvature of the element,

$$d\rho = -\frac{1}{a^2}\left(w + \frac{d^2 w}{d\theta^2}\right) \tag{5}$$

The displacement field that we shall work with is of the form

$$\left. \begin{array}{l} w(\theta, t) = A_n(t) \cos n\theta \\[2ex] v(\theta, t) = -\frac{A_n(t)}{n} \sin n\theta \end{array} \right\} \quad n = 1, 2, 3 \ldots \tag{6}$$

With the exception of the case $n = 1$ (which corresponds to a rigid body translation) this displacement field has the repetitive angular symmetry required. They are, in fact, the modes of vibration of the general problem described in the introduction: see Fig. 2.

This displacement field is inextensional in the sense implied by eqn (1). Furthermore, the area under the (almost) circular curve of radius $a + A_n(t) \cos n\theta$ is the same as that of the ring at rest. This is important as it means that the associated ideal fluid motions are volume-conserving. The surrounding fluids, in interacting with the ring structure, possess kinetic energy only.

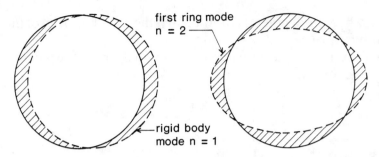

Fig. 2. Rigid body mode and first mode of vibration of a circular ring.

3 KINETIC ENERGY OF FLUID MOTION AND RING MOTION

The treatment that follows is taken from Lamb.[2] Initially, we consider the potential flow outside a circle of mean radius a. In polar coordinates we have the following expressions for the potential and stream functions respectively:

$$\phi = \sum_1^\infty r^{-n} (R_n \cos n\theta + S_n \sin n\theta) \tag{7}$$

$$\psi = \sum_1^\infty r^{-n} (S_n \cos n\theta - R_n \sin n\theta)$$

where $n \geqslant 1$. This allows the motion to be zero at infinity, while on the surface of the ring we can enforce a specific radial velocity.

We wish to have a ring mode of vibration of the form given in eqns (6),

$$w(\theta, t) = A_n(t) \cos n\theta$$

$$v(\theta, t) = -\frac{A_n(t)}{n} \sin n\theta$$

the radial velocity of the ring being

$$\frac{\partial w}{\partial t} (\theta, t) = \dot{A}_n \cos n\theta \tag{8}$$

This velocity we force on the fluid immediately in contact with the ring, that is

$$-\frac{\partial \phi}{\partial r} = \dot{A}_n \cos n\theta \quad , n \geqslant 1 \tag{9}$$

on $r = a$, where from potential flow theory, the radial velocity of the fluid is given by $-\partial\phi/\partial r$.

Therefore, for this pulsating flow exterior to the ring, the potential and stream functions are

$$
\left.
\begin{aligned}
\phi &= \dot{A}_n \frac{a^{n+1}}{nr^n} \cos n\theta \\[2em]
\psi &= -\dot{A}_n \frac{a^{n+1}}{nr^n} \sin n\theta
\end{aligned}
\right\} \quad n \geqslant 1
\tag{10}
$$

for $r \geqslant a$.

The kinetic energy of the external fluid is

$$
\text{KE} = \tfrac{1}{2}\rho_e \oint \phi \, d\psi
\tag{11}
$$

where ρ_e is the density of the external fluid, and in which the integral is evaluated around the ring itself, that is, on $r = a$. We have

$$
\text{KE} = \tfrac{1}{2}\left(\frac{\rho_e a^2 \dot{A}_n^2}{n}\right) \int_0^{2\pi} \cos^2 n\theta \, d\theta
\tag{12}
$$

or

$$
\text{KE} = \tfrac{1}{2}\left(\frac{\rho_e \pi a^2}{n}\right) \dot{A}_n^2 \quad , \quad n \geqslant 1
\tag{13}
$$

Lamb established this result for the case $n = 1$, which corresponds to a rigid cylinder translating broadside on: this leads to the classical result for the additional mass of a translating cylinder, namely $\rho_e \pi a^2$.

Clearly, however, if we do not restrict the result to $n = 1$, we have results for the effective mass of fluid external to the ring which moves in sympathy with it when a modal vibration of the form given in eqns (6),

$$
w(\theta, t) = A_n(t) \cos n\theta
$$

$$
v(\theta, t) = -\frac{A_n(t)}{n} \sin n\theta
$$

occurs. This effective mass is $\rho_e \pi a^2/n$ for $n \geqslant 1$. The effect of the additional fluid mass becomes less pronounced as the mode number increases.

For the fluid contained inside the ring, we have an ascending series for the potential and stream functions of the form

$$\phi = \sum_1^\infty r^n P_n \cos n\theta \left.\vphantom{\sum_1^\infty}\right\} \quad n \geqslant 1 \tag{14}$$

$$\psi = -\sum_1^\infty r^n P_n \sin n\theta$$

For our modal vibrations the appropriate forms are

$$\phi = \frac{r^n}{na^{n-1}} \dot A_n \cos n\theta \left.\vphantom{\frac{r^n}{na^{n-1}}}\right\} \quad n \geqslant 1 \tag{15}$$

$$\psi = -\frac{r^n}{na^{n-1}} \dot A_n \sin n\theta$$

for $r \leqslant a$.

The kinetic energy of the internal fluid (of density ρ_i) is found to be the same as given by eqn (13), namely

$$\mathrm{KE} = \tfrac{1}{2} \frac{\rho_i \pi a^2}{n} \dot A_n^2 \tag{16}$$

with the result that the effective mass of fluid internal to the ring is $\rho_i \pi a^2/n$ for $n \geqslant 1$. With the exception of the rigid body mode (i.e. $n = 1$), the velocity of the fluid at the centre is zero for all ring modes.

For the case of the ring itself, we have

$$\mathrm{KE} = \tfrac{1}{2} ma \int_0^{2\pi} \left[\left(\frac{\partial w}{\partial t} \right)^2 + \left(\frac{\partial v}{\partial t} \right)^2 \right] d\theta \tag{17}$$

or

$$\mathrm{KE} = \tfrac{1}{2} m\pi a \left(1 + \frac{1}{n^2} \right) \dot A_n^2 \quad , n \geqslant 1 \tag{18}$$

where m is the mass per unit length of the ring.

When $n = 1$ we have the rigid body mode, and the full ring mass $m\,2\pi a$ is operative. However, for higher modes, the circumferential inertia of the ring becomes quite important and in essence only about half the total mass of the ring is then effective.

The total kinetic energy is the summation of the results of eqns (13), (16) and (18), namely

$$\sum \mathrm{KE} = \tfrac{1}{2} \left[\frac{\rho_i \pi a^2}{n} + \frac{\rho_e \pi a^2}{n} + m\,\pi a \left(1 + \frac{1}{n^2} \right) \right] \dot A_n^2 \quad , n \geqslant 1 \tag{19}$$

in which ρ_i, ρ_e and m are the densities of the internal and external fluids and the mass per unit length of the ring, respectively.

4 STRAIN ENERGY OF RING BENDING

For a ring which undergoes a slight change in curvature from the circle, the bending moment at any section is (from eqn (5))

$$M = \frac{EI}{a^2}\left(w + \frac{\partial^2 w}{\partial \theta^2}\right) \tag{20}$$

and the change in rotation over the element is

$$\frac{1}{a^2}\left(w + \frac{\partial^2 w}{\partial \theta^2}\right) a\,d\theta$$

Hence the strain energy stored in the complete ring is

$$SE = \tfrac{1}{2}\frac{EI}{a^3}\int_0^{2\pi}\left(w + \frac{\partial^2 w}{\partial \theta^2}\right)^2 d\theta \tag{21}$$

For a modal vibration of the form of eqns (6),

$$w(\theta, t) = A_n(t)\cos n\theta$$

$$v(\theta, t) = -\frac{A_n(t)}{n}\sin n\theta$$

we have

$$SE = \tfrac{1}{2}\frac{EI}{a^3}A_n^2(n^2 - 1)^2\int_0^{2\pi}\cos^2 n\theta\,d\theta \tag{22}$$

or

$$SE = \tfrac{1}{2}\left(\frac{\pi(n^2 - 1)^2\,EI}{a^3}\right)A_n^2 \quad, n \geqslant 1 \tag{23}$$

and we may define the effective stiffness of the ring in bending as

$$\frac{\pi(n^2 - 1)^2\,EI}{a^3} \quad, n \geqslant 1$$

Note that when $n = 1$ we have the rigid body mode and no strain energy can be stored.

5 WORK DONE BY RING TENSION

If the ring is under tension P due to an internal pressure p, we have

$$P = pa \tag{24}$$

After radial and tangential displacements have occurred an element of the ring has rotated and, furthermore, has a change in rotation between its ends of

$$\frac{1}{a^2}\left(w + \frac{\partial^2 w}{\partial \theta^2}\right) a \, d\theta$$

The ring tension P therefore provides a radial force

$$R = \frac{P}{a^2}\left(w + \frac{\partial^2 w}{\partial \theta^2}\right) a \, d\theta \tag{25}$$

on the element because the fluid pressure p, which gives rise to P, remains *perpendicular* to the element.[3]

So, in subsequently undergoing a small radial displacement, work is done by the amount

$$\frac{1}{2}\frac{P}{a}\int_0^{2\pi}\left(w + \frac{\partial^2 w}{\partial \theta^2}\right) w \, d\theta = \frac{1}{2}\left(\frac{\pi P(n^2 - 1)}{a}\right) A_n^2 \quad , \ n \geqslant 1 \tag{26}$$

Accordingly, the effective bending stiffness of the ring may be *augmented* by the amount $\pi P(n^2 - 1)/a$ in the case of ring tension. Alternatively, if external pressure is applied, the ring is in compression and the effective bending stiffness is *reduced* by the amount $\pi P(n^2 - 1)/a$.

6 GENERAL EIGENVALUE PROBLEM

For a free vibration of the form of eqns (6),

$$w(\theta, t) = A_n(t) \cos n\theta$$

$$v(\theta, t) = -\frac{A_n(t)}{n} \sin n\theta$$

on the surface of the ring itself, the statement of energy conservation is

$$\Sigma \, \mathrm{KE} + \Sigma \, \mathrm{SE} = \text{constant}$$

in which, in line with eqn (19), the summation of kinetic energy includes contributions from the inner and outer fluids and the radial and circumferential motions of the ring. Similarly, the summation of strain energy allows the flexural strain energy in the ring to be augmented or depleted to allow for ring tension or ring compression, respectively (see eqns (23) and (26)). That is, we have

$$\tfrac{1}{2} M_{e,n} \dot{A}_n^2 + \tfrac{1}{2} K_{e,n} A_n^2 = \text{constant} \tag{27}$$

where the total effective mass in the nth mode of vibration is

$$M_{e,n} = (\rho_i + \rho_e) \frac{\pi a^2}{n} + m\pi a \left(1 + \frac{1}{n^2}\right) , \quad n \geqslant 1 \tag{28}$$

and where the total effective stiffness in the nth mode of vibration is

$$K_{e,n} = \frac{\pi EI}{a^3} (n^2 - 1)^2 \pm \frac{\pi P}{a} (n^2 - 1) , \quad n \geqslant 1 \tag{29}$$

where the positive sign is used if the ring is in tension.

By definition, the natural circular frequency of the nth mode of vibration is

$$\omega_n = \left(\frac{K_{e,n}}{M_{e,n}}\right)^{1/2} \tag{30}$$

or

$$\omega_n = \left[\frac{\dfrac{\pi EI (n^2 - 1)^2}{a^3} \pm \dfrac{\pi P (n^2 - 1)}{a}}{\dfrac{(\rho_i + \rho_e)\pi a^2}{n} + m\pi a \left(1 + \dfrac{1}{n^2}\right)} \right]^{1/2} \tag{31}$$

and we exclude the case $n = 1$ as being a rigid body mode.

It is of note that zero frequencies are also recorded if the external pressure is such that

$$P = (n^2 - 1) \frac{EI}{a^2} \tag{32}$$

This is Bresse's solution for the stability of a ring under fluid pressure (see Ref. 3). The critical load of a circular ring under external fluid pressure is (when $n = 2$)

$$P_{crit} = 3 \frac{EI}{a^2} \tag{33}$$

although in practice, on account of out-of-roundness, failure loads are a good deal less than this. The solution for the stability of partial rings under pressure loadings was first given by Hurlbrink (see Refs 3 and 4).

7 DISCUSSION

The general result, eqn (31), contains the specific results mentioned in the Introduction. For example, Rayleigh's solution for the free inextensional vibrations of the ring itself, namely

$$\omega_n = \left[\frac{EI}{ma^4} \frac{(n^2 - 1)^2}{(1 + 1/n^2)} \right]^{1/2} \quad , n \geqslant 1 \tag{34}$$

is contained there.[1] So, too, is Rayleigh's solution for vibrations of a fluid jet, namely

$$\omega_n = \left[\frac{n(n^2 - 1)P}{\rho_i a^3} \right]^{1/2} \quad , n \geqslant 1 \tag{35}$$

where P is defined as the surface tension.[2] In interpreting what is seen, one may define the wavelength of the standing wave pattern on the jet as the product of the jet velocity and the period $2\pi/\omega_n$, above.

The case of a circular membrane under internal pressure and surrounded by fluids has natural frequencies given by

$$\omega_n = \left[\frac{P(n^2 - 1)/a}{(\rho_i + \rho_e)a^2/n + ma(1 + 1/n^2)} \right]^{1/2} \quad , n \geqslant 1 \tag{36}$$

For example, the ring modes of a representative slice of, say, a blimp could be modelled in the first instance as a neutrally buoyant flexible ring under internal pressure with helium inside and air outside, by eqn (36). A problem closely related to this was given by Irvine.[5] Equation (36) is also an ideal starting point for considering the vibration of a representative slice of an air-supported barrel vault — the type used to cover tennis courts, etc. Such a representative slice is a segment of a circle in which the added mass of the surrounding air would figure significantly in the inertia forces generated by the vibration. It is probably true that the analysis presented here will give a good estimate of the fundamental natural frequencies: the only difficulty foreseen in obtaining an exact solution lies in obtaining correct expressions for the participating fluid masses.

On the other hand, the ring modes of a representative slice of, say, a submarine pressure hull would be given by the frequency equation

$$\omega_n = \left[\frac{\dfrac{\pi EI(n^2 - 1)^2}{(1 - v^2)a^3} - \dfrac{\pi P(n^2 - 1)}{a}}{\dfrac{\rho \pi a^2}{n} + m\pi a\left(1 + \dfrac{1}{n^2}\right)} \right]^{1/2}, \quad n \geqslant 1 \tag{37}$$

where E has been replaced by $E/(1 - v^2)$ to allow for Poisson's ratio effects, and only the outer confining sea water is included in the expression for additional fluid mass. The destabilizing effect of hoop compression is included: the greater the submergence the greater the effect, although, in practice, the higher modes are largely unaffected by hoop compression, fluid inertia and the circumferential inertia of the pressure hull.

REFERENCES

1. Love, A. E. H., *A Treatise on the Mathematical Theory of Elasticity*, 4th edn, Dover Publications, New York, 1944, pp. 512–13.
2. Lamb, H., *Hydrodynamics*, 6th edn, Dover Publications, New York, 1945, pp. 75–7, 471–2.
3. Timoshenko, S. P. & Gere, J., *Theory of Elastic Stability*, 2nd edn, McGraw-Hill, New York, 1961, pp. 287–8, 291, 297.
4. Simitses, G. J., *An Introduction to the Elastic Stability of Structures*, Prentice-Hall, Englewood Cliffs, NJ, 1976, pp. 171–215.
5. Irvine, H. M., *Cable Structures*, MIT Press, Cambridge, MA, 1981, pp. 254–5.

SESSION 3

Thin-Walled Structures **9** (1990) 163–174

Transverse Flange Stresses in a Simple Box Girder

L. C. Schmidt & M. Salaheldin

Department of Civil and Mining Engineering, University of Wollongong, Wollongong, New South Wales 2500, Australia

ABSTRACT

A theoretical investigation into the transverse stresses in the flanges of a simply supported box girder, under a symmetrical static concentrated load acting at the mid-span, is conducted using the finite element technique. Substantial membrane transverse stresses are detected. An explanation of this phenomenon is presented. The explanation is investigated by dividing the box girder into two identical channels. A torque is introduced by virtue of the central load being offset transversely with respect to the shear centre of each channel, and hence membrane transverse stresses are induced. In order to verify the above allocation of cause to consequence, certain lines of enquiry in connection with the behaviour of open and closed thin-walled girders are pursued. Correlation between the results revealed by the finite element analysis and those determined using simple structural mechanics principles is indicated.

NOTATION

b	Flange width
d	Depth of girder
e	Distance between the shear centre of a channel and its web
E	Young's modulus
F	Force acting laterally on the flange of channel section when the load does not act on the shear centre
l	Girder span
P	Single central static point load applied at the web/flange junction

163

Thin-Walled Structures 0263-8231/90/$03·50 © 1990 Elsevier Science Publishers Ltd, England. Printed in Great Britain

t_f, t_w Flange and web thickness, respectively
x Lateral distance across the girder measured from the web/flange junction

α Depth to width ratio of the girder $= d/b$
β Flange slenderness ratio $= b/t_f$
λ Flange aspect ratio $= b/l$
μ Poisson's ratio
σ_l Membrane longitudinal stress
σ_T Membrane transverse stress
σ_{Tmax} Maximum membrane transverse stress across the mid-span section
Ω Ratio of maximum membrane transverse stress to the corresponding membrane longitudinal stress $= \sigma_{Tmax}/\sigma_l$

1 INTRODUCTION

The problem of transverse deformation of a box girder under different types of loading has been investigated at length by others. For example, the beam on elastic foundation analogy approach has been used to describe the distortional behaviour of a box girder under unsymmetrical loading conditions,[1] while the finite element technique, using extensional–flexural quadrilateral elements, has been used to describe the torsional and distortional components of behaviour due to an eccentric point load applied on a simply supported box girder.[2] It was noted by Chapman *et al.*[2] that deformational stresses occurred under symmetrical loading if the supports were skewed or if the girder were curved.

Recently Shuskewich[3] introduced an approach to determine the longitudinal, shear and transverse membrane forces acting on a symmetrically loaded box girder based on a simple mechanics of materials relationship. The method was discussed by Avila and Cusens.[4]

The objective of this paper is to demonstrate the existence of large membrane transverse stresses in the flanges of a straight box girder under a pair of symmetrical central point loads (Fig. 1). A simple box is chosen with no stiffening of the flanges.

Following Heyman,[5] consider the box girder to be subdivided into two channels as shown in Fig. 2(a). The load $P/2$ (one quarter of the total load shown in Fig. 1) in Fig. 2(a) causes a shear flow that results in the forces shown in Fig. 2(b) for each channel. Because the force $P/2$ is located a distance e away from the shear centre, a torque of value $Pe/2$ will cause the channel to twist. However, in the case of the box the tips of the

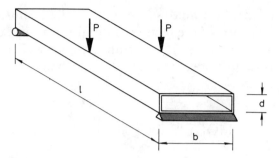

Fig. 1. Box girder — loading and boundary conditions.

channel flanges are located on the centre line; consequently, in order to restore the channel to the no-twist condition, concentrated lateral flange forces of value $Pe/2d$ are needed, as shown in Fig. 2(c). These forces can be approximated[5] as point forces which will induce transverse membrane stresses in the flanges.

This argument, as proposed by Heyman,[5] of dividing the box girder into two symmetrical channels, each of which has a loading equivalent to that on half of the original box girder, is to be examined.

An attempt is made to establish a correlation between the transverse stresses revealed by finite element analyses on the one hand, and the lateral membrane force produced across the flange as predicted using the simple mechanics of materials concept of the shear centre on the other hand.

The understanding of the transverse deformational behaviour of a flange of a box girder requires the consideration of certain lines of enquiry into the behaviour of other cross-sections. Firstly, a wide flange I-beam,

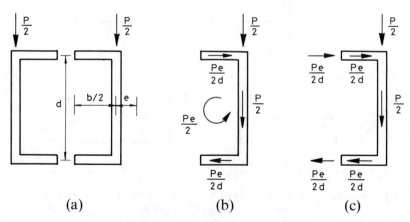

Fig. 2. Cross-section of box composed of two channels: see text.

Fig. 3(a), is considered for analysis with an applied central load acting through the shear centre of the section. Secondly, further examination of two other cross-sections, a channel and an open box girder (Fig. 3(b), (c)), enable a conclusion to be reached regarding the behaviour of the simple box girder, Fig. 3(d).

2 MODELLING TECHNIQUE

The finite element analysis employs a four-noded quadrilateral shell element. A full description of the element features is presented in Ref. 6. In all models considered for analysis no restrictions are imposed on the six degrees of freedom (three translations and three rotations) of the nodes along the web/flange junction line, and thus a full interaction between the elements of the structure is allowed. An end diaphragm of infinite in-plane stiffness and zero out-of-plane stiffness is assumed at the simple supports.

In the two cases of box girders, namely the simple closed box and the open box, a double symmetry is assumed, and hence one quarter of the box girder is modelled. For the I-beam and the channel section, half the beam is modelled.

A concentrated load is applied at the mid-span on each web/flange junction. The analysis is conducted on the assumption of linear elastic behaviour. Young's modulus E is assumed to be 200 GPa, and Poisson's ratio μ is assumed to be 0·3 for the material.

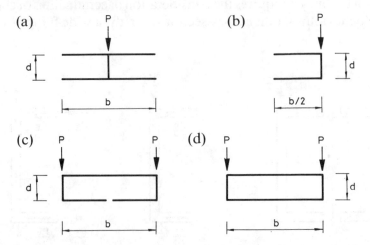

Fig. 3. Cross-sections investigated: (a) wide flange I-beam; (b) channel; (c) open box girder; (d) simple box girder.

As the central region of the girder is a highly stressed area, a biased mesh, allowing a fine discretization near the mid-span, is employed with the elements at the support 300% larger than the elements at the middle.

3 NUMERICAL RESULTS

3.1 I-Beam girder

The geometrical configurations are given as non-dimensional ratios from Fig. 3(a),

$$\alpha = d/b = 0.25$$
$$\beta = b/t_f = 40$$
$$\lambda = b/l = 0.25$$
$$t_f = t_w$$

where t_f is the flange thickness, t_w is the web thickness, and l is the span of the centrally loaded simply supported beam.

The girder is simply supported with a diaphragm preventing in-plane deformation of the cross-section at each end. The point load is applied at the mid-span on the web/flange junction, and as such it is acting through the shear centre, and therefore no twisting effect is produced.

The distribution of membrane transverse stresses across the compressive flange of the girder, at mid-span, is shown in Fig. 4(a). The stresses are tensile. Figure 4(b) displays a three-dimensional plot of the deflected shape. Magnification factors of 20, 200 and 400 are used for the vertical, longitudinal and lateral (transverse) deformation respectively. The figure shows the lateral expansion of the compressive flange and the contraction in the tensile flange of the I-beam. The lateral deflection has to be magnified using a rather large factor (400) in order to obtain a comprehensive picture of the deflection.

A complete explanation of the complex behaviour of the I-beam girder cannot be presented within the limited confines of the present paper. However, the point is made that no twisting takes place under the assumed loading condition. Consequently the web remains vertical. It is worth noting that Ω (the ratio of the maximum membrane transverse stress to the corresponding longitudinal stress) equals -14.5%.

3.2 Channel and open box girder

The boundary conditions for both models, the channel section of Fig. 3(b) and the open box girder of Fig. 3(c), are similar to those of the

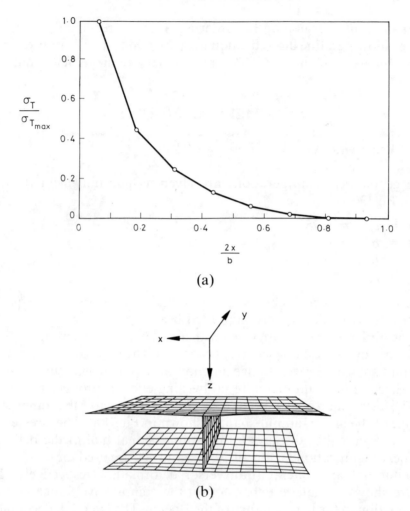

Fig. 4. (a) Membrane transverse stress distribution across the upper half flange of an I-beam (mid-span). (b) Three-dimensional deflected shape of an I-beam; magnification factors: x 400, y 200 and z 20.

I-beam girder, including the assumption of an end support diaphragm with an infinite in-plane rigidity.

The cross-sections have the values $\alpha = 0.5, \beta = 20$ and $\lambda = 0.25$ for the channel, while $\alpha = 0.25, \beta = 40$ and $\lambda = 0.5$ for the box girder. In each case $t_f = t_w$.

The interpretation of the symmetrical condition leads to the consideration of half and one quarter of the complete model for the channel and the open box girder respectively. The objective of the exercise at this stage is to examine the similarity in the behaviour of the two models.

For the channel section, the shear centre lies on its horizontal axis of symmetry and outside its vertical web. Hence the central point load, acting on the web/flange junction, does not pass through the shear centre, and consequently twisting deformation occurs.

The study of the deflected shape, as shown by the finite element analysis, shows excessive twisting deformation as shown in Fig. 5(a). The deflection magnification factors in the vertical, longitudinal and lateral directions are 5, 10 and 20 respectively.

When assuming a cut in the lower flange of the box girder the closed section becomes an open one as in Fig. 2(c), and the centre line of the lower flange gains the freedom to move laterally and rotate.

Figure 5(b) shows the deflected shape of one quarter of the open box girder. In order to facilitate the comparison between the channel and the

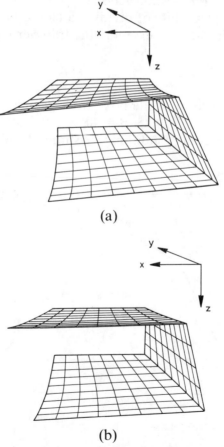

(a)

(b)

Fig. 5. Three-dimensional shape of (a) a channel section, and (b) an open box girder. Magnification factors: x 20, y 10 and z 5.

open box girder, the same magnification factors are used. The twisting action of the open box girder is clearly demonstrated through the tendency of each half of the lower flange to move away from the centre line.

The similarity between the behaviour of the lower flange of the channel (Fig. 5(a)) and the lower flange of the open box girder (Fig. 5(b)) is apparent.

The bending effect imposed on the upper flange of the open box girder, in the transverse direction, is resisted mainly by the plate flexural stiffness inducing transverse plate bending stresses. The deformation is also associated with a high value of membrane transverse stresses.

Figure 6 shows the distribution of membrane transverse stresses across the mid-span of the upper flange. An extremely high value of Ω of 2·26 is found for the geometry chosen.

The realization of the twisting action of the open box girder points the way to the logical possibility of dividing a closed box section into two channel sections in order to examine the transverse stresses.

3.3 Box girder

A non-dimensional form of the box girder geometrical configuration, Fig. 3(d), is given by $\alpha = 0·25$, $\beta = 40$, $\lambda = 0·5$ and $t_f = t_w$. Both the boundary and the loading conditions are similar to those of the open box girder.

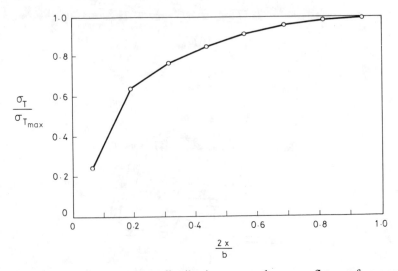

Fig. 6. Membrane transverse stress distribution across the upper flange of an open box girder (mid-span).

A comparison between Fig. 6 and Fig. 7 shows the distinct similarity between the distribution of membrane transverse stresses across the mid-span for the open and closed boxes.

For the closed box, the distribution of the membrane transverse stresses, along the upper flange, has its peak value at the centre. A rapid decay is noticed when moving away from the centre. This finding indicates that the twisting effect, which creates the compressive transverse stresses, has a localized influence near the centre.

Figure 8 displays one quarter of the deflection shape of the closed box girder. The magnification factors used in the vertical, longitudinal and lateral directions are 100, 0 and 500 respectively. Ω has a high value of 0·47.

4 DISCUSSION

The aim has been to study the variation of the membrane transverse stresses in the flange of a simply supported girder under a concentrated load acting on the web/flange junction.

Different cross-sections have been considered for the analysis. A completely symmetrical condition (geometry, boundary conditions and loading) has been assumed for the case of a box girder. A reference value $\Omega = \sigma_{Tmax}/\sigma_l$, where σ_{Tmax} is the maximum membrane transverse stress across the mid-span cross-section of the compressive flange (upper flange) and σ_l is the corresponding value of the membrane longitudinal

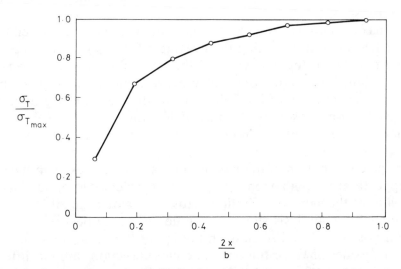

Fig. 7. Membrane transverse stress distribution across the cross-section of the compressive flange of a closed box girder.

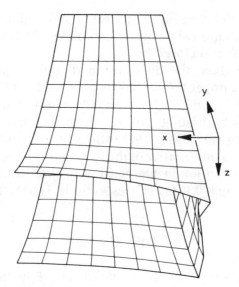

Fig. 8. Three-dimensional deflected shape of a box girder; magnification factors: x 500, y 0 and z 100.

stress, is introduced in order to assess the significance of the transverse stresses.

A review of the value of this parameter Ω, for different cases, helps to develop a greater understanding of the lateral deformation and the associated transverse stresses. In the case of an I-beam, Ω is equal to $-14 \cdot 5\%$ and the flange undergoes lateral expansion with tensile transverse stresses.

When considering the channel section and the open box girder, large lateral deformation, reflecting the twisting effects, is encountered. The similarity between the behaviour of the lower flange of the open box girder and the lower flange of the channel section furnishes a good base for the understanding of the behaviour of the closed box girder. It is through this comparison that the idea of dividing a closed box girder into two identical channels, in order to examine the membrane transverse stresses, becomes feasible.

On the examination of the membrane transverse stresses induced in the upper flange of both open and closed box girders, it is found that they have almost the same distribution across and along the girders.

Although the analysis shows very little difference between σ_T (open section) and σ_T (closed section) in the upper flange, at the same load level, the values of Ω for the open and closed sections are far different and are equal to $2 \cdot 26$ and $0 \cdot 47$ respectively. An explanation of this finding lies in the influence of the torsional deformation, in the case of an open section, which increases the shear lag effect and hence reduces the value of the longitudinal membrane stresses near the centre. It can be deduced that the high value of Ω, in the case of an open box girder, is attributed to the correspondingly small value of σ_l at the centre line resulting from the increasing influence of shear lag.

The presence of the transverse membrane stresses at the mid-section of the box, as shown by the finite element analyses, indicates that the simple mechanics of materials approach suggested by Heyman[5] can furnish a useful yardstick for their magnitude.

5 CONCLUSION

Particular attention has been paid to the finite element results of a channel girder and an open box girder. The examination of the results gives an insight into the lateral twisting effect which gives rise to the high values of membrane transverse stresses detected at the mid-span of a closed box girder. The similarity between the behaviour of the open box girder lower flange and the corresponding channel flange is demonstrated. It becomes feasible, due to the previous findings, to propose that the cross-section of the box girder can be divided into two identical channels. A simple calculation of the lateral force acting on the flange of the channel, as a result of the vertical load being offset laterally with respect to the channel shear centre, can be used to assess the importance of the membrane transverse stresses in the flange of the associated box girder.

Finally, it is pointed out that within an elastic linear analysis frame of reference, the shear lag effect on the flange of an open box girder is greater than its effect on the flange of a closed box girder.

ACKNOWLEDGEMENT

The work was carried out in the Department of Civil and Mining Engineering of the University of Wollongong; the authors are grateful for the facilities provided.

REFERENCES

1. Wright, R. N., Abdel-Samad, S. R. & Robinson, A. R., BEF analogy for analysis of box girders, *J. Struct. Div., ASCE,* **94**(ST7) (July) (1968) 1719–43.

2. Chapman, J. C., Dowling, P. J., Lim, P. T. K. & Billington, C. J., The structural behaviour of steel and concrete box girder bridges, *Struct. Engr,* **49** (March) (1971) 111.
3. Shuskewich, K. W., Membrane force acting on a box girder bridge, *J. Struct. Div., ASCE,* **112**(ST8) (August) (1986) 1900-7.
4. Avila, J. I. de S. L. & Cusens, A. R., Membrane forces acting on a box girder bridge, Discussion, *J. Struct. Div. ASCE,* **114**(4) (April) (1988) 959-62.
5. Heyman, J., *Elements of Stress Analysis,* Cambridge University Press, Cambridge, UK, 1982.
6. MacNeal, R. H., A simple quadrilateral shell element, *Comput. Struct.,* **8** (1978) 175-83.

Thin-Walled Structures **9** (1990) 175–197

Blast-Resistant Buildings for Australia's North-West Shelf Liquid Natural Gas Plant

C. Turnell

BHP Steel International Group, Level 12, Forest Centre, 221 St. George's Terrace, Perth, Western Australia 6000, Australia

N. W. Murray

Department of Civil Engineering, Monash University, Clayton, Victoria 3168, Australia

&

I. D. Bennetts

BHP Melbourne Research Laboratories, 245–273 Wellington Road, Mulgrave, Victoria 3170, Australia

ABSTRACT

In the event of an explosion at the processing plant the control equipment within the blast-resistant enclosure must remain functional for a period of time which would allow proper shutdown of external plant equipment. Thirteen blast-resistant buildings were designed to withstand blast pressures ten times greater than Australia's worst cyclonic winds. The paper describes the buildings and the novel analytical and design approach developed.

1 INTRODUCTION

The safety of critical equipment at the North-West Shelf's $A3·7 billion Liquid Natural Gas (LNG) plant, now under construction on Western Australia's Burrup Peninsula, has been secured by the installation of several blast-resistant buildings. The equipment controlling the processing

Thin-Walled Structures 0263-8231/90/$03·50 © 1990 Elsevier Science Publishers Ltd, England. Printed in Great Britain

plant operations, including links to the storage tanks and the wharf, is vital to the plant's safe operations. For protection against explosions or fires, this equipment is housed in specially reinforced buildings constructed as structural steel shells which must protect the integrity of the control equipment to enable an orderly shutdown of the external plant operation.

The shells form a protective envelope capable of withstanding an explosion equal to ten times the pressure of Australia's worst cyclonic winds. The total of 13 such buildings formed a $A45 million contract covering design, supply, fabrication and installation with delivery between January 1987 and February 1988. Kellog–Japan Gas Corp.-Raymond awarded the construction contract to a joint venture consortium of Concrete Constructions Pty Ltd and CBI Constructors Pty Ltd, with BHP Engineering undertaking the structural design as well as completing architectural detailing and electrical design.

This paper describes the buildings and the unusual features of their design.

2 STRUCTURAL REQUIREMENTS

The general arrangement of a typical building is shown in Fig. 1. They are single-storey and windowless, ranging in size from 56 m × 8 m to 32 m × 24 m. Each has a small penthouse on the roof for heating, ventilation and air conditioning services, with air-supply inlet and outlet protected by blast-resistant valves. Equipment inside the buildings is connected to the operating plant by cables running through underground trenches.

Requirements for the structure strength were specified by the contract documents principally as follows:

(a) The building must be capable of resisting an external explosion which would produce an equivalent static loading of 100 kPa on the walls and 25–50 kPa downward on the roof. Dynamic deflections of the structure must be controlled to 150 mm so as not to be detrimental to the required operational function.

(b) Provision must be made for a 2-h fire rating to be achieved *subsequent* to an explosion loading.

(c) The interior of the building must remain sealed against gas entry even after a blast, and the outer skin of the structure must be free from 'pockets' or spaces which can collect gas.

An additional construction requirement was minimisation of on-site

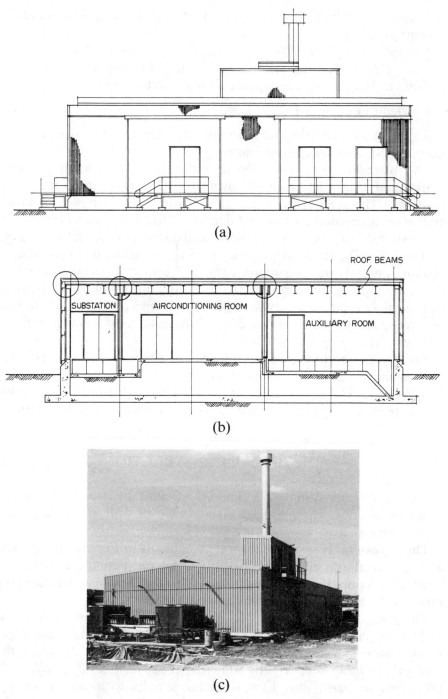

Fig. 1. (a) General elevation, and (b) general section of a typical building. (c) View of a typical building with cladding.

construction work because of the confined plant site and construction accommodation.

Ultimate strength analysis allowing plastic behaviour to the requirements of AS1250[1] was specified for blast loading resistance. The dominant design load group with ultimate factors was

1·5 Dead Load + 1·1 Blast Load

Architectural cladding and minor attachments were designed for normal AS1250 load combinations.

The blast loadings, specified as equivalent static loadings, were established from the dynamic over-pressures, diffraction and drag loadings.[2] The steel shell under blast loading is a complex dynamic system of distributed masses and degrees of freedom, consisting of wall and roof elements. These are proportioned differently for each enclosure, and with varying door openings and internal shell wall connections, a rigorous analysis was considered to be impractical, especially in view of the design contract timeframe. It is also worth noting that a steel shell can be expected to behave somewhat differently from a geometrically similar concrete structure, which was used as the basis for load specification and has been treated by Langevold.[3]

The design developed for the Joint Venture tender had to be efficient and practical, while conforming to the constraints of the Contract Specification. The key features of the design which contributed to this cause are identified and discussed in subsequent sections of this paper.

3 ENCLOSURE CONSTRUCTION

A shell made from stiffened steel plates provides the structural integrity of the enclosures. Each consists of a system of wall and roof panels assembled on-site.

The site assembly system, shown schematically in Fig. 2(a), has proved to be practical and efficient. Assembly of a typical enclosure (Fig. 2(b) and (c)) took only 12–18 days with welding proceeding over the following three weeks in conjunction with other activities.

The walls are 12 mm thick steel plate stiffened with T-section ribs at 1·015 m spacings. The chosen spacing allows use of BHP's stock 3 m width plates. The side walls incorporate an eaves section to which the roof rafters have been rigidly attached (Fig. 3(a)). The panels were fabricated in Perth into 12 m modular lengths with door openings included as required (Fig. 3(b)). Due to their light weight, steel units proved economical to transport to the North-West Shelf site.

The roof is made with 8 mm plating welded to supporting 460UB

(a)

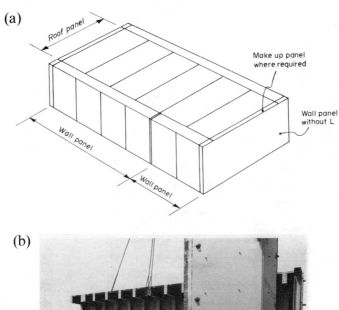

(b)

(c)

Fig. 2. (a) Structural steel box assembly; (b) erection of a typical wall panel (with connection to roof in place); (c) view of building before insulation and cladding were applied.

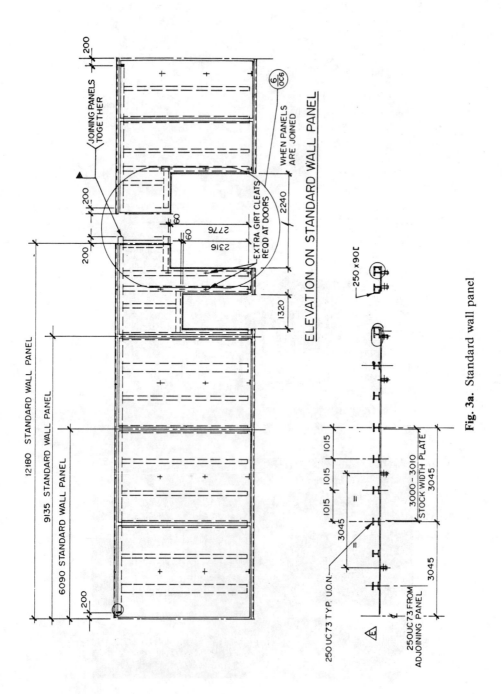

Fig. 3a. Standard wall panel

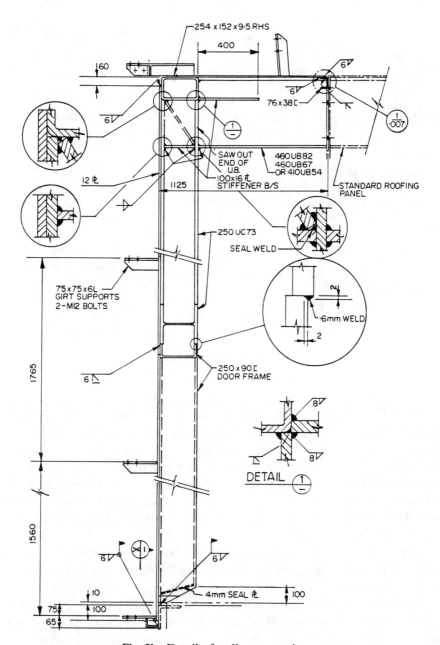

Fig. 3b. Detail of wall cross-section.

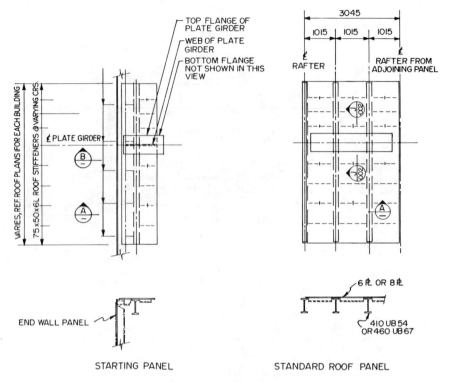

Fig. 3c. Roof panels.

rafters which align with wall ribs, while cross-stiffening of the roof plate is provided by angles welded along the toe (Fig. 3(b) and 3(c)). These angles also help to disperse the in-plane loading into the roof. For buildings wider than 8 m the roof rafters are provided with intermediate supports by longitudinal girders which frame into the rafters. The girders span between the column supports. By incorporating the girders into the panels, erection simplifies to a panel assembly procedure and minimises on-site work.

The steel shell is fire-protected with 'Kaowool', which is a blown ceramic fibre blanket or batt material. It is fastened to steel spikes welded to the plates and restrained by a wire mesh covering (Fig. 4).

The Kaowool material is porous; it will absorb gas, and will act as a 'wick' absorbing water. To achieve gas tightness and prevent water damage, the Kaowool is covered by a sisalation vapour barrier.

The steel shell is finished architecturally by a cladding of coloured light-gauge sheeting (Figs 1(c) and 4). The inside is fitted out with high standard architectural finishes selected according to room usage.

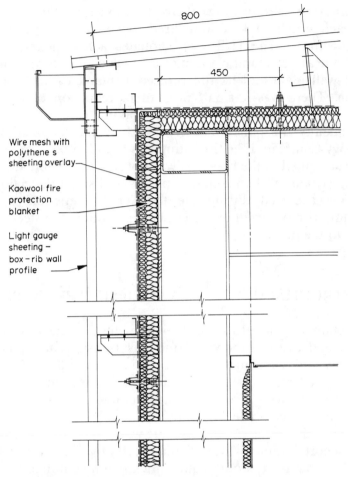

Fig. 4. Arrangement of wall and roof with insulation.

4 DETAILS OF FIREPROOFING

The lightweight Kaowool blanket is flexible and thus able to provide the fire rating to AS1530:Pt4[4] despite any distortion of the steel shell under blast loading. Alternatives of calcium silicate or ceramic board were considered too brittle, and high technology sprayed coatings are very expensive, typically four times the cost, and have unproven long-term performance.

Preliminary tests during the tender period established that the blanket was pervious to blast shock waves, and that no outer skin of protective steelwork was needed. This was proven during the design period by testing[5] a typical 3 m square wall panel using explosive TNT at the

Australian Army's testing range at Greytown, Victoria. Some 36 concrete blocks each weighing 1·5 t were used to restrain the panel and its supporting frame. The TNT was detonated a few metres away, and although the architectural cladding was buckled and torn by the blast, the steel wall plate and its fire protection blanket and fittings were unbroken. There was a small permanent reduction of the blanket thickness behind the central cladding support.

Subsequently the panel was fire-tested by the National Building Technology Centre and the fire rating was found to be in excess of 3 h. Damage sustained in the blast test was not repaired before the fire test. Minor movement of the insulation panels and small deflection of the steel panel occurred during the test. The permissible maximum temperature rise occurred at a local hot spot where the steel studs are attached to the plate.

5 STRUCTURAL ACTION AND DESIGN PRINCIPLES

In this section the general approach to the method of analysis and design is discussed. Because of the very large blast pressures acting normal to each surface and the requirements for sealing the building, it was logical to use stiffened plates as the structural elements. Thus the building resembled a box with a roof and four vertical walls, the latter being pinned to a solid concrete foundation plate.

One way of designing such a structure would have been to treat it as a number of portal frames which of course carry loads mainly by bending action. However, in view of the quite thick plating required to carry the blast loading, this seemed to be unrealistic. Thick plating is very stiff in its own plane so it was realized that a novel approach to the design should be used.

When such a building is loaded with, say, a frontal blast pressure, the key load-carrying elements are the two end walls and the roof, all of which carry in-plane direct and shear stresses. The front wall carries the pressure loading in the direction of the normal to its plane and some in-plane direct and shear stresses. The back wall carries a similar (but not identical) stress pattern.

Thus this assumed load path enabled the analysis of the superstructure to be handled in three parts as follows:

(1) Pressure loads acting normal to any surface were handled by using plastic theory. A strip of plating lying between two parallel stiffeners and welded to them was designed as a wide built-in

plastic beam with plastic hinges in the plating adjacent to the stiffeners and another at mid-span between the stiffeners. This takes care of the transfer of the normal pressure into the stiffened plating. This analysis is presented in Section 6.

(2) The loading from (1) then has to be transferred along the panel in the direction of the stiffeners. For example, when normal pressure is applied to the front wall it has to carry part of the total load down to the foundation level and the remainder up to the eaves. This load transfer is carried out by bending action of the wall. It is also considered in Section 6.

(3) Finally the load at eaves level arising from (2) above has to be resisted by 'box action' of the whole building. This was described briefly earlier in this section and is dealt with in detail in the Appendix. There it is shown that the box action of the building can be dealt with in two steps, the results being added together using the Principle of Superposition. The stress distributions in the walls and roof for part (3) of the analysis are summarised in Table A1.

The approach just described can be justified on the grounds that it is a Lower Bound Design Method (LBM). In the LBM when equilibrium is satisfied and the yield condition is not violated the structure will be safe.

6 DESIGN OF WALLS

The steel walls acting as plates are subjected to a fairly complex pattern of in-plane stresses, listed in Table A1. As seen in the last section, they arise from the action of the building as a box and they consist of the sum of the stresses from direct axial loading and shear plus bending as a cantilever. The outer skin spanning between the stiffener beams also is subjected to horizontal bending as shown in Fig. 5(a).

As stated before, in designing the wall plate the Lower Bound Theorem was invoked, i.e. provided equilibrium is satisfied and the yield condition is not violated the design will be safe. This was achieved by 'assigning' proportions of capacity to vertical bending (subscript 1) and to horizontal plate bending (subscript 2) of

$$F_{y1} = F_{y2} = F_y/\sqrt{2} = 260/\sqrt{2} \tag{1}$$

The basis of this assignment is the von Mises–Hencky yield criterion.[6] For horizontal bending (σ_x) and the vertical bending (σ_y) an effective stress σ_e must be less than F_y, i.e.

$$\sigma_e = \sqrt{\sigma_x^2 + \sigma_y^2 - \sigma_x \sigma_y + 3\tau_{xy}^2} \leqslant F_y \tag{2}$$

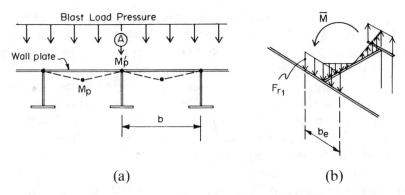

Fig. 5. (a) Plate bending action; (b) overall bending action. $\overline{M} \leqslant M_p$ of section.

The horizontal bending effect shown in Fig. 5(a) is governed by the equation

$$\text{plate capacity} = 2M_p = \frac{pb^2}{8} \tag{3}$$

where

$$M_p = \frac{F_y t_p^2}{4} = \frac{F_{y1} t_p^2}{4} \tag{4}$$

and t_p is the thickness of the wall plate.

In considering vertical bending of the wall members as stiffened plates (Fig. 5(b)) it was assumed that the effective width b_e of plate was that allowed by AS1250 Clause 4.3.2,[1] i.e.

$$b_e = \frac{560 t_p}{\sqrt{F_y}} = \frac{560 t_p}{\sqrt{F_{y2}}} \tag{5}$$

The plastic modulus and effective area of cross-section were then determined from this value of b_e. The capacity of the effective section to carry the applied moment M_u and axial load P_u was checked at the knee and at mid-height of the wall.

This approach to the design of the wall units should ensure against collapse arising from local buckling of the plating. This is because the use of an effective width means that the middle strip of plating is ignored, and secondly that the presence of the pressure loading normal to the plating should induce barrel-like deflections which suppress the lowest buckling mode. Another influence which assists the plating is that significant horizontal membrane forces should exist and thereby strengthen the outer skin.

Small penetrations were treated as in the early boiler codes, viz. their edges were reinforced with approximately the same amount of material. When a large penetration occurred the whole section of plate was deleted in the analysis.

7 ROOF DESIGN

The in-plane stresses in the roof plate arising from a frontal blast pressure loading are presented in Table A1. In addition to this loading it is necessary to consider the vertically downwards blast loading on the roof (25–50 kPa). This was handled in a similar manner to that shown in Fig. 5(a) for the wall. However, to ensure box behaviour (i.e. diaphragm action of roof plate), as assumed in Section 5, does occur, bending in the roof rafters has to be limited to elastic stress levels. The roof plate itself is still designed at ultimate loading (Fig. 6(a) and (b)).

Additional loads arise from the presence of the penthouses. They produce isolated point and patch loads which act in the plane of the roof. The point loads shown in Fig. 6(c) produce pure shear ($\tau = p/bt$) in the outer regions of the roof while there is zero shear stress in the inner region. All other stress components are zero throughout the roof for this case.

For the patch load the solution due to Michell[7] was used (Fig. 6(d)). At point $z(x, y)$ the stress components are

$$\sigma_x = -\frac{\sigma}{\pi}(\theta_1 - \theta_2) - \frac{2\sigma\,dy\,\cos(\theta_1 - \theta_2)}{\rho_1 \rho_2} \tag{6a}$$

$$\sigma_y = -\frac{\sigma}{\pi}(\theta_1 - \theta_2) + \frac{2\sigma\,dy\,\cos(\theta_1 - \theta_2)}{\rho_1 \rho_2} \tag{6b}$$

When the in-plane loadings are in the direction of the rafter centrelines the plate has a high in-plane buckling capacity[6,8] ($\sigma_{cr} \simeq 80$ MPa). When the loading is perpendicular to the rafters the plate acts as a wide column and its in-plane buckling stress is low ($\sigma_{cr} = 28$ MPa). To increase the strength of the plating, angle stiffeners as shown in Fig. 3(c) are provided.

8 FOUNDATION ANALYSIS

All of the enclosure sites were made available for construction with the ground level at -1.5 m to the finished floor level. This ground level is the specified underside of the foundation. The ground consisted of well-

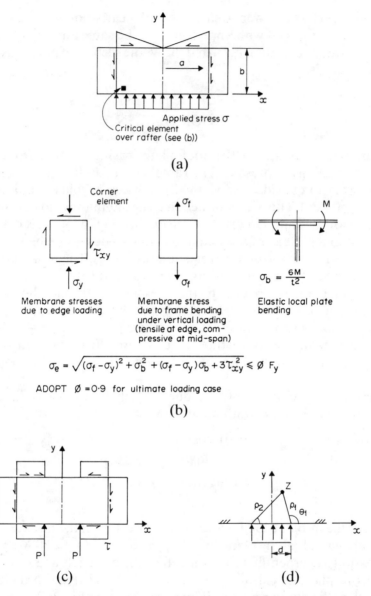

Fig. 6. (a) Stresses in roof as in Fig. A2; (b) stresses in critical element of roof plate; (c) penthouse loads; (d) patch load for Michell solution.[7]

compacted coarsely-graded rock-fill to a depth of 2·2 m generally overlying rhyodacite bedrock. Geotechnical design criteria for the blast load were:

(a) allowable nett bearing pressure 200 kPa with 150% dynamic load increase;

(b) internal friction angle 35°;

(c) foundation stability load factors: 1·1 blast, 0·9 dead loads.

The reinforced concrete foundation is designed as a rigid base to distribute the peak forces, vertical and horizontal, from the hollow box superstructure. Initially a strip footing system was investigated. To resist the overturning from horizontal forces which are applied 2·8 m above the base, and to limit bearing pressures to a maximum of 500 kPa, a 6·5 m wide footing would have been required (Fig. 7(a)). With this wide

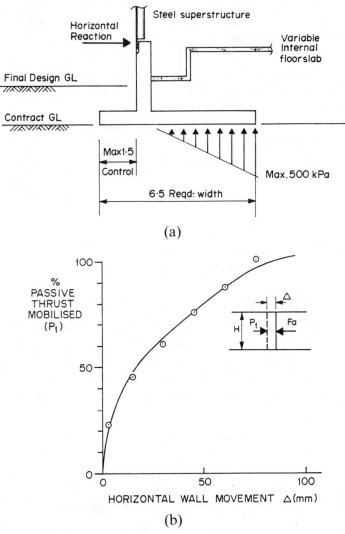

(a)

(b)

Fig. 7. (a) Strip-footing required for horizontal blast loading; (b) passive earth pressure mobilisation.

external footing around the perimeter plus internal footing pads and shear-wall strip footings, up to 80% of the plan area of the foundation was covered. To simplify the solution and increase the base stability, a 500 mm thick raft was adopted, as shown generally in Fig. 1.

The blast-resisting reinforced concrete foundation was thus a U-trough of outer perimeter wall and base raft. With this general form of foundation the detailing was standardised for all buildings, despite their differing internal wall and flooring treatments.

Floors and cabling trenches internally became localised design elements detailed individually as required and for their own loads alone.

It was, of course, important that the whole building did not move laterally as a result of a blast loading. This would disrupt underground cabling connections which are vital to its operation. Stability against sliding is provided by footing-interface shear which is mobilised at zero displacement. Additional restraint is provided by passive earth pressure against the embedded depth, but this requires a wall displacement of 75–155 mm to generate full pressure.

For most buildings adequate safety against sliding was provided by sliding shear resistance. To obtain maximum vertical mass for maximised resistance, the void area between the raft slab and floor slab was infilled with compacted sand. However, to resist blast loading in the long face of narrow buildings, additional concrete keys into the rock-fill base were necessary.

9 CONCLUSION

The paper describes the design philosophy of a rather unusual type of building. There appears to have been little published research work into box structures designed to withstand blast loadings. No doubt the design technique described here could be refined, especially if research and tests were carried out. However, given the contractual timeframe a robust, fire-resistant design which proved to be economical was achieved.

REFERENCES

1. Standards Association of Australia, AS1250–1981, *S.A.A. Steel Structures Code.*

2. Biggs, J. M., *Introduction to Structural Dynamics*, McGraw–Hill, New York, 1964.
3. Langevold, J. M., *Structural Design of Control Buildings*, Inst. of Chemical Engineers Symposium Series No. 47.
4. Standards Association of Australia, AS1530 — Pt 4, *Methods for Fire Tests on Building Materials and Structures, Fire Resistance Test of Structures*, 1975.
5. Proe, D. J. & Bennetts, I. D., *Blast Test and Fire Test on Steel Plate Wall Panel with Triton Kaowool Fire Protection*, Broken Hill Pty, MRL internal report PC 88/85/001, 1985.
6. Murray, N. W., *Introduction to the Theory of Thin-Walled Structures*, Oxford University Press, Oxford, UK, 1984.
7. Michell, J. H., The inversion of plane stress, *Proc. London Math. Soc.*, **34** (1902) 134.
8. Bulson, P. S., *The Stability of Flat Plates*, Chatto and Windus, London, 1970.

APPENDIX. ANALYSIS OF THE BUILDING AS A BOX

A1 Introduction

In this appendix the theoretical analysis of a building which consists of a rectangular parallelepiped with a flat roof and four flat, vertical walls (Fig. A1) is analysed by the Lower Bound Method.

A2 Frontal loading case

We consider the box as a wide cantilever (Fig. A1(a)) encastre at its base and carrying a frontal pressure p. In each of the roof and walls we use the Cartesian system of axes and the sign convention for positive stresses as shown. The load path into the base can be studied in two steps (Fig. A1(b) and (c)). In the first step the front face is treated as a stiffened plate spanning vertically so that a uniformly distributed force $ph/2$ per unit length of eaves is applied while the relatively small end effect is ignored. Figure A1(d) shows the positive sense of the stresses used in the following analysis.

This system of applied loads is self-equilibrating. In the second step the box is treated as a cantilever with in-plane loads applied to its end walls which are effectively the webs. These applied loads are equilibrated entirely by in-plane stresses at base level. Superposition of these two diagrams gives the actual loading, the base reactions and the internal stresses. In the following analyses it is assumed that all thicknesses of plate are equal to t. This is simply a device of convenience and does not affect the results.

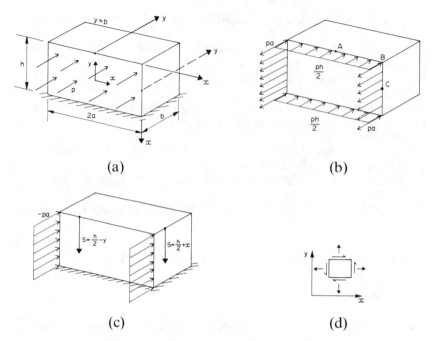

(a)   (b)

(c)   (d)

Fig. A1. (a) Box-building as loaded; (b) step 1 — self-equilibrating load; (c) step 2 — box as cantilever; (d) sign convention for positive stresses.

A3 Stress analysis of Step 1 loading case (Fig. A1(b))

A3.1 Roof and end walls

If the roof is analysed as a free body it is seen that the applied load at eaves level is equilibrated by a shear force at the roof-to-end-wall junction. Let us consider the following Airy stress function ϕ, which satisfies the biharmonic equation $\nabla^4\phi = 0$,

$$\phi = Ax^2 + Bx^2y \tag{A1}$$

where A and B are constants yet to be determined. The stresses in the roof are then

$$\sigma_x = \partial^2\phi/\partial y^2 = 0$$

$$\sigma_y = \partial^2\phi/\partial x^2 = 2A + 2By \tag{A2}$$

$$\tau_{xy} = -\partial^2\phi/\partial x\partial y = -2Bx$$

The following boundary conditions are used to obtain A and B.
When $y = 0$, $\sigma_y = -ph/2t$, and when $y = b$, $\sigma_y = 0$, whence

$$A = -ph/4t$$

$$B = ph/4tb \tag{A3}$$

i.e. in the roof at a point (x, y) the stresses are

$$\sigma_x = 0$$

$$\sigma_y = -\frac{ph}{2t}\left(1 - \frac{y}{b}\right) \tag{A4}$$

$$\tau_{xy} = -phx/2tb$$

The same form of Airy stress function as in eqn (A1) can be used to obtain the stresses in the end walls. With the coordinate system shown in Fig. A1(a) the stress distribution is

$$\sigma_x = 0$$

$$\sigma_y = \frac{pa}{t}\left(1 - \frac{y}{b}\right) \tag{A5}$$

$$\tau_{xy} = pax/tb$$

These stresses are plotted in Fig. A2 for the boundaries of the roof and end walls on an exploded view of half of the building.

A3.2 Front and rear walls

To obtain the stress distribution on the front wall we use the Airy stress function (D being a constant and ψ a biharmonic function),

$$\psi = D(y^4 - 3x^2y^2) \tag{A6}$$

The stress distribution is

$$\sigma_x = \partial^2\psi/\partial y^2 = D(12y^2 - 6x^2)$$

$$\sigma_y = \partial^2\psi/\partial x^2 = -6Dy^2 \tag{A7}$$

$$\tau_{xy} = -\partial^2\psi/\partial x\partial y = 12Dxy$$

In order to match all of the boundary conditions for τ_{xy} (Fig. A2) we let

$$D = -p/12bt \tag{A8}$$

It is now necessary to add some stresses in order to satisfy the boundary conditions for σ_y and σ_x. Along AB (where $y = h/2$) σ_y should be zero and inspection of eqns (A7) shows that this condition can be satisfied by adding a uniform stress $6D(h/2)^2$ in the y-direction. Hence this boundary condition is satisfied when

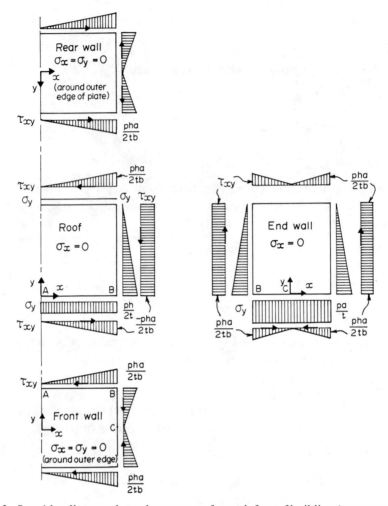

Fig. A2. Step 1 loading case boundary stresses for each face of building (on an exploded view of one half of building).

$$\sigma_y = -\frac{p}{2bt}\left(\frac{h^2}{4} - y^2\right) \tag{A9}$$

All boundary conditions except $\sigma_x = 0$ along BC (where $x = a$) are now satisfied. Inspection of eqns (A7) shows that there is an unwanted stress of $\frac{p}{bt}\left(\frac{a^2}{4} - y^2\right)$. While it is not possible to remove this stress with a simple stress function, it is possible to remove its average value which is $\frac{p}{bt}\left(\frac{a^2}{2} - \frac{h^2}{12}\right)$; i.e. the final stress σ_x is taken as

TABLE A1
Summary of Stress Distributions

		Step 1	Step 2
Roof	σ_x	0	0
	σ_y	$-\dfrac{ph}{2t}\left(1-\dfrac{y}{b}\right)$	0
	τ_{xy}	$-\dfrac{phx}{2tb}$	0
End wall	σ_x	0	$\dfrac{pa}{I}\left(\dfrac{b}{2}-y\right)\left(\dfrac{h}{2}+x\right)^2$
	σ_y	$\dfrac{pa}{t}\left(1-\dfrac{y}{b}\right)$	0
	τ_{xy}	$\dfrac{pax}{tb}$	$\dfrac{-pa[ab+y(b-y)]\left(\dfrac{h}{2}+x\right)}{2I}$
Front wall	σ_x	$\dfrac{p}{bt}\left(\dfrac{x^2-a^2}{2}+\dfrac{h^2}{12}-y^2\right)$	0
	σ_y	$-\dfrac{p}{2bt}\left(\dfrac{h^2}{4}-y^2\right)$	$\dfrac{pab\left(\dfrac{h}{2}-y\right)^2}{2I}$
	τ_{xy}	$-\dfrac{pxy}{bt}$	$\dfrac{pabx\left(\dfrac{h}{2}-y\right)}{2I}$
Rear wall	σ_x	$-\dfrac{p}{bt}\left(\dfrac{x^2-a^2}{2}+\dfrac{h^2}{12}-y^2\right)$	0
	σ_y	$\dfrac{p}{2bt}\left(\dfrac{h^2}{4}-y^2\right)$	$\dfrac{-pab\left(\dfrac{h}{2}-y\right)^2}{2I}$
	τ_{xy}	$\dfrac{pxy}{bt}$	$\dfrac{-pabx\left(\dfrac{h}{2}-y\right)}{2I}$

$$\sigma_x = \frac{p}{bt}\left(\frac{x^2 - a^2}{2} + \frac{h^2}{12} - y^2\right) \tag{A10}$$

so there is no resultant force in the wall acting in the x-direction along the edges $x = \pm a$.

The expressions given for σ_x, σ_y and τ_{xy} in eqns (A10), (A9) and (A7), respectively, are seen to be approximate. That they are sufficiently accurate for practical purposes can be justified in two ways. Firstly, the resultant force along BC is zero and by Saint Venant's Principle any errors in stress distribution will be localised. Secondly, the greatest error occurs at the corner B where the stress σ_x should be zero, but in the solution it is $ph^2/6bt$. This is a relatively low stress. Hence the solution given above is usable.

For the rear wall the stress distribution is the same but the signs must be reversed.

The stresses derived in Step 1 are summarised in Table A1.

A4 Stress analysis of Step 2 loading case (Fig. A1(c))

In this case the building is analysed using engineers' theory[6] as a thin-walled tube built-in at its base (Fig. A3(a)). The second moment of area about its neutral axis is

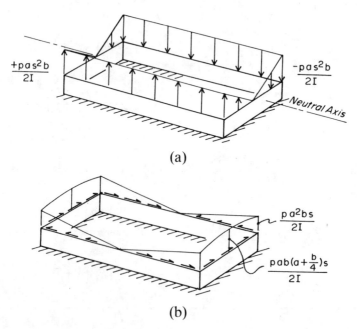

(a)

(b)

Fig. A3. Step 2 loading case stresses: (a) direct, and (b) shear stresses acting at section distance s below roof level.

$$I = atb^2 + \frac{tb^3}{6} \tag{A11}$$

The bending moment at a height s below the roof is pas^2 and the in-plane stresses due to bending are shown in Fig. A3(b) for a general value of s. If shear lag effects are neglected the shear stress distribution is also given by engineers' theory.[6] The horizontal shear force to be resisted at a distance s below the roof is $2pas$. The shear stress in the front wall is obtained using the usual expression $VA\bar{y}/It$, i.e.

$$\tau(x, s) = \frac{pabx \left(\frac{h}{2} - y \right)}{2I} \tag{A12}$$

and in the end walls it is

$$\tau(y, s) = -\frac{pa[ab + y(b - y)] \left(\frac{h}{2} + x \right)}{2I} \tag{A13}$$

Figure A3(b) shows the distribution of these shear stresses for a general value of s while Table A1 is a summary of the stress distributions for the two steps which must be combined algebraically.

Thin-Walled Structures **9** (1990) 199–240

Theoretical Investigation on the Behaviour of a Plate Strip Undergoing Local and Global Deformation

P. H. Dayawansa* & N. W. Murray

Department of Civil Engineering, Monash University, Clayton, Victoria 3168, Australia

ABSTRACT

The behaviour of a plate strip with local as well as global imperfections is investigated in this paper. The function used to describe the deformation of the plate was based on a previously conducted experimental investigation. The behaviour of the plate well into the large-deflection post-buckling range has been considered. It is shown that various buckling modes are possible and the effects of the imperfections on the buckling and post-buckling behaviour are presented.

1 INTRODUCTION

Buckling and post-buckling behaviour of thin plates is an important aspect of structural mechanics which forms the basis for understanding the behaviour of more complicated thin-walled structural forms. The elastic behaviour of a perfectly flat plate is governed by von Kármán's[1] equations. These equations were modified by Marguerre[2] to analyse initially imperfect plates but this latter theory is more general and includes perfect plates as well. These equations therefore become the governing equations of the plate problem discussed here. Exact closed-form solutions for Marguerre's equations have not been obtained so far. However, approximate solutions of these equations for rectangular plates under edge compression have been obtained by several researchers.[3-8]

*Present address: BHP Melbourne Research Laboratories, 245–273 Wellington Road, Mulgrave, Victoria 3170, Australia.

Thin-Walled Structures 0263–8231/90/$03·50 © 1990 Elsevier Science Publishers Ltd, England, Printed in Great Britain

The series solutions obtained by Levy,[3-5] Coan[6] and Yamaki[7] are particularly interesting because practically exact answers can be obtained by truncating the series at desired levels. These authors used the Marguerre equations in combination with Galerkin's method of minimization of complementary energy. Similar analysis was carried out by Murray[9] using one component of the Fourier series for displacement. In his analysis, he included three different types of boundary conditions in the same solution using two coefficients which take the values of either zero or one for each type of boundary condition. Supple[10] obtained solutions for rectangular plates using the same method as Levy,[3-5] Coan[6] and others. In his analysis the plate was treated as a two degree of freedom system and the out-of-plane plate displacement was expressed using two Fourier components. Some of the results obtained by him become directly relevant to the investigation reported here. Bulson[11] used a method similar to that of Levy,[3-5] Coan[6] and Yamaki[7] to demonstrate the post-buckling behaviour of flat plates. Instead of Galerkin's minimization, he used the minimization of total potential energy. In this analysis only one component of the double Fourier series for out-of-plane displacement was used.

All the investigations discussed in the above paragraphs were concerned with either perfect plates or plates with local imperfections. Imperfections of a global nature (as shown in Fig. 1) were not considered in any of them. Global imperfections of this type can commonly be found in structures such as stiffened plates. The behaviour of a plate with global imperfections can also be important in understanding the interactive buckling behaviour of these structures.

A plate with global imperfections was considered as a shallow shell and was analysed using Marguerre's equations and Galerkin's minimization. The plate was modelled as a two degree of freedom system and its out-of-plane displacement was based on the experimental results reported by Dayawansa.[12] It was noticed that the inclusion of global imperfections tends to make the algebra of the problem much more complicated. However, if the number of terms used in the Fourier series for displacement is limited, the geometry, boundary conditions and loading conditions of the present problem are quite amenable to this method of solving Marguerre's differential equations. As the first step of the investigation, a plate with global imperfections alone was analysed. The method was then extended to include the imperfections of the two local buckling modes as well. Some of the theoretical relationships for the extended analysis could be deduced from the corresponding expressions of the previous analysis. This approach was found to reduce the mathematical effort needed in the analysis substantially.

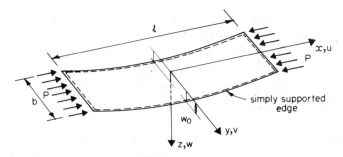

Fig. 1. Configuration of the plate.

2 ELASTIC ANALYSIS

2.1 General

The theory was developed first for a plate with global imperfections only and it was extended to cover the more general case of globally and locally imperfect plates as a second stage. The out-of-plane deformation of the plate under the applied axial load was described by two Fourier components. The Airy stress function was obtained by solving Marguerre's compatibility equation using the assumed displacement components and boundary conditions. This stress function was then used to obtain the membrane strain energy of the plate. It was noticed that certain mathematical simplifications had been possible in the solutions of Levy,[3-5] Coan[6] and Yamaki[7] due to the orthogonality property of the trigonometric functions. However, in the present solution, the general pattern leading to these simplifications is destroyed due to the presence of the global imperfection. For this reason the integrations involved in evaluating the membrane strain energy of the plate became very tedious. In order to overcome this difficulty the membrane strain energy was expressed in terms of eight coefficients and these coefficients were evaluated by using a computer program written for this purpose. The expressions for bending strain energy and total potential energy of applied loads were obtained much more easily than those for the membrane strain energy.

Two equilibrium equations are obtained by specifying that the total potential energy of the system should be stationary. The extension of the method to include the two Fourier components of the local imperfections was carried out at this juncture. The evaluation of membrane strain energy for this general case is much more tedious than for the case of global imperfections only. However, it was possible to deduce the expression for the membrane strain energy for the plate with both local and global imperfections using the expressions derived for the plate with global imperfections only. Theoretical results for all possible combinations of imperfections are discussed.

The model of the plate analysed here is exactly the same as the plate which was tested in the laboratory by Dayawansa.[12] Therefore, the results of this theoretical investigation can be compared directly with his experimental results. The boundary conditions of the problem have to be slightly modified if this method is to be used to study the interactive buckling behaviour of stiffened plates, but these modifications can be made without too much difficulty.

2.2 Analysis of the globally imperfect plate

2.2.1 Assumptions and boundary conditions

The system of coordinate axes, the dimensions of the plate analysed and its initial global deflection are shown in Fig. 1. The analysis is based on the following assumptions:

(1) The material of the plate is linearly elastic and homogeneous.
(2) All four edges of the plate are simply supported.
(3) The plate is compressed between two rigid platens and hence the loaded edges remain straight and parallel to each other.
(4) No other loads except the axial load are considered. The axial load is expressed as a non-dimensional parameter $P = \sigma_{av}/E$.
(5) The longitudinal edges remain stress free. They can deflect freely in the plane of the plate.
(6) Only symmetric imperfections and out-of-plane deformations are considered.
(7) The l/b ratio is always taken as an odd integer number denoted by n. The lowest mode of local buckling is determined by this. Values of $n > 3$ are considered. The plate strip with $n = 3$ is assumed to be too short for a representative stiffened plate encountered in practice.
(8) The shape of the global deformation of a wide stiffened plate panel (one half buckle) can be approximated by trigonometric functions. Therefore the initial global imperfection for this analysis is assumed to be

$$w_0 = C_0 \cos\left(\frac{\pi x}{l}\right) \tag{1}$$

The curvature of the plate introduced by the imperfections is assumed to be small.

(9) The deformation of the plate measured in the z-direction from its initial shape is modelled with two degrees of freedom:

$$w = A \cos\left(\frac{n\pi x}{l}\right) \cos\left(\frac{\pi y}{b}\right) + B \cos\left(\frac{\pi x}{l}\right) \cos\left(\frac{\pi y}{b}\right) \tag{2}$$

The basis of this assumption has been given by Dayawansa.[12] The shapes of various components of deformation are given in Fig. 2.

Based on the assumptions described in the previous section, the mathematical representation of the boundary conditions of the plate can be given as follows.

Longitudinal edges, $y = \pm b/2$:

$$(w)_{y = \pm b/2} \qquad = 0 \tag{3a}$$

$$(\partial^2 w/\partial y^2)_{y = \pm b/2} \qquad = 0 \tag{3b}$$

$$(\sigma_y)_{y = \pm b/2} \qquad = 0 \tag{3c}$$

$$(\sigma_{xy})_{y = \pm b/2} \qquad = 0 \tag{3d}$$

Loaded edges, $x = \pm l/2$:

$$(w)_{x = \pm l/2} \qquad = 0 \tag{4a}$$

$$(\partial^2 w/\partial x^2)_{x = \pm l/2} \qquad = 0 \tag{4b}$$

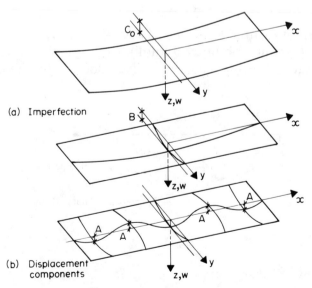

(a) Imperfection

(b) Displacement components

Fig. 2. (a) The shape of the imperfection; (b) the components of displacement (for $n = 5$).

$$\int_{-b/2}^{+b/2} t(\sigma_x)_{x = \pm l/2} dy = Etb\ P \tag{4c}$$

$$(\sigma_{xy})_{x = \pm l/2} \qquad\qquad = 0 \tag{4d}$$

The physical representation of the boundaries is shown in Fig. 3. The boundary conditions given by eqns (3a), (3b), (4a) and (4b) are automatically satisfied by the assumed function for out-of-plane displacement.

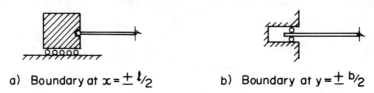

a) Boundary at $x = \pm l/2$ b) Boundary at $y = \pm b/2$

Fig. 3. The physical representation of the boundary conditions.

2.2.2 Governing equations and their solution

The initial imperfection of the plate given by eqn (1) can also be expressed as follows:

$$w_0 = C_0 \cos \beta x \tag{5}$$

Similarly the out-of-plane displacement of the plate can be expressed as follows:

$$w = A \cos n\beta x \cos \alpha y + B \cos \beta x \cos \alpha y \tag{6}$$

w and w_0 are measured as shown in Fig. 4.

Marguerre's compatibility and equililbrium equations are respectively given by the following equations. The dot (·) in these equations

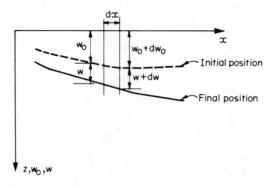

Fig. 4. The displacements defined by w and w_0.

represents the partial derivative with respect to x, and the prime ($'$) represents the partial derivative with respect to y:

$$\nabla^4\Phi + Et(w_0'' w^{\cdot\cdot} - 2w_0' w'^{\cdot} + w_0^{\cdot\cdot} w'' + w'' w^{\cdot\cdot} - w'^{\cdot 2} = 0 \tag{7}$$

$$D\nabla^4 w - [\Phi^{\cdot\cdot}(w_0 + w)'' - 2\Phi'^{\cdot}(w_0 + w)'^{\cdot} + \Phi''(w_0 + w)^{\cdot\cdot}] - W$$
$$= 0 \tag{8}$$

Closed form solutions of these equations are not yet available. The present method is based on satisfying the compatibility equation (eqn (7)) first and then satisfying equilibrium by a process of minimization of total potential energy. Therefore, Marguerre's equilibrium equation is not used in the form given in eqn (8). The following equation which has to be solved for the stress function is obtained by substituting eqns (5) and (6) in eqn (7):

$$\nabla^4\Phi = -\tfrac{1}{4}Et\alpha^2\beta^2[+ 2BC_0 \cos\alpha y + 2(n^2 A^2 + B^2)\cos 2\alpha y$$
$$+ 2B^2 \cos n_1\beta x + n_2^2 AB \cos n_2\beta x$$
$$+ n_3^2 AB \cos n_3\beta x + 2n^2 A^2 \cos n_4\beta x$$
$$+ 2BC_0 \cos n_1\beta x \cos\alpha y + 2AC_0 \cos n_2\beta x \cos\alpha y$$
$$+ 2AC_0 \cos n_3\beta x \cos\alpha y + n_3^2 AB \cos n_2\beta x \cos 2\alpha y$$
$$+ n_2^2 AB \cos n_3\beta x \cos 2\alpha y] \tag{9}$$

The general solution of eqn (9) can be written as follows:

$$\Phi = \Phi_c + \Phi_p \tag{10}$$

where Φ_c and Φ_p are complementary and particular solutions, respectively. The complementary solution of eqn (9) can be written as shown below:

$$\frac{\Phi_c}{Et} = \sum_q (\bar{L}_q \cosh q\beta y + \bar{M}_q y \sinh q\beta y)\cos q\beta x + \bar{N}x^2 + \bar{Q}y^2 \tag{11}$$

and $q = n_1, n_2, n_3, n_4$, where $\bar{L}_q, \bar{M}_q, \bar{N}$ and $\bar{Q}$ are integration constants. A particular solution for the stress function was derived and is given by the following equation:

$$\frac{\Phi_p}{Et} = (-)[+ \bar{K}_1 BC_0 \cos\alpha y$$
$$+ \bar{K}_2(n^2 A^2 + B^2)\cos 2\alpha y$$
$$+ \bar{K}_3 B^2 \cos n_1\beta x$$
$$+ \bar{K}_4 AB \cos n_2\beta x$$

$$+ \bar{K}_5 AB \cos n_3 \beta x$$
$$+ \bar{K}_6 A^2 \cos n_4 \beta x$$
$$+ \bar{K}_7 BC_0 \cos n_1 \beta x \cos \alpha y$$
$$+ \bar{K}_8 AC_0 \cos n_2 \beta x \cos \alpha y$$
$$+ \bar{K}_9 AC_0 \cos n_3 \beta x \cos \alpha y$$
$$+ \bar{K}_{10} AB \cos n_2 \beta x \cos 2\alpha y$$
$$+ \bar{K}_{11} AB \cos n_3 \beta x \cos 2\alpha y] \tag{12}$$

where

$$\bar{K}_1 = (1/2)\gamma^2 \qquad\qquad\qquad \bar{K}_2 = (1/32)\gamma^2$$
$$\bar{K}_3 = \gamma^2/32 \qquad\qquad\qquad \bar{K}_4 = \gamma^2/4n_2^2$$
$$\bar{K}_5 = \gamma^2/4n_3^2 \qquad\qquad\qquad \bar{K}_6 = \gamma^2/32n^2$$
$$\bar{K}_7 = \gamma^2/2(\gamma^2 + n_1^2)^2 \qquad\qquad \bar{K}_8 = \gamma^2/2(\gamma^2 + n_2^2)^2$$
$$\bar{K}_9 = \gamma^2/2(\gamma^2 + n_3^2)^2 \qquad\qquad \bar{K}_{10} = \gamma^2 n_3^2/4(4\gamma^2 + n_2^2)^2$$
$$\bar{K}_{11} = \gamma^2 n_2^2/4(4\gamma^2 + n_3^2)^2 \qquad\qquad \gamma = \alpha/\beta \tag{13}$$

Thus the general solution for the stress function is expressed as

$$\frac{\Phi}{Et} = (-)[+ \bar{K}_1 BC_0 \cos \alpha y$$
$$+ \bar{K}_2(n^2 A^2 + B^2) \cos 2\alpha y$$
$$+ \bar{K}_3 B^2 \cos n_1 \beta x$$
$$+ \bar{K}_4 AB \cos n_2 \beta x$$
$$+ \bar{K}_5 AB \cos n_3 \beta x$$
$$+ \bar{K}_6 A^2 \cos n_4 \beta x$$
$$+ \bar{K}_7 BC_0 \cos n_1 \beta x \cos \alpha y$$
$$+ \bar{K}_8 AC_0 \cos n_2 \beta x \cos \alpha y$$
$$+ \bar{K}_9 AC_0 \cos n_3 \beta x \cos \alpha y$$
$$+ \bar{K}_{10} AB \cos n_2 \beta x \cos 2\alpha y$$
$$+ \bar{K}_{11} AB \cos n_3 \beta x \cos 2\alpha y] + \bar{N} x^2 + \bar{Q} y^2$$
$$+ \Sigma_q(\bar{L}_q \cosh q\beta y + \bar{M}_q y \sinh q\beta y) \cos q\beta x \tag{14}$$

and $q = n_1, n_2, n_3, n_4$. The ten integration constants $\bar{L}_q, \bar{M}_q, \bar{N}$ and $\bar{Q}$ are to be evaluated using the boundary conditions.

The following equation is obtained as the complete solution of the Airy's stress function Φ for the problem after application of the boundary conditions:

$$
\begin{aligned}
\frac{\Phi}{Et} = (-)[&+ \bar{K}_1 BC_0 \cos \alpha y \\
&+ \bar{K}_2 (n^2 A^2 + B^2) \cos 2\alpha y \\
&+ \bar{K}_3 B^2 \cos n_1 \beta x \\
&+ \bar{K}_4 AB \cos n_2 \beta x \\
&+ \bar{K}_5 AB \cos n_3 \beta x \\
&+ \bar{K}_6 A^2 \cos n_4 \beta x \\
&+ \bar{K}_7 BC_0 \cos n_1 \beta x \cos \alpha y \\
&+ \bar{K}_8 AC_0 \cos \alpha y \cos n_2 \beta x \\
&+ \bar{K}_9 AC_0 \cos n_3 \beta x \cos \alpha y \\
&+ \bar{K}_{10} AB \cos n_2 \beta x \cos 2\alpha y \\
&+ \bar{K}_{11} AB \cos n_3 \beta x \cos 2\alpha y] + \left(\frac{P}{2} - \frac{\alpha \bar{K}_1}{b} BC_0\right) y^2 \\
&+ \Sigma_q (\bar{L}_q \cosh q\beta y + \bar{M}_q y \sinh q\beta y) \cos q\beta x
\end{aligned}
\tag{15}
$$

where

$$
\bar{L}_q = \frac{\bar{R1}_q \left(q\beta b \cosh \dfrac{q\beta b}{2} + 2 \sinh \dfrac{q\beta b}{2}\right) + \bar{R2}_q \, q\beta b \sinh \dfrac{q\beta b}{2}}{q\beta b + \sinh q\beta b}
\tag{16}
$$

$$
\bar{M}_q = \frac{-2q\beta \left(\bar{R1}_q \sinh \dfrac{q\beta b}{2} \, \bar{R2}_q \cosh \dfrac{q\beta b}{2}\right)}{q\beta b + \sinh q\beta b}
\tag{17}
$$

$$
\begin{aligned}
\bar{R1}_{n_1} &= \bar{K}_3 B^2 \\
\bar{R1}_{n_2} &= (\bar{K}_4 - \bar{K}_{10}) AB \\
\bar{R1}_{n_3} &= (\bar{K}_5 - \bar{K}_{11}) AB \\
\bar{R1}_{n_4} &= \bar{K}_6 A^2
\end{aligned}
\tag{18}
$$

$$
\bar{R2}_{n_1} = \frac{\bar{K}_7 \gamma}{n_1} BC_0
$$

$$
\bar{R2}_{n_2} = \frac{\bar{K}_8 \gamma}{n_2} AC_0
$$

$$\overline{R2}_{n_3} = \frac{\overline{K}_9 \gamma}{n_3} A C_0$$

$$\overline{R2}_{n_4} = 0 \tag{19}$$

and $q = n_1, n_2, n_3, n_4$. It is interesting to note that the form of the stress function given by eqn (15) is different from those obtained by Levy,[3-5] Coan[6] and Yamaki[7] due to the effects of the global initial imperfection. The boundary conditions used to derive the integration constants of the stress function did not use the assumption that the plate is compressed between two rigid platens. However, this condition is automatically satisfied by the boundary conditions used.

2.2.3 Energy function and equilibrium equations

The total potential energy of the plate is evaluated taking the unstressed initial state as the datum. The derivation of expressions for potential energy of the applied loads and bending strain energy of the plate is quite straightforward but the evaluation of the membrane strain energy would be very tedious due to the length of the expression in terms of a set of coefficients and these coefficients are evaluated by using a computer program. The total potential energy of the plate can be expressed as follows:

$$U = U_m + U_b + V \tag{20}$$

Bending and membrane energies are given by the following well-known expressions:

$$U_b = \frac{D}{2} \int\int \left[\left(\frac{\partial^2 w}{\partial x^2} + \frac{\partial^2 w}{\partial y^2} \right)^2 - 2(1-v) \left\{ \frac{\partial^2 w}{\partial x^2} \frac{\partial^2 w}{\partial y^2} \right.\right.$$
$$\left.\left. - \left(\frac{\partial^2 w}{\partial x \, \partial y} \right)^2 \right\} \right] dx \, dy \tag{21}$$

$$U_m = \frac{1}{2Et} \int\int \left[\left(\frac{\partial^2 \Phi}{\partial x^2} + \frac{\partial^2 \Phi}{\partial y^2} \right)^2 - 2(1+v) \left\{ \frac{\partial^2 \Phi}{\partial x^2} \frac{\partial^2 \Phi}{\partial y^2} \right.\right.$$
$$\left.\left. - \left(\frac{\partial^2 \Phi}{\partial x \, \partial y} \right)^2 \right\} \right] dx \, dy \tag{22}$$

The curvature of the plate due to initial imperfections is assumed to be small. Therefore the bending strain energy is not affected by the initial imperfections. The potential energy of the applied axial load at the ends of the plate can be expressed as follows:

$$V = P Etb \left[\frac{\beta^2 l}{8ab} (n^2 abA^2 + abB^2 + 8 BC_0) - lP \right] \tag{23}$$

Substituting eqn (6) in eqn (21), the following expression is obtained for the bending strain energy of the plate:

$$U_b = \frac{Dbl}{8} [(\alpha^2 + n^2\beta^2)^2 A^2 + (\alpha^2 + \beta^2)^2 B^2] \tag{24}$$

The mathematics involved in the process of evaluating U_m is very tedious. It becomes quite difficult to handle the very long expressions encountered in this calculation. Therefore the expression is subdivided into 15 different parts and each part is integrated separately and expressed in terms of the variables A, B and C_0. The coefficient of each term, which is a constant for a given plate, is evaluated by the computer program ESTRIP. Finally the membrane strain energy is expressed as shown below.

$$U_m = \frac{Et}{2} (T_1 A^4 + T_2 B^4 + T_3 A^2 B^2 + T_4 B^3 C_0 + T_5 B^2 C_0^2$$

$$+ T_6 A^2 C_0^2 + T_7 A^2 BC_0 + T_{11} PBC_0 + blP^2) \tag{25}$$

where T_i are coefficients calculated by the computer program ESTRIP. Combining eqns (23), (24) and (25), the total potential energy of the plate can now be written as follows:

$$U = + \bar{c}_1 A^4 + \bar{c}_2 B^4 + \bar{c}_3 A^2 B^2 + \bar{c}_4 B^3 C_0$$

$$+ \bar{c}_5 B^2 C_0^2 + \bar{c}_6 A^2 C_0^2 + \bar{c}_7 A^2 BC_0 + \bar{c}_8 A^2$$

$$+ \bar{c}_9 B^2 + \bar{c}_{12} P A^2 + \bar{c}_{13} P B^2 + \bar{c}_{15} P BC_0 + \bar{c}_{16} P^2 \tag{26}$$

where $\bar{c}_i$ are defined as follows:

$$\bar{c}_i = \frac{Et}{2} T_i \quad \text{for} \quad i = 1, \dots, 7$$

$$\bar{c}_8 = \frac{Dbl}{8} (\alpha^2 + n^2\beta^2)^2$$

$$\bar{c}_9 = \frac{Dbl}{8} (\alpha^2 + \beta^2)^2$$

$$\bar{c}_{12} = \frac{Et}{8} bln^2\beta^2$$

$$\bar{c}_{13} = \frac{Et}{8} bl\beta^2$$

$$\bar{c}_{15} = \frac{Et}{2} \left(\frac{2l\beta^2}{\alpha} + T_{11} \right)$$

$$\bar{c}_{16} = -\frac{Et}{2} bl \tag{27}$$

The total potential energy is now specified as stationary in order to obtain the equilibrium equations. Thus

$$\partial U/\partial A = 0$$

$$\partial U/\partial B = 0$$

Therefore,

$$4\bar{c}_1 A^3 + 2\bar{c}_3 AB^2 + 2\bar{c}_6 AC_0 + 2\bar{c}_7 ABC_0 + 2\bar{c}_8 A + 2\bar{c}_{12} PA = 0 \tag{28}$$

$$4\bar{c}_2 B^3 + 2\bar{c}_3 A^2 B + 3\bar{c}_4 B^2 C_0 + 2\bar{c}_5 BC_0^2 + \bar{c}_7 A^2 C_0 + 2\bar{c}_9 B$$
$$+ 2\bar{c}_{13} PB + \bar{c}_{15} PC_0 = 0 \tag{29}$$

These two equilibrium equations can be solved to obtain the solutions of the problem.

2.3 Analysis of the locally and globally imperfect plate

The same method used to obtain the equilibrium equations for the globally imperfect plate in Section 2.2 is extended here to incorporate two types of local imperfections A_0 and B_0 corresponding to the local deformations A and B. The physical shapes of the imperfections and the modes of deformation are shown in Fig. 5. In this case also the expressions for potential energy of applied loads and bending strain energy remain quite straightforward but the evaluation of membrane strain energy becomes even more tedious. It is found that for a plate which has both the local and global imperfections, the stress function can easily be obtained by replacing certain terms of the corresponding solution for the globally imperfect plate. The membrane strain energy for the case discussed in this section is also obtained by using the same technique. Many tedious mathematical derivations involved in the solution are eliminated by the use of this method.

2.3.1 Assumptions and boundary conditions
All of the assumptions described in Section 2.2 except the assumption described by eqn (1) are valid for the case discussed here. The initial imperfections of the plate are assumed to be

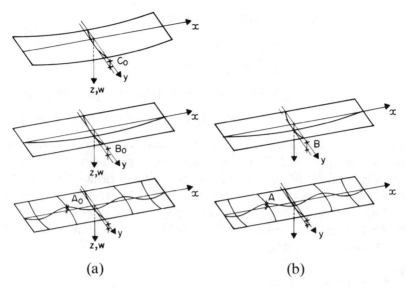

Fig. 5. (a) The types of imperfections considered; (b) the modes of deformation.

$$w_0 = A_0 \cos n\beta x \cos \alpha y + B_0 \cos \beta x \cos \alpha y + C_0 \cos \beta x \qquad (30)$$

The imperfections with magnitudes B_0 and C_0 become relevant for stiffened plates used in practice. These two types become almost unavoidable for stiffened panels which are the top and bottom flanges of a horizontal box beam. It has been noticed that the imperfections introduced due to welding of stiffeners approximately take the shape of the imperfection described by B_0. Furthermore the self-weight and any additional transverse distributed loads, such as deck loads and the loads due to surface finishes, tend to introduce imperfections of the same shape. The global sagging or hogging of the box section can introduce imperfection of the type described by C_0.

2.3.2 *Governing equations and their solution*
The following expression is obtained by substituting eqns (6) and (30) into eqn (7):

$$
\begin{aligned}
\nabla^4 \Phi = (-) \frac{Et\alpha^2\beta^2}{4} [&+ 2BC_0 \cos \alpha y \\
&+ 2\{n^2(A^2 + 2AA_0) + (B^2 + 2BB_0)\} \cos 2\alpha y \\
&+ 2(B^2 + 2BB_0) \cos n_1 \beta x \\
&+ n_2^2(AB + A_0B + AB_0) \cos n_2 \beta x \\
&+ n_3^2(AB + A_0B + AB_0) \cos n_3 \beta x \\
&+ 2n^2(A^2 + 2AA_0) \cos n_4 \beta x
\end{aligned}
$$

$$+ 2BC_0 \cos n_1\beta x \cos \alpha y$$

$$+ 2AC_0 \cos \alpha y \cos n_2\beta x$$

$$+ 2AC_0 \cos n_3\beta x \cos \alpha y$$

$$+ n_3^2(AB + A_0B + AB_0) \cos n_2\beta x \cos 2\alpha y$$

$$+ n_2^2(AB + A_0B + AB_0) \cos n_3\beta x \cos 2\alpha y] \quad (31)$$

It is noticed here that eqn (31) can be obtained simply by replacing some terms in eqn (9). These replacements are given in Table 1. This relationship between two problems is used to obtain the complete solution for the stress function and equilibrium equations for the plate with global and local imperfections from the corresponding expressions for the plate with global imperfections only. The complete solution for Φ can be written as follows:

$$\frac{\Phi}{Et} = (-)[+ K_1 BC_0 \cos \alpha y$$

$$+ K_2\{n^2(A^2 + 2AA_0) + (B^2 + 2BB_0)\} \cos 2\alpha y$$

$$+ K_3(B^2 + 2BB_0) \cos n_1\beta x$$

$$+ K_4(AB + A_0B + AB_0) \cos n_2\beta x$$

$$+ K_5(AB + A_0B + AB_0) \cos n_3\beta x$$

$$+ K_6(A^2 + 2AA_0) \cos n_4\beta x$$

$$+ K_7 BC_0 \cos n_1\beta x \cos \alpha y$$

$$+ K_8 AC_0 \cos \alpha y \cos n_2\beta x$$

$$+ K_9 AC_0 \cos n_3\beta x \cos \alpha y$$

$$+ K_{10}(AB + A_0B + AB_0) \cos n_2\beta x \cos 2\alpha y$$

$$+ K_{11}(AB + A_0B + AB_0) \cos n_3\beta x \cos 2\alpha y]$$

$$+ \left(\frac{P}{2} - \frac{\alpha K_1}{b} BC_0\right) y^2$$

$$+ \sum_q (L_q \cosh q\beta y + M_q y \sinh q\beta x) \cos q\beta x \quad (32)$$

where K_i are the same as $\bar{K}_i$ given by eqn (13), and $q = n_1, n_2, n_3, n_4$. The expressions obtained for the integration constants are

$$L_q = \frac{R1_q\left(q\beta b \cosh \dfrac{q\beta b}{2} + 2 \sinh \dfrac{q\beta b}{2}\right) + R2_q\, q\beta b \sinh \dfrac{q\beta b}{2}}{q\beta b + \sinh q\beta b} \quad (33)$$

$$M_q = \frac{-2\beta b \left(R1_q \sinh \frac{q\beta b}{2} R2_q \cosh \frac{q\beta b}{2} \right)}{q\beta b + \sinh q\beta b} \tag{34}$$

where

$$R1_{n_2} = K_3(B^2 + 2BB_0)$$

$$R1_{n_1} = (K_4 - K_{10})(AB + AB_0 + A_0B)$$

$$R1_{n_3} = (K_5 - K_{11})(AB + AB_0 + A_0B)$$

$$R1_{n_4} = K_6(A^2 + 2AA_0) \tag{35}$$

$$R2_{n_1} = -\frac{K_7\gamma}{n_1}BC_0$$

$$R2_{n_2} = -\frac{K_8\gamma}{n_2}AC_0$$

$$R2_{n_3} = -\frac{K_9\gamma}{n_3}AC_0$$

$$R2_{n_4} = 0 \tag{36}$$

TABLE 1
Replacement Terms Required to Get Eqn (31)
from Eqn (9)

Term in eqn (9)	Replacement
A^2	$A^2 + 2AA_0$
B^2	$B^2 + 2BB_0$
AB	$AB + A_0B + AB_0$

2.3.3 Energy functional and equilibrium equations
The equilibrium equations for this case are derived in exactly the same way as was done in Section 2 for the plate with only global imperfections. The energy functional U is defined by eqn (20). Bending and membrane strain energies are evaluated by using eqns (21) and (22), respectively. The membrane strain energy for the plate with global and local imperfections is derived by replacing certain terms of the corresponding expression for the plate with global imperfections only. The increase in potential energy of the applied load is expressed as follows:

$$V = P \, Etb \left[\frac{\beta^2 l}{8\alpha b} \{ n^2 \alpha b (A^2 + 2AA_0) + \alpha b (B^2 + 2BB_0) \right.$$

$$\left. + 8 \, BC_0 \} - lP \right] \tag{37}$$

Since the curvatures of the plate introduced by the imperfections are assumed to be small, the bending strain energy for this case is also given by eqn (24). The expression for membrane strain energy obtained by using the method of replacement of terms is as follows:

$$\begin{aligned}
U_m = \tfrac{1}{2} Et [& + T_1 A^4 \\
& + 4T_1 A_0 A^3 \\
& + (4T_1 A_0^2 + T_3^* B_0^2 + T_6 C_0^2 + T_7^* B_0 C_0) A^2 \\
& + T_2 B^4 \\
& + (4T_2 B_0 + T_4 C_0) B^3 \\
& + (4T_2 B_0^2 + T_3^* A_0^2 + T_5 C_0^2 + 2T_4 B_0 C_0) B^2 \\
& + (T_3^* + T_{12}) A^2 B^2 \\
& + \{ 2(T_3^* + T_{12}) B_0 + (T_7^* + T_{13}) C_0 \} A^2 B \\
& + 2(T_3^* + T_{12}) A_0 AB^2 \\
& + \{ 2(T_3^* + 2T_{12}) A_0 B_0 + (T_7^* + 2T_{13}) A_0 C_0 \} AB \\
& + T_{11} C_0 PB + blP^2]
\end{aligned} \tag{38}$$

The coefficients T_i and T_i^* which are constants for a given plate can be evaluated by the computer program ESTRIP. By adding the three components of energy, the energy functional of the plate is expressed as follows:

$$\begin{aligned}
U = {} & c_1 A^4 + c_2 A^3 + c_3 A^2 + c_4 B^4 + c_5 B^3 + c_6 B^2 + c_7 A^2 B^2 + c_8 A^2 B \\
& + c_9 AB^2 + c_{10} AB + c_{11} PA^2 + c_{12} PB^2 + c_{13} PA + c_{14} PB + c_{15} P^2
\end{aligned} \tag{39}$$

where the coefficients c_i are defined as follows:

$$c_1 = \frac{Et}{2} T_1$$

$$c_2 = 2Et \, T_1 A_0$$

$$c_3 = \frac{Et}{2} (4T_1 A_0^2 + T_3^* B_0^2 + T_6 C_0^2 + T_7^* B_0 C_0) + \frac{Dbl}{8} (\alpha^2 + n^2 \beta^2)^2$$

$$c_4 = \frac{Et}{2}T_2$$

$$c_5 = \frac{Et}{2}(4T_2 B_0 + T_4 C_0)$$

$$c_6 = \frac{Et}{2}(4T_2 B_0^2 + T_3^* A_0^2 + T_5 C_0^2 + 2T_4 B_0 C_0) + \frac{Dbl}{8}(\alpha^2 + \beta^2)^2$$

$$c_7 = \frac{Et}{2}T_3$$

$$c_8 = \frac{Et}{2}(2T_3 B_0 + T_7 C_0)$$

$$c_9 = Et\, T_3 A_0$$

$$c_{10} = \frac{Et}{2}\{2(T_3 + T_{12})A_0 B_0 + (T_7 + T_{13})A_0 C_0\}$$

$$c_{11} = \frac{Et}{8}n\beta^2 bl$$

$$c_{12} = \frac{Et}{8}\beta^2 bl$$

$$c_{13} = \frac{Et}{4}n\beta^2 blA_0$$

$$c_{14} = \frac{Et}{4\alpha}(2\alpha T_{11} C_0 + \alpha\beta^2 blB_0 + 4\beta^2 lC_0)$$

$$c_{15} = \frac{Et}{2}bl \tag{40}$$

The equilibrium equations of the system are now obtained when the total potential energy has a stationary value with respect to A and B. The equilibrium equations are as follows:

$$\partial U/\partial A = 0$$
$$4c_1 A^3 + 3c_2 A^2 + 2c_3 A + 2c_7 AB^2 + 2c_8 AB + c_9 B^2 + c_{10} B$$
$$\qquad + 2c_{11} PA + c_{13} P = 0 \tag{41}$$

$$\partial U/\partial B = 0$$
$$4c_4 B^3 + 3c_5 B^2 + 2c_6 B + 2c_7 A^2 B + c_8 A^2 + 2c_9 AB + c_{10} A$$
$$\qquad + 2c_{12} PB + c_{14} P = 0 \tag{42}$$

Solutions are obtained by solving these two equations simultaneously.

3 THEORETICAL RESULTS

The solutions for the plate problem discussed above can be obtained by solving the two equilibrium equations given by eqns (41) and (42). Although these equations are non-linear due to the large deformations considered in the problem, it is possible to solve them without having to use numerical techniques.

The solutions can be obtained for eight different combinations of imperfections as shown in Table 2. Four of these cases correspond to plates with no global initial imperfections while the other four relate to plates with global initial imperfections. The solutions for the cases with no global initial imperfections are similar to those obtained by Supple.[10] However, the boundary conditions of the problem solved by Supple[10] were different from those considered in the present problem. In the following discussion, a greater emphasis is given to cases with global initial imperfections. The other cases are discussed briefly for the purpose of completeness.

The solutions of the eight cases defined in Table 2 can be categorized into four different *Types* based on the nature of the solution. For example, the equilibrium equations for Cases 2, 5 and 6 could be solved in exactly the same manner yielding solutions of exactly the same characteristics. Details of the four solution types have been presented by Dayawansa.[12]

The basic non-dimensional parameters required to describe the geometry of the plate are l/b and b/t. The solutions of the problem mainly

TABLE 2
The Combinations of Imperfections Considered

	Case	Imperfection combinations			Solution type
		A_0	B_0	C_0	
Plate with	1	zero	zero	zero	1
local imp.	2	zero	non zero	zero	2
only	3	non zero	zero	zero	3
	4	non zero	non zero	zero	4
Plate with	5	zero	zero	non zero	2
local and	6	zero	non zero	non zero	2
global imp.	7	non zero	zero	non zero	4
	8	non zero	non zero	non zero	4

for $l/b = 5$ are given in this section. These solutions can be directly compared with the results of the experiments carried out by Dayawansa.[12] The non-dimensional forms of various relationships presented are independent of the b/t ratio of the plate.

Solutions for elastic buckling and post-buckling of plates available in the literature are numerous but global plate imperfections are not included in any of them. Therefore only a few parts of the solutions obtained by the present analysis could be checked with available results. The solutions obtained by Murray using the Ritz–Galerkin approach are used to verify some of the solutions obtained by the present model. The uncoupled solutions obtained by the present models for Cases 1, 2 and 3 are verified by using Murray's solutions. The two methods produced exactly the same solutions for the above three cases.

3.1 Solution for Case 1

The plate is considered to have no imperfection in this case. There are four possible solutions of the equilibrium equations for this case as follows:

(1) pre-buckled solution with $A = 0$, $B = 0$;
(2) uncoupled solution with $A \neq 0$, $B = 0$;
(3) uncoupled solution with $A = 0$, $B \neq 0$;
(4) coupled solution with $A \neq 0$, $B \neq 0$.

The characteristics of this case are similar to the corresponding examples treated by Supple.[10] The solutions for the other cases approach the solution for Case 1 asymptotically. A three-dimensional plot of the solution for a plate having l/b ratio of 5 and b/t ratio of 88 is shown in Fig. 6(a). The projections of the same solution on the three planes of coordinate axes are shown in Fig. 6(b). In these figures, the pre-buckled solution is given by *oef*. The uncoupled solution with $A \neq 0$ and $B = 0$ which has the lower critical stress bifurcates at *e*. The solution for this mode is given by *ee'* and *ee''*. The other uncoupled solution which has a higher critical stress bifurcates at *f*. This solution is given by *ff'* and *ff''*. From here onwards these two uncoupled modes will be referred to as the *lower mode* and the *higher mode*, respectively. The coupled solution for this case branches out from the higher mode symmetrically at *g* and *h* as shown in Fig. 6. These solutions are given by *gg'*, *gg''*, *hh'* and *hh''*. It can also be seen from Fig. 6 that all three post-buckling solutions described above for Case 1 have monotonically increasing deformations with the increase of the load. In Fig. 6(a), the graphs *ee''* and *ff''* lie on the

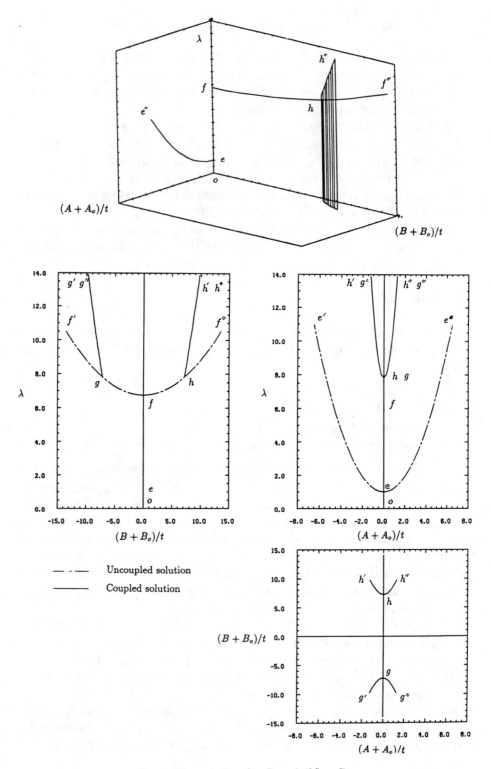

Fig. 6. The solution for Case 1 ($l/b = 5$).

coordinate planes. The graph hh'' comes out of the coordinate planes. A fencing between hh'' and its projection on the $[(A + A_0)/t, (B + B_0)/t]$ plane is used to show this feature clearly. The same method of fencing is used in all similar three-dimensional figures presented.

3.2 Solutions for Cases 2, 3 and 4

For all of these three cases the plate does not contain any global imperfections. These solutions are very similar to those obtained by Supple.[10] Therefore these three cases will not be discussed in detail here.

The solution for Case 2 belongs to the Type 2 category and contains a coupled mode and an uncoupled mode. The solution for the coupled mode yields one natural loading path and a complementary loading path as shown in Fig. 7. The solution for the coupled mode yields three loading paths, one branching out from the complementary loading path and the other two branching out from the natural loading path. These solutions are symmetrical about the $(B + B_0)/t$ axis of the three-dimensional load–displacement plot. When B_0/t takes a value of 2·4798 (for $l/b = 5$ and $b/t = 88$) the two branching points on the natural loading path (labelled as $B1$ and $B2$ in Fig. 7) coincide at one point. This value of the imperfection is called the critical imperfection. For values of imperfections higher than the critical imperfection, there are no bifurcation points on the natural loading path.

Case 3 also has two solutions for the uncoupled mode, one as the natural loading path and the other as the complementary loading path, but for this case there is only one real solution for the bifurcation point. This bifurcation point always lies on the complementary uncoupled loading path. There are no branching points on the natural loading path. A typical solution of Case 3 is given in Fig. 8.

The solution for Case 4 has only one solution in Fig. 9. The nature of this solution is very similar to that of Case 8. More details of the solution for Case 4 will be discussed under Case 8.

3.3 Solutions for Case 5

The solutions of the equilibrium equations for this case have one uncoupled mode and one coupled mode. Each mode has several loading paths. There is one value of the imperfection beyond which the nature of the buckling behaviour of the plate changes. This value of the imperfection is called the critical imperfection $(C_0)_{cr}$. Two solutions of Case 5, when the initial imperfection is sub-critical and super-critical, are shown in Figs 10 and 11. In these figures, the natural loading paths

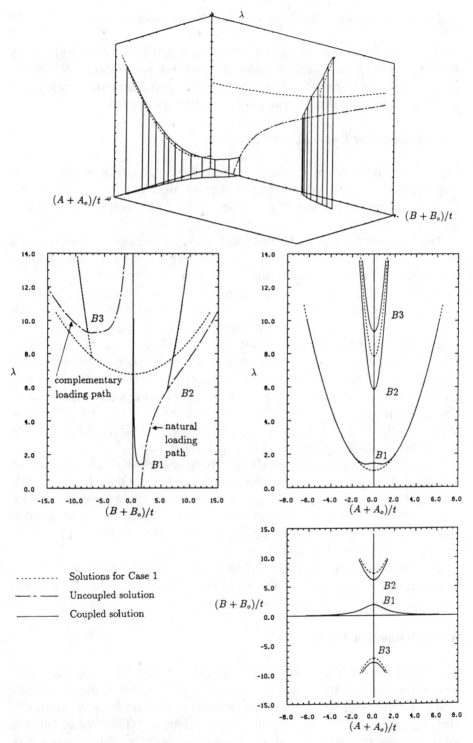

Fig. 7. A typical solution for Case 2 ($A_0/t = 0$, $B_0/t = 1.5$, $C_0/t = 0$).

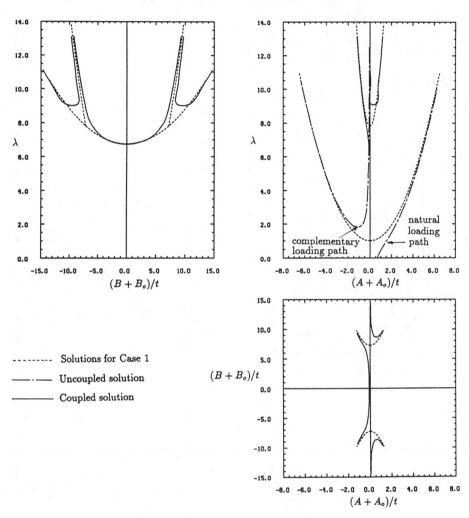

Fig. 8. A typical solution for Case 3 ($A_0/t = 0.67$, $B_0/t = 0$, $C_0/t = 0$).

are shown as *oabc* and *oa* respectively. The complementary loading paths appear beyond the range of the load axis. The uncoupled solutions for Case 5 become asymptotic to the higher mode of the perfect plate.

The coupled solutions branch out from the uncoupled solutions. Two of the bifurcation points, viz. *a* and *b* (Fig. 10), lie on the natural loading path while the other lies on the complementary loading path. For the coupled mode loading path described by *ad* or *ad'* which has the lowest critical stress, the displacement component *A* increases with an increase of the load while *B* decreases. Furthermore this loading path shows snap-through buckling characteristics for higher values of C_0. This can be seen

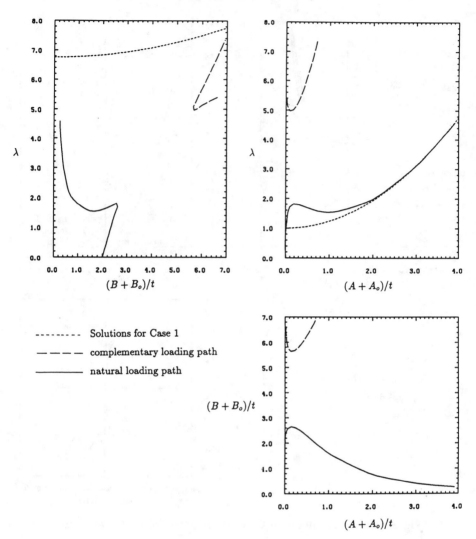

Fig. 9. A typical solution for Case 4 ($A_0/t = 0.01$, $B_0/t = 2.0$, $C_0/t = 0$).

in Fig. 10. In practice, an axially loaded plate generally follows this loading path unless it is forced to behave otherwise. This loading path becomes asymptotic to the lower mode of the perfect plate. The other coupled mode loading path which bifurcates out from the natural loading path is described by be or be' in Fig. 10. This becomes asymptotic to the coupled mode of the perfect plate.

The load factors at the two bifurcation points a and b that are on the natural loading path are plotted in Fig. 11. These two bifurcation points become closer when the value of C_0 is increased. The value of C_0 at which these two bifurcation points coincide is called the critical imperfection

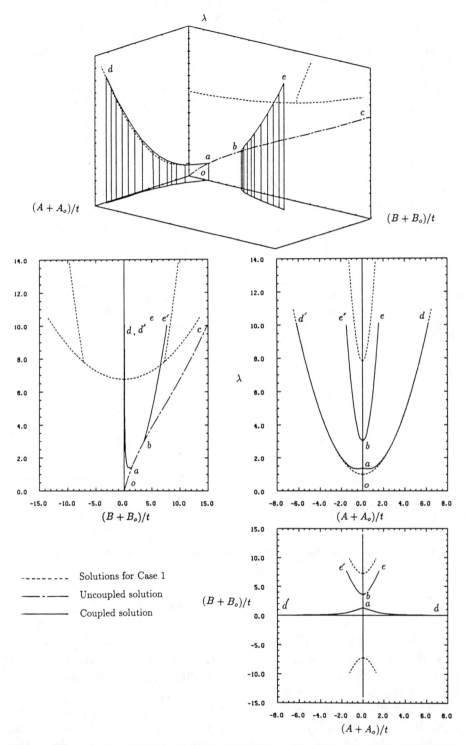

Fig. 10. The solution for Case 5 when $C_0 < (C_0)_{cr}$; $l/b = 5 \cdot 0$, $A_0/t = 0 \cdot 0$, $B_0/t = 0 \cdot 0$, $C_0/t = 4 \cdot 5$.

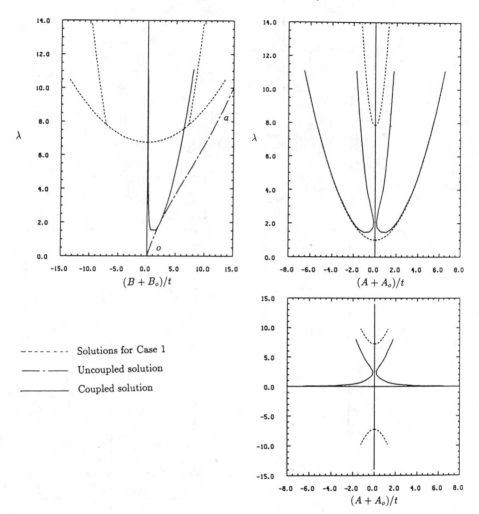

Fig. 11. The solution for Case 5 when $C_0 > (C_0)_{cr}$; $l/b = 5.0$, $A_0/t = 0.0$, $B_0/t = 0.0$, $C_0/t = 5.26$.

$(C_0)_{cr}$. This point is denoted by h in Fig. 11. For a plate with $l/b = 5$, the critical imperfection $(C_0)_{cr}/t$ is found to be 5·236 irrespective of its b/t value. The value of $(C_0)_{cr}/t$ for the case where $l/b = 7$ is 11·333. When the so-called *secondary local deformation* (B) is omitted in the displacement function, the energy solution shows negligible increase in the bifurcation load. This case for $l/b = 5$ is also shown in Fig. 11.

For values of imperfection C_0 which are greater than $(C_0)_{cr}$ the equilibrium equations have only one real solution which lies on the complementary loading path and there are no bifurcation points on the natural loading path. This feature can be seen in Fig. 12. It is seen that the

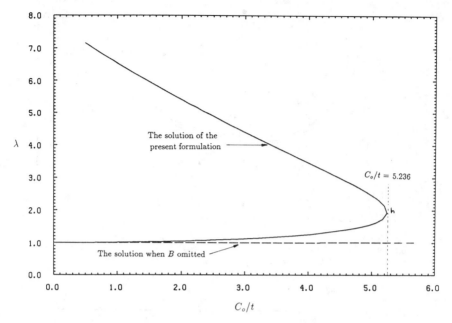

Fig. 12. The variation of the bifurcation load with C_0.

coupled mode loading paths which branched out from the natural loading path at a and b when C_0 was less than $(C_0)_{cr}$ (Fig. 10) are now completely detached from the natural loading path (Fig. 12). Therefore when the imperfection is super-critical the plate will continue to deform into the shape of the so-called *secondary local deformation*, i.e. $A = 0$ and $B \neq 0$. This is a significant change in the behaviour of the plate which depends entirely on the magnitude of the global imperfection C_0.

In Figs 10 and 12, the complete load–deformation characteristics of the plate are shown in order to describe the mechanics of its behaviour. However, in practice, these plates will rarely carry a load in excess of two and a half times their critical buckling load (i.e. $\lambda = 2\cdot5$). An enlarged view of the load–displacement characteristics for different values of the imperfection C_0 is shown in Fig. 13.

The axial stiffness of the plate is another important aspect of its behaviour. It is seen from Fig. 14 that both pre-buckling and post-buckling stiffness of the plate is reduced when the magnitude of the imperfection is increased. Furthermore it can be seen from Fig. 14 that the axial stiffness of the imperfect plate approaches asymptotically that of its perfect plate at higher loads. The snap-through buckling characteristics of the plate for higher values of imperfections are also observed in the axial stiffness curves.

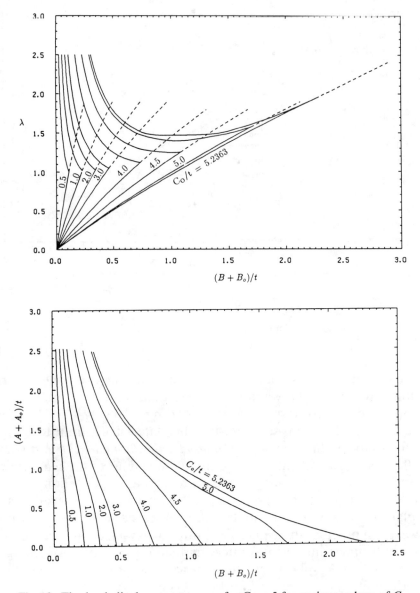

Fig. 13. The load–displacement curves for Case 5 for various values of C_0.

3.4 Solutions for Case 6

In this case the plate has two imperfections whose magnitudes are given by B_0 and C_0 while A_0 is zero. Similarly to Case 5, the solution for Case 6

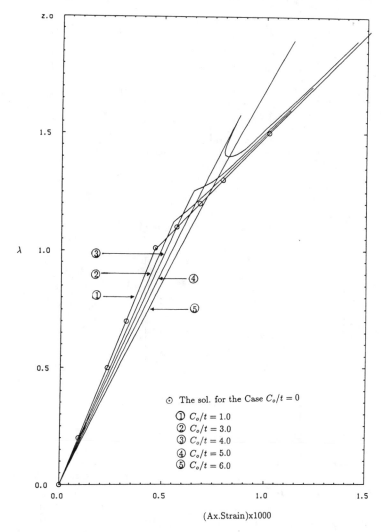

Fig. 14. The load–axial load plots for Case 5 for various values of C_0.

also belongs to the solution category of Type 2. Therefore the methods of solving the equilibrium equations and the features of the solutions for these two cases are identical.

A typical load–displacement solution for Case 6 is given in Fig. 15. Most of the general features of this solution are similar to those given in Fig. 10 for the solution of Case 5. As in Case 5 the plate first deforms into the mode with magnitude B. Then it bifurcates into a coupled mode with both A and B. The complementary loading path and the bifurcation

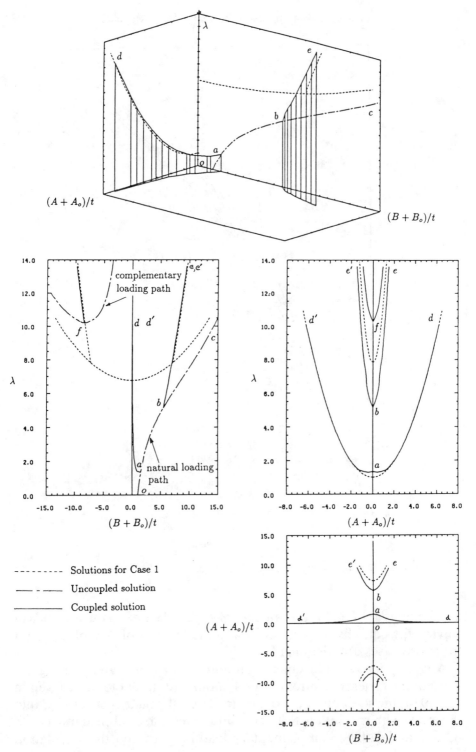

Fig. 15. A typical solution for Case 6 (Type 2); $l/b = 5{\cdot}0, A_0/t = 0{\cdot}0, B_0/t = 1{\cdot}0, C_0/t = 1{\cdot}0$.

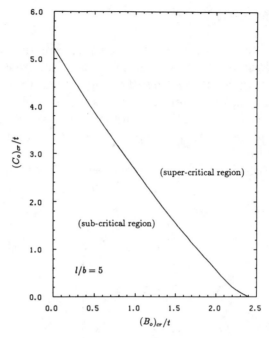

Fig. 16. Sub-critical, critical and super-critical combinations of imperfections for Case 6.

point on it are within the range of the graph for the case shown in Fig. 15. The two bifurcation points *a* and *b* which are on the natural loading path converge onto one point for certain combinations of imperfections. If the magnitude of either of the imperfections is further increased, the coupled solution detaches from the uncoupled solution in exactly the same way as it did in Case 5. Therefore, instead of one single value of critical imperfection, Case 6 can have an infinite number of critical combinations of B_0 and C_0. The critical combinations of imperfections for Case 6 are described by the graph shown in Fig. 16.

It can be seen from Table 2 that the solutions for three cases, namely Cases 2, 5 and 6, belong to Type 2. In all of these cases the magnitude of A_0 is zero and either B_0 or C_0 or both B_0 and C_0 are non-zero. It is also found that the load–displacement characteristics of these three cases are similar. All of these similarities suggest that the imperfections B_0 and C_0 have similar effects on the behaviour of the plate. This feature is further demonstrated by the combinations of critical imperfections for Case 6 given in Fig. 16. When one imperfection is increased the magnitude of the other imperfection required to achieve the critical conditions is decreased, showing that the effects of the two types of imperfections are additive.

3.5 Solutions for Case 7

For this case the magnitudes of A_0 and C_0 are non-zero while the magnitude of B_0 is zero. The solution for Case 7 belongs to the solution category Type 4. In all of the other three types of solutions discussed so far, at least one equilibrium equation separated into two equations, resulting in multi-mode solutions. But for cases that belong to Type 4, the equilibrium equations do not separate and only one coupled mode solution is obtained.

Two typical solutions for Case 7 are given in Figs 17 and 18 for a plate

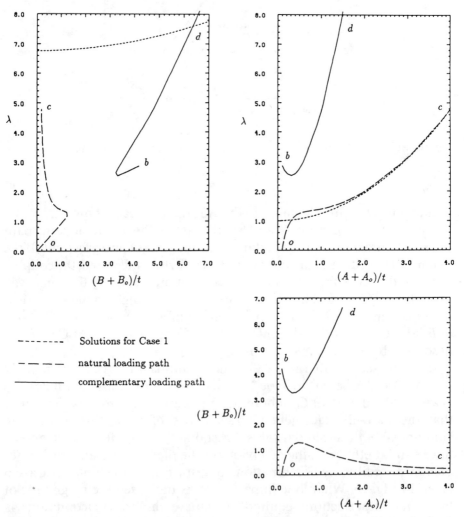

- - - - - - -   Solutions for Case 1

- - - - -   natural loading path

————   complementary loading path

Fig. 17. A typical solution for Case 7 for a sub-critical combination of imperfections; $l/b = 5$, $A_0/t = 0.15$, $B_0/t = 0$, $C_0/t = 9.0$.

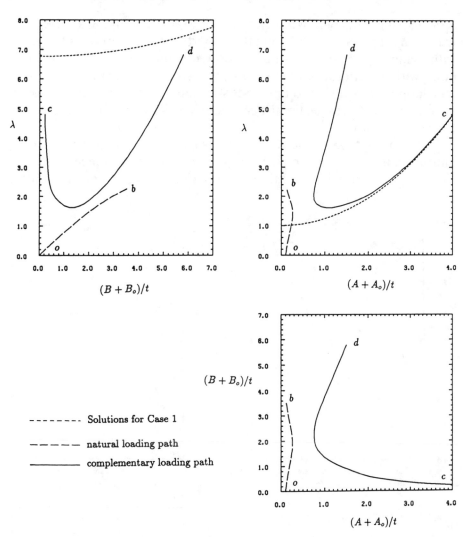

Fig. 18. A typical solution for Case 7 for a super-critical combination of imperfections; $l/b = 5$, $A_0/t = 0.15$, $B_0/t = 0$, $C_0/t = 11.0$.

with an l/b ratio of 5 and a b/t ratio of 88. It can be seen from these two figures that the plate does not now have a branching type of buckling behaviour. The complementary loading paths are included in these figures for the purpose of completeness and to explain the behaviour under critical imperfection combinations. During the initial loading, the magnitudes of both A and B increase with the increase of the load (see the natural loading paths in both Figs 17 and 18). Then the magnitude of A starts to increase rapidly while the magnitude of B starts to decrease for the case shown in Fig. 17. For the case given in Fig. 18, B increases while A

is decreasing. This behaviour can be easily seen by looking at $(A + A_0)/t$ vs $(B + B_0)/t$ plots. It is clear that the imperfection C_0 promotes the mode with magnitude B and the imperfection A_0 promotes the local buckling mode with magnitude A. For the case given in Fig. 17, the imperfection A_0 was dominant over C_0 and the mode with magnitude A was promoted in the post-buckling range. For the case covered by Fig. 18, the imperfection C_0 was dominant.

The two solutions described above suggest that there should be a limiting combination of imperfections at which the influences of A_0 and C_0 are equal. This combination of imperfections is called the critical

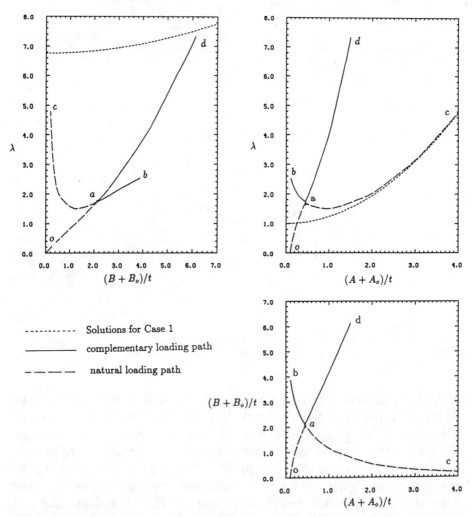

Fig. 19. A solution for Case 7 for critical combination of imperfections; $l/b = 5$, $A_0/t = 0.15$, $B_0/t = 0$, $C_0/t = 10.193$.

combination of imperfections for Case 7. The solution for a plate having a critical combination of imperfections is given in Fig. 19. It is seen that for this special case the plate exhibits a bifurcation type of buckling behaviour. The bifurcation point is given by the point *a* in Fig. 19. In this solution the natural loading path *ob* and the complementary loading path *cd* of Fig. 18 have joined at point *a* to give the load–displacement curves shown in Fig. 19.

A complete definition for the term *critical imperfection* can be given at this point of the discussion. The plate without any imperfections (Case 1) has a lowest buckling mode with magnitude *A* (for the case of *l/b* = 5, the 5th mode will be the lowest buckling mode). An imperfection or a combination of imperfections which can completely prevent or make the magnitude of the lowest mode decrease during its post-buckling range will be a super-critical imperfection. If the lowest mode continues to increase in magnitude during the post-buckling range, then the imperfections of the plate are sub-critical. A plate with critical imperfections will have a bifurcation type of buckling. In general imperfect plates do not exhibit the bifurcation type of buckling.

The critical imperfection combinations for the Case 7 solution are given in Fig. 20. It is based on plate dimensions given in the same figure.

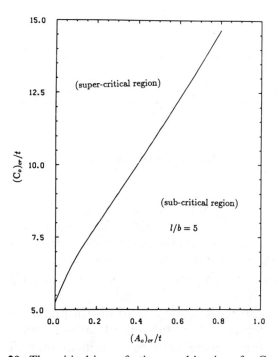

Fig. 20. The critical imperfection combinations for Case 7.

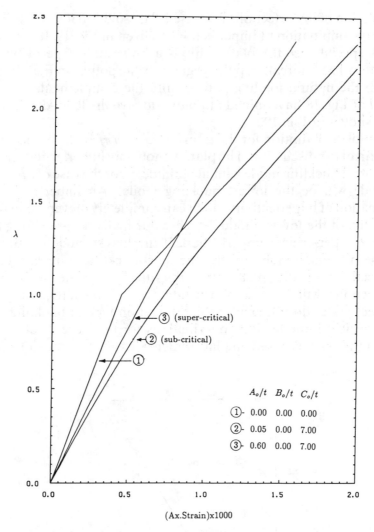

Fig. 21. Axial strain vs load factor for Case 7.

It can be seen from Fig. 20 that a small increase in the magnitude of A_0 significantly increases the magnitude of C_0 required to obtain the critical conditions. It is interesting to note that the effect of B_0 on C_0 given by Fig. 16 was exactly the opposite of this. A comparison of results for Cases 4, 6 and 7 further confirms that the imperfections B_0 and C_0 have a similar influence on the behaviour of the plate.

The stiffness of the plate changes significantly as the conditions of its imperfections alter. A plate with sub-critical imperfections shows less axial stiffness than a plate with super-critical imperfections. In the

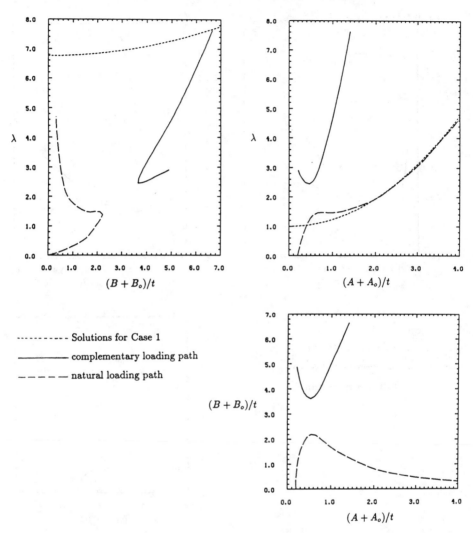

Fig. 22. A solution for Case 8 with a sub-critical combination of imperfections; $l/b = 5$, $A_0 = 0\cdot2$, $B_0/t = 1\cdot0$, $C_0/t = 4\cdot333$.

former, the post-buckling deformation pattern is dominated by the mode with magnitude A, and the mode with magnitude B is dominant in the latter. Therefore, this result agrees well with the observation that the mode with magnitude B is stiffer than the mode with magnitude A. Two load-axial strain solutions of Case 7 are compared with the same for the flat plate of Case 1 in Fig. 21. The solution of the plate with a sub-criticial combination of imperfections becomes asymptotic to the Case 1 solution. The stiffness for the plate with a super-critical combination of

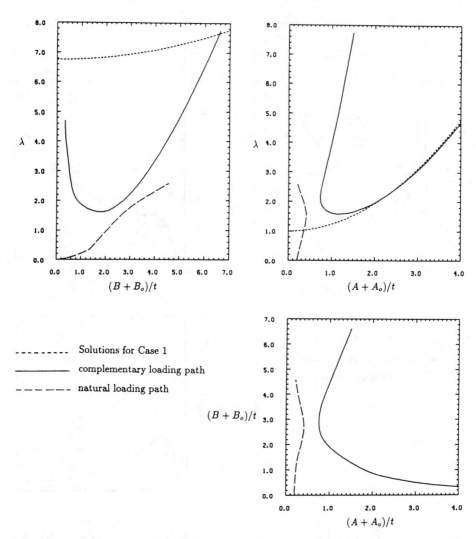

Fig. 23. A solution for Case 8 with a super-critical combination of imperfections; $l/b = 5$, $A_0/t = 0.2$, $B_0/t = 1.0$, $C_0/t = 5.333$.

imperfections remains higher than each of the others in the post-buckling range.

3.6 Solution for Case 8

This is the most general case where all three types of imperfections are present in the plate. The solution for this case also belongs to solution category Type 4. The description of the general features of the behaviour

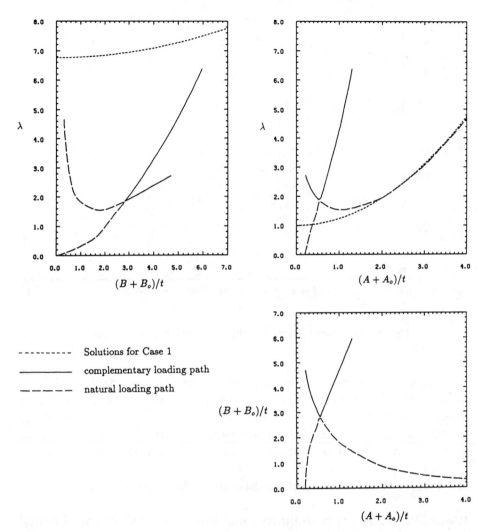

Fig. 24. A solution for Case 8 with a critical combination of imperfections; $l/b = 5$, $A_0/t = 0.2$, $B_0/t = 1.0$, $C_0/t = 5.0419$.

of the plate is given under the solution for Case 7. Therefore only a brief discussion of the Case 8 solution is given below.

Three solutions of Case 8 are given in Figs 22–24. In the solution given in Fig. 22, the effect of the imperfection A_0 has a higher influence than does that of B_0 and C_0 on the post-buckling behaviour of the plate. The combined effect of B_0 and C_0 is more predominant over that of A_0 in case of the solution given in Fig. 22. Figure 23 refers to a plate which has a critical combination of imperfections in it.

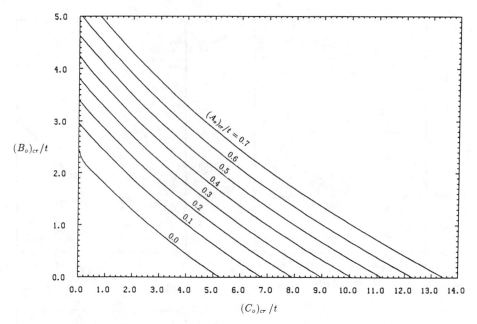

Fig. 25. The combinations of critical imperfections for Case 8.

Once again it is seen that the imperfections of magnitudes B_0 and C_0 try to suppress the displacement component A, and the imperfection of magnitude A_0 tries to suppress the displacement component B, in the post-buckling range. The relationship of the magnitudes of imperfections to obtain the critical conditions on the plate is given in Fig. 25.

3.7 Effects of l/b ratios on the behaviour of the plate

It was found that the non-dimensional forms of the solutions obtained for the eight cases described above are independent of the b/t ratio of the plate but dependent on the l/b ratio. The difference between the critical loads of the modes A and B is increased when the l/b ratio is increased. As expected, the influence of the secondary local deformations on the behaviour of the plate is reduced when the l/b ratio is increased.

The solutions for the critical imperfections of the plate for $l/b = 5$ are given in Figs 16, 20 and 25. These three figures can be combined together to give a critical imperfection surface as shown in Fig. 26. When the point which represents the combination of imperfections is on the surface *abcd* then the critical conditions are achieved. When the point is outside the domain enclosed by the surface *abcd* and the coordinate planes, either the mode A is completely suppressed or it is dominated by B during the post-buckling range. When the point which represents the imperfection combination is inside the domain mentioned above then mode *B* will be suppressed by mode *A* during the post-buckling range. When the *l/b* ratio is increased the critical imperfection surface is moved out as shown in Fig. 26. The surfaces *abcd* and *fghk* then represent the critical imperfection surfaces for *l/b* ratios 5 and 7, respectively.

4 CONCLUSIONS

The mechanics of the buckling and post-buckling behaviour of a plate with a global imperfection of a particular type are explained using a theoretical model based on an energy method. The general behaviour observed during the experimental programme described by Dayawansa[12] is well supported by the results of this theoretical investigation. The concept of critical imperfections described by Supple[10] for a flat plate with local imperfections has been further extended for plates with both local and global imperfections. The analysis showed that certain imperfections can have cumulative effects to promote one aspect of behaviour of the plate while other imperfections tend to suppress that aspect. The results of the investigation also show that theoretically there can be a bifurcation type of buckling even when imperfections of all three types considered here are present in the plate.

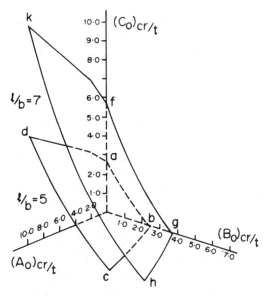

Fig. 26. Critical imperfection surfaces for *l/b* = 5 and 7.

REFERENCES

1. von Kármán, T., *Festigkeit Problems in Maschinenbau Encyklopaedie der mathematischen Wissenschaften,* **4** (1910) 349.
2. Marguerre, K., Eur Theorie der Gekruemmter Platte grosser Formaenderung. *Proc. Fifth Int. Congr. Applied Mech.,* Cambridge, 1938.
3. Levy, S., Bending of rectangular plates with large deflections. NACA, Report No. 737, 1942.
4. Levy, S., Bending of rectangular plates with large deflections. NACA, TN No. 846, 1942.
5. Levy, S., Square plate with clamped edges under normal pressure producing large deflections. NACA, TN No. 847, 1942.
6. Coan, J. M., Large deflection theory for plates with small initial curvature loaded in edge compression. *J. Appl. Mech.,* **18** (2) (June) (1951) 143–51.
7. Yamaki, N., Post-buckling behaviour of rectangular plates with small initial curvature, loaded in edge compression. *J. Appl. Mech.,* **26** (1959) 407–14.
8. Marguerre, K., The apparent width of plate in compression. NACA, TM No. 833, July, 1937.
9. Murray, N. W., *Introduction to the Theory of Thin-Walled Structures.* Oxford University Press, Oxford, UK, 1984.
10. Supple, W. J., Changes of wave-form of plates in the post-buckling range. *Int. J. Sol. Struct.,* **6** (1970) 1243–58.
11. Bulson, P. S., *The Stability of Flat Plates,* Chatto and Windus, London, 1970.
12. Dayawansa, P. H., Elastic post-buckling behaviour of isolated and stiffened plates in the large deflection range. PhD Thesis, Dept of Civil Engineering, Monash University, Australia, 1986.

SESSION 4

Thin-Walled Structures **9** (1990) 241–256

Thin-Walled Structures and Related Optimization Problems

Georg Thierauf

Department of Civil Engineering, University of Essen, Universitätsstrasse 15, D4300
Essen 1, FRG

ABSTRACT

The present paper deals with specific methods for optimal design of thin-walled structures and with the problem of optimal design for serviceability and ultimate limit state. A brief classification of structural optimization is given first, followed by a general formulation of the optimal design problem for thin-walled structures and by a discussion of the design models involved. Specific solution techniques which have been found to be suited for structural optimization and selected applications are presented.

1 INTRODUCTION

Optimization of structures and design of thin-walled structures are two wide-reaching areas of research with a long tradition and a rapidly growing number of publications.

Most publications on thin-walled structures are concerned with analysis and design, and in structural optimization the specific problems of thin-walled structures are often excluded, although they reveal the most difficult problems of optimal design and could be considered as representatives of the 'One-Hoss-Shay' philosophy.[1]

In fact, if minimum weight is the ultimate goal, and if the constraints are too simplified, structural optimization can be considered as a 'generator of structural instability'[2] with unexpected nonlinear coupling

241

Thin-Walled Structures 0263-8231/90/$03·50 © 1990 Elsevier Science Publishers Ltd, England. Printed in Great Britain

of bifurcation modes. But even a constraint space derived from existing design codes might lead to unexpected results and necessitate a critical inspection of the inevitable idealizations.

An example of such a conflicting situation is the acceptance of local buckling in thin-walled structures under service loads.[3] Taken as a constraint for optimal design, one might well end up with certain types of optimal structures which are generally at the border of local instability under service load: the acceptable exemption of the design code becomes a regular feature for the optimal design.

2 CLASSIFICATION OF STRUCTURAL OPTIMIZATION PROBLEMS

In the following a short classification of problems in structural optimization is attempted. Structural optimization includes three main fields. First, there is the 'classical' problem of *optimal design*, where the overall geometry of the structure is fixed and 'member-sizing' for given stress- and displacement-constraints is required. The second field, *shape optimization*, is concerned with additional variables stemming from the geometry of the structure. The third field, *topological optimization*, involves integer variables or discrete variables, such as the number of stiffeners in thin-walled structures.

In applications a strict distinction between these fields is difficult, in particular because a priori decisions of the designer with respect to the constraints and the objective function are involved.

Optimization of thin-walled structures involves optimal design, shape optimization and topological optimization and is best characterized by the necessity to include bifurcation of stability into the constraints of the optimization problem.

3 STRUCTURAL OPTIMIZATION AND QUADRATIC APPROXIMATIONS

In most early applications the total weight of the structure was chosen as the objective function together with stress or displacement constraints. The 'fully-stressed-design'[4] as an intuitive concept of structural optimization and 'optimality-criterion' algorithms[5] were used extensively for minimum weight design of structures. In both bases a criterion that defines the optimum is established first and then a recursive relation is derived for an iterative solution.

Later applications of mathematical programming showed that most optimality criteria can be derived from the well-known Kuhn–Tucker criterion and that the iterative methods are special variants of the Lagrange-multiplier method together with an active set strategy.[6]

A general survey on the development of structural optimization is given by Vanderplaats;[7] the particular development of optimum design with plate bending elements is discussed by Hafta and Prasad.[8]

In order to provide a common terminology for discussion, the underlying mathematical programming problem will be stated first: for $\mathbf{x} \in R^n$

minimize W$(\mathbf{x})$, (objective function)

and

$$g_i(\mathbf{x}) = 0 \text{ for } i = 1, \ldots, m \tag{1}$$

$$g_i(\mathbf{x}) \leqslant 0 \text{ for } i = m + 1, \ldots, M \text{ (constraints)}$$

where W and g_i are continuously differentiable functions.

The objective function W could be the total weight of the structure or an approximation of the total cost, for example.

The constraints are equilibrium or compatibility conditions or criteria for structural stability. Generally speaking, the constraints should incorporate all relevant design principles.

Before going into detail, some general design principles and specific properties of the constraints will be given.

If the objective function is the total volume of the structure and the design requires a constant potential, then an equivalent design principle is a structure with a minimum potential for a given constant volume.[9] This well-known principle shows a direct relation between an elementary optimization problem and the principle of minimum potential energy, which is the common basis of finite element analysis of structures.

Modern design codes for thin-walled structures rely on two limit states: ultimate load capacity and serviceability (*cf.*, e.g., ECCS).[3] Let $\mathbf{F}_i$, $i = 1, 2, \ldots, s$ be the vector of generalized stress of the structure; then the ultimate load capacity can be expressed by

$$\psi_i(\mathbf{F}_i) \leqslant y_i \tag{2}$$

where ψ_i is the yield function for element i of a discretized structure, e.g. a plate discretized by triangular finite elements as shown in Fig. 1.

Assuming Drucker's[10] postulate, the yield function is convex for all $\mathbf{F}$ in static equilibrium with the external loads $\mathbf{R}$. Furthermore, the yield

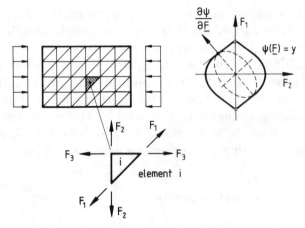

Fig. 1. Finite element and quadratic approximation of limit state.

function is assumed to be at least piecewise differentiable and the normality rule states that

$$(\mathbf{F} - \tilde{\mathbf{F}})^T \frac{\partial \psi}{\partial \mathbf{F}} \bigg|_{\tilde{\mathbf{F}}} = 0 \qquad (3)$$

An optimal design problem can be obtained by assuming $\mathbf{y} = \{y_i\}$ as the vector of design variables and an approximating linear function $W(\mathbf{y})$ for the cost or weight of the structure. Then the mathematical programming problem (1) takes the following form:

$$\text{minimize}\{W(\mathbf{y}) = c_1 y_1 + c_2 y_2 + \ldots + c_s y_s\} \qquad (4)$$

subject to

$$\psi_i(\mathbf{F}_i) \leqslant y_i, i = 1, \ldots, s \qquad (5)$$

and

$$\mathbf{a}^T \mathbf{F} = \mathbf{R} \qquad (6)$$

where the equality constraint describes the linear equilibrium condition of a finite element system ($\mathbf{a}^T$ is an $n \times m$ matrix, the transpose of the structural compatibility matrix $\mathbf{a}$) and c_i are constants.

Efficient solution techniques for the general nonlinear programming problem (1) can be obtained by successive quadratic approximations[11] of the Lagrange function subject to linearized constraints. With regard to the special programming problem (4), a quadratic approximation of the nonlinear constraints[12] leads to the following sub-problem which has to be solved in each iteration:

minimize $\{W = \mathbf{c}^T \mathbf{y}\}$

subject to

$$\mathbf{F}_i^T \, \mathbf{A}_i \, \mathbf{F}_i \leqslant y_i \tag{7}$$

$$\mathbf{a}^T \mathbf{F} = \mathbf{R}$$

Introducing slack-variables d_i^2 and Lagrange-parameters u_i and r_k $(k = 1, 2, \ldots, n)$, the following Lagrange-function $\mathscr{L}$ is obtained:

$$\mathscr{L}(\mathbf{y}, \mathbf{F}, \mathbf{u}, \mathbf{d}, \mathbf{r}) = \sum_{i=1}^{s} [c_i y_i + u_i(\mathbf{F}_i^T \, \mathbf{A}_i \, \mathbf{F}_i - y_i + d_i^2)] + \mathbf{r}^T(\mathbf{R} - \mathbf{a}^T \mathbf{F}) \tag{8}$$

The necessary and sufficient conditions are related to the design principle of 'minimum volume–constant potential' as stated above and also to the well-known Prager–Shield condition;[13] it can be shown that the complementary energy $\frac{1}{2}\mathbf{F}^T\mathbf{f}\mathbf{F}$ of an associated elastic structure equals the minimum W. This second design principle offers direct access to the following iterative numerical solution of (1) by finite element methods. In each iteration a finite element solution of

$$\mathbf{K}\,\mathbf{r} = \mathbf{R} \tag{9}$$

has to be computed; $\mathbf{K}$ is the $n \times n$ stiffness matrix of an associated elastic structure with flexibility $\mathbf{f} = 2 \times \mathrm{diag}(c_i \, \mathbf{A}_i)$. The Lagrange-parameters $\mathbf{r}$ are the nodal displacements of this elastic structure.

The optimal design of thin-walled structures requires a first generalization of this approach to include elastic stability. For a neighbouring state of equilibrium and proportional loading $\lambda \mathbf{R}_0$ we obtain

$$(\mathbf{a}^T + \delta \mathbf{a}^T)\mathbf{F} = \lambda \mathbf{R}_0 \tag{10}$$

The variation of $\mathbf{a}^T$ is assumed to be caused by self-equilibrating stresses, and instead of eqn (9) we have to solve the stability equation

$$(\mathbf{K} + \lambda \mathbf{K}^g)\mathbf{r} = \mathbf{0} \tag{11}$$

where the geometric stiffness matrix $\mathbf{K}^g$ is obtained from

$$\mathbf{K}^g|_{\mathbf{R}_0} = \delta \mathbf{a}^T \mathbf{f}^{-1} \delta \mathbf{a} \tag{12}$$

For shape optimization additional variables, the coordinates $\mathbf{x}$ of selected nodes of the structure, are introduced as variables. In a constant volume shape optimization the size of the finite elements is kept constant and only the position of the nodes is variable. Therefore only the equilibrium condition of eqn (6) has to be modified. But even for the most elementary optimization problems the elements of $\mathbf{a}^T$ are nonlinear functions of the coordinates x_i. Two-stage optimization techniques can be used for an iterative solution based on successive quadratic approximations of the constraints.

For problems with only a small number of variables, e.g. for shape optimization of cold-formed prismatic beams, a direct application of sequential quadratic programming packages[14] can cost more computing time but does not require the development of specialized programs.

4 CONSTRAINTS FOR OPTIMAL THIN-WALLED STRUCTURES

At first glance the accepted design models for thin-walled structures are hardly amenable to a simplified optimization problem as described in the previous section. The latest European Recommendations[3] claim that 'full consideration of the post-buckled strength' is necessary and 'elastic–plastic redistribution of forces may be advantageously considered'. However, the recommended 'effective width' analysis is based on *local* elastic buckling of thin square plates with correction factors derived from tests ('Winter formula'[3]).

Consider a quadratic plate hinged on all sides with stress gradient as shown in Fig. 2. The buckling coefficient[3] is $k_\sigma = 13\cdot16$, which is the theoretical bifurcation factor as obtained from linear elastic theory. The effective width depends on the yield stress, the buckling coefficient and the width b and t of the plate. If side B is clamped instead of hinged, we obtain $k_\sigma \approx 15\cdot6$, and for both sides clamped $k_\sigma \approx 23\cdot5$. The plate element as shown (in Fig. 2) is part of a thin-walled structure and all values of k_σ given above are approximations. According to ECCS[3] the square root of these k_σ values is directly proportional to the effective cross-section. If the real structural behaviour tends to the second boundary condition we would get 9% more of the effective cross-section and in the third case even 33%. It will be objected that a simple design code has to give conservative values, which is certainly true. On the other

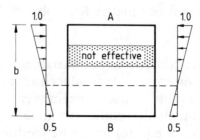

Fig. 2. Effective width design.

hand it would be unrealistic to expect higher gains than 5–15% from optimization, in particular when looking at thin-walled prefabricated elements which have been improved by experiments in each generation. Therefore the effective width design is not suited for evaluating the constraints for optimal design of thin-walled structures.

Optimal design for post-buckling and elastic–plastic redistribution of forces is far too complicated and for this reason the following approach will be adopted:

(1) Stability constraints are assumed to be given as

$$G(\sigma, \sigma_{ki}, \beta_s) \leqslant 0 \tag{13}$$

where σ_{ki} is the ideal buckling stress of the complete structure, β_s is the yield stress, and G is a differentiable function which may also include empirical reduction factors.

(2) An optimal solution is verified by sensitivity studies and experiments.

5 SELECTED APPLICATIONS

5.1 Constant and minimum volume, thin-walled compression members

The first two examples demonstrate the capability of the iterative methods and the improvements which can be achieved by shape optimization of thin-walled structures.

In accordance with DIN 18800, we assume the following reduction:

$$G: \begin{cases} \sigma - \beta_s \leqslant 0 & \text{for } \lambda \leqslant 0.2 \\ \sigma - \dfrac{\beta_s}{k + \sqrt{k^2 - \lambda^2}} \leqslant 0 & \text{for } \lambda > 0.2 \end{cases} \tag{14}$$

where $\lambda = \sqrt{\beta_s/\sigma_{ki}}$ and $k = 0.5[1.00 + 0.34(\lambda - 0.2) + \lambda^2]$.

A cold-formed, L-shaped cross-section from an St37 steel plate measuring 1250 mm × 230 mm × 2 mm had to be designed for maximum load capacity in compression. We assume an Euler column as shown in Fig. 3, where nonlinear mode interaction (local and global buckling) may occur.

The Euler buckling stress was computed by the finite strip method (computer program PLATE[15]). Two typical suboptimal cross-sections (*a* and *b*) and the final design (*c*) are shown in Fig. 3. The load capacity is 26·50 kN for the first, 48·6 kN for the second and 57·4 kN for the final design (relative improvement: 117%).

The second example is a minimum volume–constant load design which

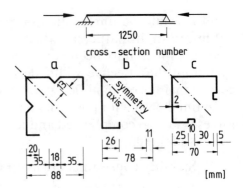

Fig. 3. Constant volume, maximum load design.

demonstrates an application of sequential quadratic programming.[11] The following optimization problem is solved (Fig. 4):

  minimize x_n (thickness)

subject to

  $-\pi \leqslant x_i \leqslant \pi$ for $i = 1, 2, \ldots, n-1$

  $1 \leqslant x_n \leqslant 10$ (x_n: thickness)

Stability constraints:

$$\frac{\pi^2 EI_{\min}}{l^2 R} - 1 \geqslant 0$$

where $EI_{\min}$ is the minimal bending stiffness.

$$\frac{\sigma bt}{R} - 1 \geqslant 0$$

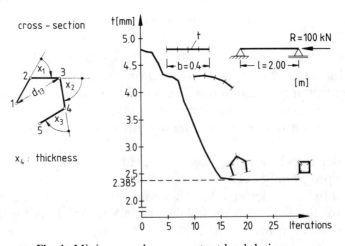

Fig. 4. Minimum volume, constant load design.

$$G(\sigma, \sigma_{ki}, \beta_s) \leqslant 0$$

Nodal distance constraint:

$$\frac{n}{b} \cdot d_{jk} - 1 \geqslant 0 \qquad \text{for } k > j, \quad j, k = 1, \ldots, n-1 \tag{15}$$

where d_{ij} is the distance between nodes i and j)

5.2 Shape optimization of trapezoidal roof decks

Shape optimization of trapezoidal roof decks from cold-formed steel was carried out by the author in 1981. Trapezoidal roof decks have been fabricated for more than 40 years and are sold on a competitive market. Dramatic reductions in weight or cost cannot be expected because of the successive improvements based on numerous tests.

The situation in the European market in 1981 can be described by comparing available products (Fig. 5). For a standard design load of $1 \cdot 20 \text{ kN/m}^2$ on a continuous beam over three equal spans $L(\text{m})$ the self-weight g of available trapezoidal steel decks is marked by triangles ($\triangledown$). At first sight the shape optimization seems to be a problem of minimum weight design.

For a typical cross-section as shown in Fig. 6 the relative weight is obtained as

$$g = \frac{\rho t}{b} \sum_{i=1}^{n-1} l_i$$

where

ρ = nominal specific weight (80 kN/m^3)
t = nominal thickness (min. $t = 0 \cdot 71 \text{ mm}$)

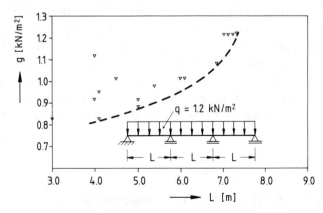

Fig. 5. Available trapezoidal steel decks (1981).

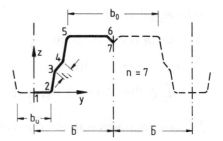

Fig. 6. Typical trapezoidal cross-section.

l_i = length of element i
$\bar{b}$ = width of half cross-section

The total loading is

$q = p + g\bar{b}$

and the span for standardized cross-sections as shown in Fig. 4 ranges from 4 to 8 m. Although self-weight plays an essential role, the objective function turns out to be far more complicated: in fact we have to deal with a nonlinear benefit–cost optimization problem with mixed real and integer variable. The number of different types of cross-sections produced to cover the desired range of spans $L_1 \leqslant L \leqslant L_u$ defines the first integer variable. Other integer variables are the number of stiffeners in the upper and lower flange and in the web. A most important integer variable is the number of different coil-widths to be used and kept for disposition. Available coil-widths range from 1200 to 1750 mm, and due to the production process only a limited number of geometric variations of the final cross-section are possible.

The problem was formulated as a multi-objective optimization problem and solved approximately by parametric optimization. In principle the different criteria were ordered first in terms of importance. Most important is a minimum number of coil-widths; next is the number of different cross-sections to be produced; and finally the criterion 'minimum weight with maximum load capacity' was set up.

Starting with only one coil-width, an optimal value was computed for a maximal number of feasible cross-sections. For the geometric variables **x** of these types of cross-section the nonlinear fractional optimization problem

minimize $g(\mathbf{x})/L(\mathbf{x})$
    $\mathbf{x} \in X$

was solved for a standard beam with either two or three equal spans and an external loading of

$\gamma \times 1.20 \text{ kN/m}^2$ ($\gamma = 1.5$, limit load).

From the numerous constraints X only a few typical ones will be given here. The web-inclination $x_1 = \varphi$ was constrained by

$$50° \leqslant \varphi \leqslant 80°$$

the lower bound following from DIN 18807 and the upper bound preventing clamping. For structural reasons the width of the upper flange was constrained by

$$\frac{b_0}{2b} \geqslant 0.4$$

and the width of the lower flange by

$$b_u \geqslant 40 \text{ (mm)}$$

Local buckling was considered for a maximum bending moment and for an interaction of a bending moment M and a reaction force R at supports (Fig. 7).

A linear stress distribution due to bending moments was assumed and the critical stress $\lambda \equiv \sigma_{ki}$ was computed by the *finite strip method* as the lowest eigenvalue $\lambda_{min} > 0$ of

$$(\mathbf{K} + \lambda \, \mathbf{K}^g)\mathbf{r} = \mathbf{0}$$

The reduced allowable stress was obtained from

$$\sigma = \beta_s \left(\frac{1}{1 + \lambda^5}\right)^{0.4}$$

where $\lambda = \sqrt{\beta_s/\sigma_{ki}}$. The displacements were limited to $L/300$ for service loads.

With preliminary grid-searches and sensitivity studies, the number of constraints could be reduced so that the final nonlinear optimization problem had to be solved only for a small number of variables and nonlinear constraints.

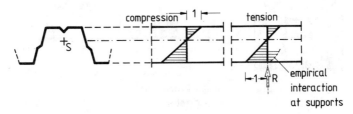

Fig. 7. Stress distribution for stability constraints.

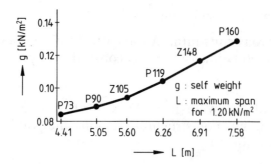

Fig. 8. Optimized trapezoidal roof decks (P73, ..., P160).

The result of the final optimal design for two different coil-widths (1500 and 1200 mm) is shown in Fig. 8.

The final set of cross-sections was submitted to performance tests which were required in Germany at that time by the building authorities. With respect to the allowable span, test results and theory differed only by a maximum of 4%. In most cases the allowable deflections were reached before local buckling occurred.

5.3 Shape optimization of a three-span girder for a rack structure

The last example is an integral part of a rack structure. A three-span girder had to be designed for loads from a transportation unit moving on wheels in the longitudinal direction on the lower flange (Fig. 9) and storing paper rolls (800–1500 mm diameter) on the upper flange.

At the time (1988) when this shape optimization problem was presented to the author, the principal dimensions of the transportation unit were fixed already and an initial shape of the girder as shown in Fig.

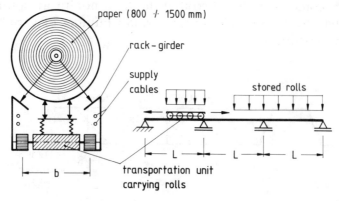

Fig. 9. Rack structure for paper rolls.

10 was discussed. Significant distortions, longitudinal bending stress and torsional shear stress had to be expected for the initial shape due to the great distance between the shear centre M and the centroid S.

It was also obvious that either deformation constraints or lateral instability with nonlinear buckling mode interaction could become active in a shape optimization.

Forced by the limited time available, shape optimization was based on the assumption that lateral instability could be adequately constrained by assuming a longitudinal stress distribution as shown in Fig. 10.

The allowable longitudinal stress was computed by the finite strip method.[16] Computation of the principal stress required the iterative solution of the nonlinear equations of thin-walled beam theory, including all stress components for bending and torsion.[17] Initial deformations were taken into account according to DIN 18800 ($\pm L/200$ in the direction of the principal axes).

The weight per unit length was taken as the objective function. The optimized shape is shown in Fig. 11.

A comparison with the initial shape shows that the distance d between the centre of shear and the centroid is reduced considerably, with the effect that torsional shear stress is small for the dominant loading cases.

The supporting construction was designed as shown in Fig. 12 and cold-formed cross-sections were used for all parts except for the supporting rack structure (U-girders, Fig. 12). Approximately 1700 t of the optimized girder are now produced with a total length of nearly 80 km for one rack structure.

Before the fabrication tools for cold-forming were designed, a full-scale model girder was set up for performance tests (Fig. 13).

The maximum difference between theoretical and experimental mid-

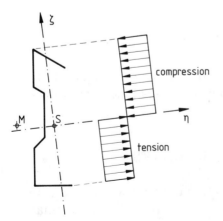

Fig. 10. Stress distribution for stability constraints. M, Shear centre; S, centroid.

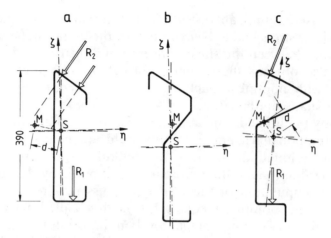

Fig. 11. Suboptimal and optimal cross-sections.

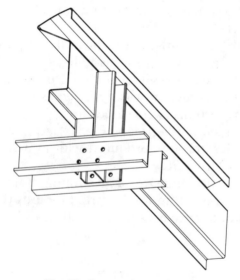

Fig. 12. Supporting structure.

field deformations was 5%. In agreement with the building authorities, no strain measurements were performed, because all deformations were fully elastic.

6 CONCLUDING REMARKS

It has been shown that shape optimization of thin-walled, cold-formed steel sections can be formulated as a problem of mathematical

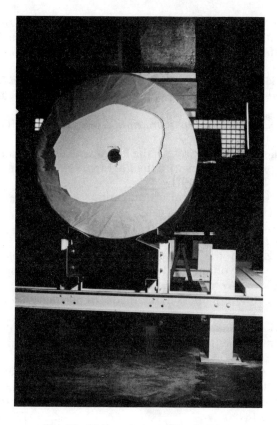

Fig. 13. Full-scale test of rack structure.

programming with functional constraints arising from local and global buckling, nonlinear mode interaction and stress or displacement constraints.

The iterative solutions discussed are based on quadratic approximations. A direct iterative method can be used if the constraints are approximated by quadratic functions, and in general a sequential quadratic approximation of the augmented Lagrange function can be used. The examples presented show that optimization can be used successfully for a great variety of thin-walled structures.

REFERENCES

1. Fox, R. L., *Optimization Methods for Engineering Design*, Addison–Wesley, Reading, MA, 1971.
2. Thompson, J. M. T. & Hunt, G. W., *A General Theory of Elastic Stability*, John Wiley & Sons, London, 1973.

3. ECCS, Technical Committee 7, Working Group 7.1. Design of cold formed steel sheeting and sections, *'European Recommendations for the Design of Light Gauge Steel Members'*, European Convention for Constructional Steelwork, No. 49 (1987).
4. Gallagher, R. H., Fully stressed design, in *Optimum Structural Design, Theory and Applications*, ed. R. H. Gallagher, and O. C. Zienkiewicz, John Wiley & Sons, London, 1973.
5. Gellatly, R. A. & Berke, L., *Optimal structural design*, USAF AFFDL-TR-70-165, 1971.
6. Lipp, W. & Thierauf, G., The role of the force- and displacement method for the optimization of structures with the Lagrange-multiplier-technique, *10th Congr. IABSE*, Tokyo, Sept. 1976.
7. Vanderplaats, G. N., Structural optimization — past, present and future, *AIAA J.,* **20**(7) (1981) 992–1000.
8. Hafta, R. T. & Prasad, B., Optimal structural design with plate bending element — a survey, *AIAA J.,* **19**(4) (1981) 517–22.
9. Wasiutyński, Z., On the equivalence of design principles: minimum potential – constant volume and minimum volume – constant potential, *Bull. Acad. Pol. Sci., Sér. Sci. Tech.,* **14**(9) (1966) 537–9.
10. Drucker, D. C., On uniqueness in the theory of plasticity, *Q. Appl. Math.,* **14** (1956) 35–42.
11. Schittkowski, K., The nonlinear programming method of Wilson, Han and Powell with an augmented Lagrangian type line search function, Part 1: Convergence Analysis, *Numer. Math.,* **38** (1981) 83–114.
12. Thierauf, G., A method for optimal limit design of structures with alternative loads, *Comp. Meth. Appl. Mech. Eng.,* **16** (1978) 135–49.
13. Prager, W. & Shield, R. T., A general theory of optimal plastic design, *J. Appl. Mech.,* **34** (1967) 184–6.
14. Kaneko, I., Lawo, M. & Thierauf, G., On computational procedures for the force method, *Int. J. Numer. Meth. Eng.,* **19** (1982) 1469–95.
15. Murray, N. W. & Thierauf, G., *Tables for the Design and Analysis of Stiffened Steel Plates*, Vieweg, Braunschweig, FRG, 1981.
16. Mahendran, M. & Murray, N. W., Elastic buckling analysis of ideal thin-walled structures under combined loading using a finite strip method, *Thin-Walled Structures,* **4** (1986) 329–62.
17. Murray, N. W., *Introduction to the Theory of Thin-Walled Structures,* Clarendon Press, Oxford, UK, 1984.

Thin-Walled Structures **9** (1990) 257–267

Probabilistic Properties of Thin-Walled Elements

R. E. Melchers

Department of Civil Engineering and Surveying, The University of Newcastle, Newcastle, New South Wales 2308, Australia

ABSTRACT

Thin-walled structures are relatively complicated structural systems governed by many parameters. These include the dimensions, the material properties and imperfection measures. In principle all of these are not known with certainty at the design stage, and even after construction some degree of uncertainty remains.

The present paper reviews briefly how such uncertainties are considered in modern structural reliability theory to estimate nominal probabilities of failure. An example application will be given to illustrate the process of estimating the probability density function for the failure stress of stiffened plates subject to axial forces.

1 INTRODUCTION

It has been traditional to use a 'safety factor' or 'load factor' as a measure of safety of a structure against collapse (or even loss of serviceability). There are good reasons to adopt a probabilistic approach in setting such factors (or their modern 'equivalents' — 'partial safety factors'); an important one is consistency between safety measures for different structures and for different structural elements.

In setting 'partial factors' the concept of limit states is conventionally adopted. Herein attention will be restricted only to the 'collapse' limit state, that is, to the conditions under which the structure is considered in conventional professional practice to have 'failed'. For buckling

Thin-Walled Structures 0263-8231/90/$03·50 © 1990 Elsevier Science Publishers Ltd, England. Printed in Great Britain

problems, for example, this is commonly taken to be when the extreme fibre of the structure in a buckling situation has reached the yield capacity of the material. Any greater load capacity of the structure, due, for example, to overt strain-hardening, is ignored.

The partial factors of limit state design codes are obtained by reference to so-called 'nominal' failure probabilities, calculated from statistical data on loads, material strengths, dimensions, etc., but not recognising errors in design or construction other than those due to natural variability in construction tolerances, etc. Thus, gross errors are specifically neglected.

The process of 'design code calibration' consists of integrating existing design practice, statistical data and nominal failure probability estimates to produce partial factors. This process is well documented in the literature[1] and will not be considered herein. This paper will be concerned, however, with the estimation of a (nominal) probability of failure (in the 'collapse' sense) for a realistic structure — a necessary preliminary for any code calibration work.

2 STRUCTURAL RELIABILITY THEORY

The load acting on the structure in general will be a time dependent quantity, $Q(t)$. During any one time interval, the maximum value of $Q(t)$ will be of interest and during the lifetime $[0, T]$ of the structure the maximum of all such maxima will be critical. For all real loads $Q(t)$ is a probabilistic variable. At any point in time only its expected value can be given, perhaps with estimates of the uncertainty in that expected value. It follows that $Q_{max}|_{[0, T]} = X_1$ also can be best described in probabilistic terms. An extreme value distribution is usually appropriate.[1]

Let attention now be restricted to problems in which there is only one load process Q for which X_1 is the time invariant random variable describing its uncertainty in the lifetime $[0, T]$. Also let the material strengths, dimensions, etc., be assumed not to change with time, and let such parameters be described by the random variables $X_2, \ldots, X_n$. The probability of failure of a structure described by the random vector $\mathbf{X}$ is then

$$p_f = \int \cdots \cdots \int f_{\mathbf{X}}(\mathbf{x}) \, d\mathbf{x} \tag{1}$$

$$\bigcup_i G_i(\mathbf{X}) \leqslant 0$$

where $f_{\mathbf{X}}(\mathbf{x})$ is the (known) joint probability density function (p.d.f.) of $\mathbf{X}$ and $\bigcup_i G_i(\mathbf{X}) \leqslant 0$ describes the region of integration (i.e. the so-called failure domain), composed of the union of the $G_i(\ )$, which are individual 'limit state' functions. The problem is sketched in Fig. 1 in two-dimensional space. In general the integration required in eqn (1) is not straightforward, particularly for large n. Various approximate methods have been proposed.[1] An important issue is the definition of the $G_i(\ )$ terms.

For the present problem it is unlikely that the load X_1 will depend on any other X_i, so that eqn (1) may be written as

$$p_f = \int \cdots \cdots \int f_{X_1}(x_1)\ f_{X_{(n-1)}}(\mathbf{x})\ d\mathbf{x} \tag{2}$$

$$\bigcup_i G_i(\mathbf{X}) \leqslant 0$$

where $f_{X_{(n-1)}}$ is the p.d.f. for the structural resistance described by the vector $\mathbf{X}_{(n-1)} = [X_2, X_3, \ldots, X_n]$. The integral can be further simplified to

$$p_f = \int_{-\infty}^{\infty} f_Q(x)\ F_R(x)\ dx \tag{3}$$

if $f_{X_{(n-1)}}$ can be separately evaluated. In eqn (3) $F_R(x)$ represents the cumulative distribution function $= \int \ldots \int f_{X(n-1)}(\mathbf{x})\ d\mathbf{x}_{(n-1)}$ which is the probability that the structure will fail given that the load $(X_1 = Q)$ has the value x. Expression (3) is known also as the 'fundamental' problem, and can be evaluated readily by numerical integration provided $F_R(x)$ is known.[1] How the expression for $F_R(x)$ may be obtained for a stiffened plate is the subject of this paper.

$F_R(\ )$ may be obtained from the p.d.f. for R, i.e. from $f_R(\ )$, since

$$F_R(x) = \int_{-\infty}^{\infty} f_R(v)\ dv \tag{4}$$

so that it is sufficient to focus attention on deriving $f_R(\ )$.

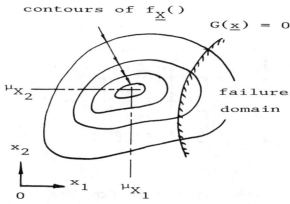

Fig. 1. Contours of $f_X(\ )$ and limit state function $G(\mathbf{x}) = 0$ for two-dimensional case.

For a specific structure or structural element $f_R(\ )$ may be obtained through so-called 'second moment' analysis if all variables are represented only by their mean and variance. More generally, however, recourse must be had to simulation methods using the Monte Carlo technique. In all cases, an accurate description of the structural or element resistance (or structural capacity) must be available, as well as statistical data for the parameters which affect the resistance. These matters are addressed in the sections to follow for the special case of stiffened plates.

3 BUCKLING OF STIFFENED PLATES UNDER AXIAL LOAD

Estimates for the collapse load associated with the buckling of longitudinally stiffened steel plates may be obtained in a number of different ways, including methods based on modifications of the Perry–Robertson equation.[2] Of the latter, the somewhat simplified theory developed by Murray[3] will be applied herein to illustrate the procedures which may be used in a probabilistic analysis.

For sections of the type shown in Fig. 2, subject to an axial load initially located on the original centre of gravity, buckling may occur in the plate, or in the stiffeners; these occur, respectively, when the initial imperfection, δ_0, measured at mid-length ($x = L/2$) and the eccentricity of the load due to deformation of the cross-section Δ sum to a positive or negative value (see Fig. 2).

As is well known, the stress distribution in the plate is not uniform and a widely used approach is to consider an equivalent section having equivalent plate width S' (S is the stiffener spacing). (All primed values relate to the effective cross-section.) A critical issue is how the effective width S' is to be obtained. Various approaches have been suggested in the literature.[2]

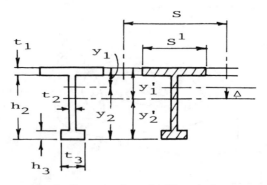

Fig. 2. Cross-section of stiffened plate.

Murray[3] suggested that a semi-rational method based on observations of the relationship between the failure stress and the membrane stresses in initially deformed square plates could be used to obtain an estimate of S':

$$S' = \frac{\sigma_m}{\sigma_y} S \qquad (5)$$

where σ_m/σ_y is obtained from a nonlinear relationship (Fig. 3) with $(\sigma_y/\sigma_c)^{1/2}$ and where σ_c is the critical stress for the buckling of an in-plane loaded plate of width S and thickness t, given by

$$\sigma_c = \frac{\pi^2 E}{3(1 - v^2)} \left(\frac{t}{S}\right)^2 \qquad (6)$$

The error in estimating real buckling loads by σ_c is usually considerable, largely due to the influence of imperfections. This has been allowed for in the relationship of Fig. 3, in which the curve shown was chosen to bound, from below, all known experimental results.[3] It is clear that Fig. 3 is generally similar in form, and analogous in meaning, to the type of curves obtained for column buckling. The slenderness ratio (S/t) is contained in (σ_y/σ_c) through expression (6).

Once the effective section is known, the Perry–Robertson formula may be used to estimate the nominal stress on the effective section at failure (buckling), given by

$$\sigma'_f = \tfrac{1}{2}([\sigma_y + (1 + \eta)\sigma'_e] - \{[\sigma_y + (1 + \eta)\sigma'_e]^2 - \sigma'_e\}^{1/2}) \qquad (7)$$

where all parameters are nominal (see below) and where

σ'_e $= \pi^2 E(r'/L)^2$, the elastic buckling stress for the equivalent Euler column, assuming the plate–stiffener assembly is pinned at $x = 0, L$;

r' = radius of gyration of the effective cross-section;

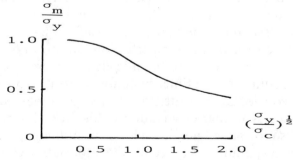

Fig. 3. Relationship between σ_m/σ_y and $(\sigma_y/\sigma_c)^{1/2}$ (see Ref. 3).

η = imperfection parameter = $A'y'(\delta_0 + \Delta')/I'$;

A', I', y' = area, second moment of area and distance to the extreme fibre for the effective cross-section; and

σ_y = material yield-strength.

Expression (7) results, of course, from the assumption that buckling occurs when the critical extreme fibre stress reaches the yield stress σ_y; this is somewhat conservative, but appears to correlate well with experimental observations.

The eccentricity of the load, Δ, due to deformation of the whole plate assembly is given by the change in location of the centre of gravity before and after loading, thus (see Fig. 2):

$$\Delta = y_1 - y_1' \tag{8}$$

According to Murray,[3] the eccentricity of load relative to the effective section occurs at an applied stress σ_c in the original section. This is equivalent to an applied stress of $\sigma_c A/A'$ in the effective section. Further, since Δ is equivalent to a load eccentricity of Δ' when the effective section carries zero load,[3] it follows that

$$\Delta' = \Delta \left(1 - \frac{\sigma_c A/A'}{\sigma_e'} \right) \tag{9}$$

with σ_e' as defined before. The failure stress on the effective cross-section σ_f' is obtained from expression (7) using the properties based on the effective cross-section. Once σ_f' has been obtained, σ_f, the nominal stress at failure on the original cross-section, follows simply from $\sigma_f = \sigma_f' A'/A$.

4 PROBABILISTIC MODELLING

To develop a measure of the uncertainty in σ_f estimation it is necessary to be able to estimate the uncertainties in the parameters which contribute to σ_f through eqn (7) and its subsidiaries. It will be clear that the 'input' parameters are essentially the dimensions, such as s, t_i, L, etc., the yield strength σ_y of the steel, and the imperfection parameter δ_0. The derived parameters $\sigma_c, \sigma_e, \sigma_m$, etc., are of little direct interest. Compared to experimental results, σ_e, the Euler buckling stress of a pin-ended strut, may display considerable scatter, as is well documented in column buckling studies. A similar observation holds for σ_c for plate buckling and for σ_m, also for plate buckling. However, in the present case σ_c, σ_e and σ_m are merely parameters reflecting the information contained in the 'input' parameters. They should not be seen as parameters which need to be compared to observations. It may be useful to think of all uncertainty in these parameters as being ultimately reflected in σ_f. It may be convenient also to think of eqn (7) and its subsidiaries as representing a 'black box', which predicts σ_f for given, well-defined (but probabilistically described) input parameters.

The uncertainties in the physical dimensions S, t_i, L, etc., are in practice very small and unlikely to have much influence on σ_f. A useful first approximation is therefore to treat these all as deterministic variables, not subject to uncertainty (as noted, the possibility of gross error, such as in S, has been specifically excluded).

Statistical data for the plate yield stress σ_y are directly available from the literature.[1] Typically a lognormal distribution is appropriate. If nominal values are used in design, allowance must be made for a bias due to the estimated mean being generally greater than the specified mean (or nominal value). Typically, the ratio is 1·03. The yield strength itself may have a coefficient of variation typically about 0·1.

Undoubtedly the parameter of greatest importance and also of greatest uncertainty is δ_0, the measure of initial imperfections measured at mid-length $x = L/2$. According to Murray,[3] eqn (7) produces good predictions of the failure stress when accurately measured values of δ_0 are used together with actual values of the other parameters. This suggests that the model represented by eqn (7) is a good one. It also suggests that for design, good estimates for the expected value of δ_0 and the corresponding variance are needed. Since at the design stage only predictions about standards of workmanship, and hence about imperfections, can be made, it is clear that estimates for δ_0 will be subject to much uncertainty. Probabilistic estimates for the uncertainty in δ_0 are not readily available for real plates used in different ways in real structures. Some information exists for laboratory specimens.[2] There are also guidelines for conventional (non-probabilistic) design,[2] but these are, again, bounds of uncertain definition. In view of this, it is appropriate to adopt as a mean value for δ_0 the best estimate made by expert designers for a particular design situation and also to estimate the uncertainty of this estimate in terms of a standard deviation (or similar measure). δ_0 may then be represented in 'second-moment' terms. This is an acceptable procedure and consistent with the notions of 'subjective probability' and 'nominal' failure probability.[1]

The final form of uncertainty to be considered is model uncertainty. This represents the statistical relationship between the value of failure stress predicted by the model (eqn (7)) and observations of failure stress. As noted, the model (eqn (7)) predicts the actual failure stress rather well using the actual value for δ_0, the actual values for the other input parameters and the various models for σ_m/σ_y, σ_c and σ_e. Models generally similar to eqn (7) have been found[2] to have ratios (measured failure stress/theoretical failure stress) of about 1·04 with a standard deviation of about 0·05. Thus a multiplier X_m with these statistical properties will be used to represent model uncertainty in eqn (7). In the absence of information to the contrary, a 'second-moment' approximation for the probability distribution for X_m will be adopted.

5 EXAMPLE

As noted earlier, the estimation of the probability density function $f_{\sigma_f}()$ for σ_f may proceed in broadly two distinct ways.[1] For relatively simple models of strength, the Second Moment approximation may be valid for all parameters and relatively simple Second Moment algebra can be applied.[4] More generally, however, recourse must be had to simulation using Monte Carlo methods. Such an approach will now be outlined.

Let the dimensions s, t_i, L, etc., be given[3] (see Table 1). Let it be assumed that the yield stress σ_y is estimated to have a mean $\mu_y = 377$ and be lognormally distributed. The standard deviation will be varied to study its effect: see Table 2. Further, as noted, it will be assumed that δ_0 is normally distributed, with parameters as given in Table 2.

Simulation now proceeds by taking a random sample from each of the distributions for σ_y, δ_0 and X_m (also assumed normal) and for the three values so obtained determining the sample value $\hat{\sigma}_{f_i}$ using the rules of Section 3. This process is repeated a sufficiently large number of times, N. From the ensemble of $\hat{\sigma}_{f_i}$ values, the (sample) mean m_{σ_f}, the (sample) standard deviation s_{σ_f} and higher moments may be calculated from (with $x = \sigma_f$)

$$m_x = \frac{1}{N} \sum_{i=1}^{N} \hat{x}_i \tag{10}$$

$$s_x^2 = \frac{1}{N-1} \left(\sum_{i=1}^{N} \hat{x}_i^2 - N m_x^2 \right) \tag{11}$$

Statistical tests may then be used to infer a probability density function for σ_f. This may then be used in subsequent reliability analyses.

Table 2 summarises some results using the above analysis for the stiffened plate described in Fig. 2 and Table 1. The mean values of δ_0 were taken from Murray[3] as typical of plate buckling ($\delta_0 = -0·25$ mm) and

TABLE 1
Dimensions of Stiffened
Plate Example

s	=	533 mm
t_1	=	9·85 mm
t_2	=	7·36 mm
t_3	=	28·6 mm
h_2	=	152 mm
h_3	=	15·9 mm
L	=	3 450 mm
E	=	210 Mpa
v	=	0·3

stiffener buckling ($\delta_0 = -2\cdot41$ mm) for the plate assemblies having the properties shown in Table 1. It is clear from Table 2 that the mean value of σ_f/σ_y decreases and the standard deviation increases in both cases with greater uncertainty (i.e. standard deviation) in δ_0. This is entirely as expected. However, except for very high uncertainty in δ_0 relative to its mean value, the estimates for the mean of σ_f/σ_y were closely similar.

It is clear also that changing the standard deviation of σ_y has little effect on the mean of σ_f/σ_y but a considerable effect on its standard deviation. Fortunately, in practice the standard deviation of σ_y can be reasonably closely predicted.

TABLE 2
Effect of Main Parameters on Mean and Standard Deviation of σ_f/σ_y

Case	μ_{δ_0}	$SD(\delta)$	μ_{σ_y}	$SD(\sigma_y)$	μ_{X_m}	$SD(X_m)$	μ_{σ_f/σ_y}	$SD(\sigma_f/\sigma_y)$
1	−0·25	0·25	377·0	30·0	1·04	0·05	0·704	0·045
2	—	0·50	—	—	—	—	0·705	0·046
3	—	1·0	—	—	—	—	0·704	0·050
4	—	1·0	—	60·0	—	—	0·702	0·068
5	—	2·0	—	30·0	—	—	0·682	0·061
6	—	1·0	—	—	—	0·10	0·703	0·078
7	—	—	—	—	—	0·20	0·703	0·142
8	−2·41	0·10	—	—	—	0·05	0·678	0·037
9	—	0·50	—	—	—	—	0·682	0·054
10	—	1·0	—	—	—	—	0·675	0·068
11	—	1·0	—	60·0	—	—	0·673	0·075
12	—	2·0	—	30·0	—	—	0·652	0·082
13	—	3·0	—	—	—	—	0·632	0·092
14	—	1·0	—	—	—	0·10	0·675	0·089
15	—	—	—	—	—	0·20	0·674	0·145

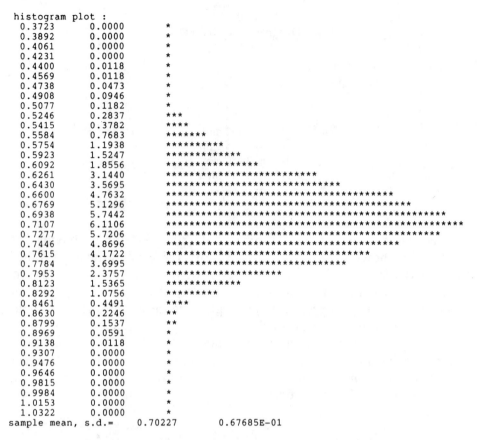

```
histogram plot :
    0.3723      0.0000      *
    0.3892      0.0000      *
    0.4061      0.0000      *
    0.4231      0.0000      *
    0.4400      0.0118      *
    0.4569      0.0118      *
    0.4738      0.0473      *
    0.4908      0.0946      *
    0.5077      0.1182      *
    0.5246      0.2837      ***
    0.5415      0.3782      ****
    0.5584      0.7683      *******
    0.5754      1.1938      *********
    0.5923      1.5247      ************
    0.6092      1.8556      ****************
    0.6261      3.1440      **************************
    0.6430      3.5695      *******************************
    0.6600      4.7632      ********************************************
    0.6769      5.1296      ***************************************************
    0.6938      5.7442      ********************************************************
    0.7107      6.1106      ***************************************************************
    0.7277      5.7206      ********************************************************
    0.7446      4.8696      *******************************************
    0.7615      4.1722      *************************************
    0.7784      3.6995      *****************************
    0.7953      2.3757      *******************
    0.8123      1.5365      *************
    0.8292      1.0756      *********
    0.8461      0.4491      ****
    0.8630      0.2246      **
    0.8799      0.1537      **
    0.8969      0.0591      *
    0.9138      0.0118      *
    0.9307      0.0000      *
    0.9476      0.0000      *
    0.9646      0.0000      *
    0.9815      0.0000      *
    0.9984      0.0000      *
    1.0153      0.0000      *
    1.0322      0.0000      *
sample mean, s.d.=     0.70227        0.67685E-01
```

Fig. 4. Typical histogram for σ_f/σ_y obtained by simulation.

The effect of changing the standard deviation of the model uncertainty parameter X_m is also shown in Table 2. It is clear that the mean of σ_f/σ_y is hardly affected, but that the standard deviation is roughly proportional to the changes in the standard deviation of X_m. This is entirely as expected and highlights the importance of accurate modelling. Figure 4 shows a typical histogram obtained from one such analysis. It is evident that the results are closely Gaussian in distribution, a result which was also found for the other cases of Table 2.

6 CONCLUSION

The parameters having greatest uncertainty for axially loaded stiffened plates are conventionally considered to be (i) the initial out-of-plane imperfections δ_0 of the plate; and (ii) the yield strength σ_y of the material. In a reliability analysis the accuracy of mathematical modelling of the physical situation must also be considered; this was done through the modelling parameter X_m.

The importance of these parameters in obtaining a probability density function for the failure stress, $f_{\sigma_f}(\ )$ was indicated through a parametric study on a typical structure. The use of $f_{\sigma_f}(\ )$ in obtaining a formal estimate of reliability of the stiffened plate under axial load was also indicated. Cross-sectional sizes and plate length generally have such low variances that they may be assumed deterministic for reliability analyses.

REFERENCES

1. Melchers, R. E., *Structural Reliability Analysis and Prediction,* Ellis Horwood/ John Wiley, Chichester, UK, 1987.
2. Murray, N. W., *Introduction to the Theory of Thin-Walled Structures,* Oxford University Press, Oxford, UK, 1984.
3. Murray, N. W., Analysis and design of stiffened plates for collapse load, *The Structural Engineer,* **53** (March 1987) 153–8.
4. Ditlevsen, O., *Uncertainty Modelling,* McGraw-Hill, New York, 1981.

SESSION 5

Thin-Walled Structures **9** (1990) 269–307

Elastic Biaxial Bending and Torsion of Thin-Walled Members

N. S. Trahair

School of Civil and Mining Engineering, University of Sydney, Sydney,
New South Wales 2006, Australia

&

S. Bild

Bild Consulting Engineers, D-5800 Hagen, FRG

ABSTRACT

This paper presents a detailed treatment of the non-linear elastic biaxial bending and torsion of thin-walled open section members. The treatment is valid for uniform members of linear elastic material, and is limited to small strains and rotations, and moderate deflections. Shear straining of the mid-surface of the member wall is neglected, and it is assumed that the member does not distort or buckle locally. The effects of initial deformations, loads, stresses, and strains are incorporated.

The treatment is based on non-linear strain–displacement relationships, and these are used to derive the non-linear equilibrium and tangent stiffness equations in forms which are suitable for computer solution by the finite element method.

Approximate linear and non-linear differential equilibrium equations are derived, as are the differential equilibrium equations and the energy equation for neutral equilibrium at bifurcation buckling, and these are then related to the classical equations developed by Timoshenko, Vlasov, and others.

NOTATION

[*a*]	Matrix of shape function coefficients (eqn (144))
A	Cross-sectional area

269

Thin-Walled Structures 0263-8231/90/$03·50 © 1990 Elsevier Science Publishers Ltd, England. Printed in Great Britain.

$[A_L], [A_Q]$ Matrices for linear and quadratic potential energy contributions of $\{q\}$

$[A_{LQ}], [A_{QQ}]$ Matrices for linear and quadratic potential energy contributions of $\{Q\}$

b Distributed bimoment per unit length

b_i Initial value of b

B Bimoment

B_i Initial value of B

$[B_L], [B_Q]$ Matrices for linear and quadratic strains

$[D]$ Tangent modulus constitutive matrix

$\{e\}$ Vector of equilibrium equation errors

E Young's modulus of elasticity

$[E]$ Elasticity matrix (eqn (44))

$\{F_E\}$ Vector of external applied actions

$\{F_I\}$ Vector of equivalent internal resistances

G Shear modulus of elasticity

i, j, k Integers

$I_P, I_{PP}, I_{Px}, I_{Py}$ Section properties (eqn (2))

I_{Pw} Section property (eqn (6))

I_w Warping section constant (eqn (6))

I_x, I_y Major and minor axis second moments of area (eqn (2))

J Torsion section constant (eqn (7))

$[K_T]$ Total tangent stiffness matrix

L Element length, or member length

L, M, N Direction cosines between rotated shear centre axes and original x, y, z axes

m_x, m_y, m_z Distributed moments and torque per unit length about x, y, z axes

m_{xi}, m_{yi}, m_{zi} Initial values of m_x, m_y, m_z

M End moment

M_{qij} Elements of $[M_q]$

$[M_Q], [M_q]$ Geometric matrices associated with actions $\{Q\}, \{q\}$

M_x, M_y, M_z Moments and torque about x, y, z axes

M_{xi}, M_{yi}, M_{zi} Initial values of M_x, M_y, M_z

M_{yz} Flexural–torsional buckling moment of a beam in uniform bending

$[M_\sigma]$ Geometric matrix associated with stresses

$M_{\sigma ij}$ Elements of $[M_\sigma]$

n $= n_{u, v, w, \phi}$

$n_{u, v, w, \phi}$ Four integers to indicate order of the representations of the deformations u, v, w, ϕ

$[N]$	Matrix relating $\{u, v, w, \phi\}^{\mathrm{T}}$ to $\{\delta\}$ (eqn (71))
$[N_Q], [N_q]$	Matrices relating $\{\theta_1^{\mathrm{T}}, \theta_2^{\mathrm{T}}\}^{\mathrm{T}}$, $\{\theta\}$ to $\{\delta\}$ (eqns (74), (75))
$\{N_u\}$	Vector relating u to $\{\delta_u\}$ (eqn (143))
$[N_\sigma]$	Matrix relating $\{\Phi\}$ to $\{\delta\}$ (eqn (73))
P	Axial force
P_x, P_y, P_z	Flexural and torsional buckling loads of a straight column
$\{q\}$	Load vector $\{q_x, q_y, q_z, m_x, m_y, m_z, b\}^{\mathrm{T}}$ (eqn (56))
q_x, q_y, q_z	Distributed forces per unit length in x, y, z directions
q_{xi}, q_{yi}, q_{zi}	Initial values of q_x, q_y, q_z
Q_x, Q_y, Q_z	Loads acting in x, y, z directions
Q_{xi}, Q_{yi}, Q_{zi}	Initial values of Q_x, Q_y, Q_z
$\{Q\}$	Load vector $\{Q_x, Q_y, Q_z, M_x, M_y, M_z, B\}^{\mathrm{T}}$ (eqn (57))
r_1	$= \sqrt{(I_p/A + y_0^2)}$
r_2	$= \sqrt{(I_p/A + x_0^2 + y_0^2)}$
s_c	Distance around thin-walled section
$[S]$	Matrix of cross-section coordinates of P
t	Thickness of thin-walled section
t_p	Distance from mid-thickness surface
$[T_R]$	Transformation matrix for rotations about x, y, z axes
$[T_x], [T_y], [T_z]$	Individual transformation matrices
$\{u\}$	Vector of load point displacements, rotations, and twist (eqn (58))
u, v, w_s	Displacements of the shear centre in the x, y, z directions
u_b, v_b, w_b	Buckling displacements
u_c	Central value of u
u_i, v_i, w_{si}	Initial values of u, v, w_s
$\{u_L\}, \{u_Q\}$	Linear and quadratic components of $\{u\}$ (eqns (59), (60))
u_L, v_L, w_L	Linear components of u_P, v_P, w_P
u_P, v_P, w_P	Displacements of P in the x, y, z directions
u_Q, v_Q, w_Q	Quadratic components of u_P, v_P, w_P
U	Strain energy
U_T	Total potential
$U_{\sigma\varepsilon i}$	Strain energy associated with initial stresses
V	Volume of element
w	Displacement of the centroid in the z direction
W	Potential energy
x, y, z	Coordinate axes at centroid of section
x_m, y_m	Point of action of m_x, m_y
x_M, y_M	Point of action of M_x, M_y
x_q, y_q	Point of action of q_x, q_y, q_z
x_Q, y_Q	Point of action of Q_x, Q_y, Q_z

x_{s1}, y_{s1}, z_{s1}	Axes at displaced and rotated shear centre
x_0, y_0	Shear centre coordinates
$\{z\}$	Vector of powers of z
$\{a\}$	Vector of coefficients of powers of z
β_x	$= I_{Px}/I_x - 2y_0$
γ	Load factor
γ_P	Shear strain at P due to uniform torsion
γ_{Pi}	Initial value of γ_P
γ_{PL}, γ_{PQ}	Linear and quadratic components of γ_P
$\gamma_{P\delta}$	Value of γ_P associated with total deformations
$\gamma_{P\delta i}$	Value of γ_P associated with initial deformations
$\{\delta\}$	Vector of nodal deformations
$\{\delta_b\}$	Vector of buckling nodal deformations
$\{\delta_{E2}\}, \{\delta_{E3}\}$	Additional nodal degrees of freedom of higher elements
$\{\delta_u\}$	Vector of nodal deformations associated with u
Δ	Indicates the change or increment in the value following
$\{\varepsilon\}$	Vector of generalised strains
ε_P	Normal axial strain at P
ε_{Pi}	Initial value of ε_P
$\varepsilon_{PL}, \varepsilon_{PQ}$	Linear and quadratic components of ε_P
$\varepsilon_{P\delta}$	Value of ε_P associated with total deformations
$\varepsilon_{P\delta i}$	Value of ε_P associated with initial deformations
$\{\varepsilon_{\delta i}\}$	Vector of generalised strains associated with initial deformations
$\{\theta\}$	Vector of displacements, rotations, curvatures, twists (eqn (63))
$\theta_x, \theta_y, \theta_z$	Rotations about x, y, z axes
κ_x, κ_y	Curvatures about x, y axes
κ_z	Twist about z axis
κ_{zi}	Initial value of κ_z
ρ_0	Perpendicular distance from shear centre
$\{\sigma\}$	Generalised stress resultants
σ_P	Normal stress at P
σ_{Pi}	Initial value of σ_P
$\{\sigma_{\sigma i}\}$	Initial values of $\{\sigma\}$
$\sigma_1 - \sigma_6$	Elements of $\{\sigma\}$
σ_5	'Wagner' stress resultant
σ_{5i}	Initial value of σ_5
τ_P	Shear stress at P
τ_{Pi}	Initial value of τ_P
ϕ	Twist rotation of cross-section about z axis
ϕ_b	Buckling twist rotation

ϕ_c	Central twist rotation
ϕ_i	Initial value of ϕ
$\{\Phi\}$	Vector of generalised curvatures
ω	Section warping function (eqn (4))

1 INTRODUCTION

The development over the past 30 years of the use of digital computers to solve structural problems has proceeded to such an advanced stage that it is now appropriate to review and restate the currently accepted theory for the elastic non-linear biaxial bending and torsion of thin-walled members.

Historically, the current theory of biaxial bending and torsion has developed as a series of extensions from the previously accepted theories, with the occasional review which drew together the then state of the art into a coherent and acceptable statement of the theory. Thus, the early linear engineering theory of beam bending was modified to account for the effects of flexural buckling predicted by Euler[1] in 1759 to produce an approximate theory for the elastic non-linear in-plane bending behaviour of beam-columns.

The linear theory of uniform torsion developed by Saint-Venant[2] in 1855 was extended in 1905 to include warping torsion by Timoshenko,[3,4] and comprehensive treatments of the linear theories of bending and torsion were given in 1940 by Vlasov[5] and in 1945 by Timoshenko.[6] Subsequently, these treatments have been repeated in many texts, such as those of Timoshenko and Gere,[7] Trahair and Bradford,[8] Murray,[9] and many others.

The first non-linear treatments of combined bending and torsion were given in 1899 by Michell[10] and Prandtl[11] in their studies of the flexural–torsional buckling of narrow rectangular beams out of the plane of initial bending. These were extended in 1905 by Timoshenko[3,4] to include the effects of warping torsion.

Subsequent work in 1929 by Wagner[12] and later work by others led to the development of a non-linear theory for the torsional and flexural–torsional behaviour of axially loaded columns, as stated by Timoshenko[6] and Vlasov.[5] These latter treatments provided the bases not only of a flexural–torsional buckling theory, but also of a non-linear elastic biaxial bending and torsion theory which was thought to be valid for small deflections.

This non-linear theory has been used from time to time in a number of studies, such as those of Horne,[13] and a number of extensions have been made, including those for the effects of initial crookedness and twist, restaints, non-uniform members, interaction between members, pre-buckling deflections, curved members and directed loading.

The method of making these extensions was generally to start with the commonly accepted non-linear differential equations of elastic biaxial bending and torsion, and to include additional terms to describe the particular extension being made. Alternatively, another process was used, which started from one of the commonly accepted energy equations for elastic buckling, most of which have developed from the early work of Timoshenko.[3, 4] Unfortunately, some of these extensions have not received general acceptance, and there are at present widely differing views on both the effect of axial loads on torsional buckling[14] and on the flexural–torsional buckling of arches.[15]

These difficulties suggest that a more general and basic method than that of making isolated extensions to previous studies is needed to develop a generally acceptable theory for non-linear behaviour. Such a method is available, through the use of non-linear relationships between the displacements and twists of the member and the strains developed in the member. The use of these relationships with the principle of virtual work allows the non-linear matrix stiffness equations of equilibrium to be formulated. The differential equilibrium equations can be derived from these, as can the energy equation for elastic buckling.

However, the resulting non-linear equations have many more terms than are commonly found in the extensions of previous studies, indicating that approximations or simplifications have been introduced. These additional terms make it impractical to attempt to find general closed-form solutions, except in very special cases.

Solutions are best found numerically using computer programs, such as those based on the finite element method.[16–19] The matrix formulation of the non-linear stiffness equations is well suited to such a method, and the use of the power of a modern computer means that there is no need to simplify the formulation by omitting terms which might be thought to be unimportant. In addition, the repetitions of the iterative method of solution required by the non-linear nature of the stiffness equations virtually require the use of a computer, as does the application of the method to any but the simplest of structures.

The purposes of this paper are to demonstrate the general method of formulating non-linear structural problems by developing the non-linear strain–displacement relationships for the biaxial bending and torsion of elastic members, and by deriving the non-linear matrix equilibrium and tangent stiffness equations; and from these

(a) to obtain the differential equilibrium equations for non-linear behaviour;
(b) to obtain the energy equations for elastic buckling;
(c) to demonstrate the approximations made for the commonly accepted Timoshenko–Vlasov theory; and
(d) to outline the finite element method of solution.

Other investigators have had similar or related purposes, including Roberts,[20] Rajasekaran,[21] Hasegawa *et al.*,[22] Yang and McGuire,[23] Attard,[24] and Attard and Somervaille.[25]

For this paper, it is assumed that the material is linear elastic; the member is of thin-walled open cross-section; the strains and rotations are small and the deflections are moderate; the shear strains in the mid-surface of the member can be neglected; and the cross-section of the member does not distort in its plane. The making of these assumptions immediately suggests topics which should be investigated in the future in order to make the method more general.

2 ANALYSIS

2.1 Member and section properties

The member of length L shown in Fig. 1(a) is of thin-walled cross-section, and is straight and untwisted. The principal centroidal axes x, y of the cross-section are shown in Fig. 1(b). The positions of these axes are defined by the conditions

$$\int_A x \, dA = \int_A y \, dA = \int_A xy \, dA = 0 \tag{1}$$

The following section properties are defined:

$$\left.\begin{aligned}
A &= \int_A dA \\
I_x &= \int_A y^2 \, dA \\
I_y &= \int_A x^2 \, dA \\
I_P &= \int_A (x^2 + y^2) \, dA \\
I_{Px} &= \int_A y(x^2 + y^2) \, dA \\
I_{Py} &= \int_A x(x^2 + y^2) \, dA \\
I_{PP} &= \int_A (x^2 + y^2)^2 \, dA
\end{aligned}\right\} \tag{2}$$

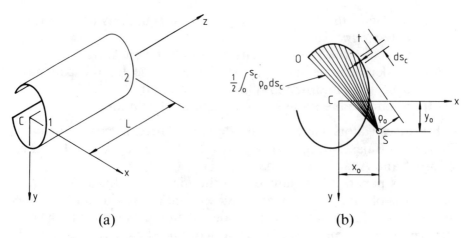

Fig. 1. (a) Thin-walled member; (b) its cross-section.

The position of the shear centre $S(x_0, y_0)$ of the cross-section shown in Fig. 1(b) is defined by the conditions

$$\int_A x\omega \, dA = \int_A y\omega \, dA = 0 \tag{3}$$

in which ω is a warping function[5] defined by

$$\omega = \frac{1}{A} \int_A \left\{ \int_0^{s_c} \rho_0 \, ds_c \right\} t \, ds_c - \int_0^{s_c} \rho_0 \, ds_c \tag{4}$$

which satisfies

$$\int_A \omega \, dA = 0 \tag{5}$$

In eqn (4), t is the wall thickness, ρ_0 is the perpendicular distance from the shear centre to the mid-thickness tangent, and s_c is the distance around the mid-thickness line. The following section properties are defined:

$$\left. \begin{aligned} I_w &= \int_A \omega^2 \, dA \\ I_{Pw} &= \int_A \omega(x^2 + y^2) \, dA \end{aligned} \right\} \tag{6}$$

Also defined is the section property

$$J = \int_A 4t_P^2 \, dA \tag{7}$$

in which t_P is the perpendicular distance of a point P in the cross-section from the mid-thickness line.

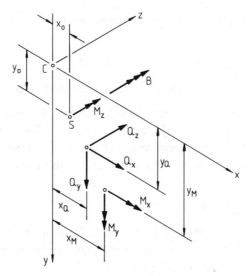

Fig. 2. End actions.

2.2 Loading

The member is acted on by end forces $Q_{x1}, Q_{y1}, Q_{z1}, Q_{x2}, Q_{y2}, Q_{z2}$, end moments $M_{x1}, M_{y1}, M_{z1}, M_{x2}, M_{y2}, M_{z2}$, and end bimoments B_1, B_2 (Fig. 2), and distributed forces per unit length q_x, q_y, q_z, distributed moments per unit length m_x, m_y, m_z, and distributed bimoment per unit length b. The forces act through points defined by x_Q, y_Q, x_q, or y_q, and the moments in planes defined by x_M, y_M, x_m, or y_m. These actions move with the beam, but remain parallel to their original directions and planes defined by the x, y, z axes of a straight, untwisted member.

2.3 Displacements, rotations, curvatures and twist

A typical cross-section of the member has an initial position defined by shear centre displacements u_i, v_i, w_{si} parallel to the x, y, z axes and corresponding rotations $\theta_{xi}, \theta_{yi}, \theta_{zi}$ about the x, y, z axes, and is warped $\omega\kappa_{zi}$ out of its plane, in which κ_{zi} is the initial twist of the member. In this position the member has an initial set of actions $\{Q_{xi}, Q_{yi}, Q_{zi}, M_{xi}, M_{yi}, M_{zi}, B_i\}$ at its ends, distributed actions $\{q_{xi}, q_{yi}, q_{zi}, m_{xi}, m_{yi}, m_{zi}, b_i\}$, and initial strains $\{\varepsilon_{Pi}, \gamma_{Pi}\}$ and stresses $\{\sigma_{Pi}, \tau_{Pi}\} = \{E\varepsilon_{Pi}, G\gamma_{Pi}\}$ at a typical point $P(x, y)$ in the cross-section.

After an increment in the set of actions, the shear centre displaces (Δu, $\Delta v, \Delta w_s$) parallel to the x, y, z axes to S_1 and the axes through S rotate $\Delta\theta_x$,

$\Delta\theta_y$, $\Delta\theta_z$, so that the total displacements and rotations shown in Fig. 3 are given by

$$\{u, v, w_s, \theta_x, \theta_y, \theta_z\} = \{u_i, v_i, w_{si}, \theta_{xi}, \theta_{yi}, \theta_{zi}\}^T$$

$$+ \{\Delta u, \Delta v, \Delta w_s, \Delta\theta_x, \Delta\theta_y, \Delta\theta_z\}^T \quad (8)$$

In addition, the cross-section warps $\omega\Delta\kappa_z$ out of its plane, so that the total warping is $\omega\kappa_z = \omega\kappa_{zi} + \omega\Delta\kappa_z$, as shown in Fig. 3. The total axis rotations $\theta_x, \theta_y, \theta_z$ can be expressed approximately in terms of the displacements u and v and the angle of twist rotation ϕ about the unrotated shear centre axis as

$$\{\theta_x, \theta_y, \theta_z\} = \{-v', u', \phi\} \quad (9)$$

in which the prime (') denotes differentiation with respect to z. These approximations ignore the effects of normal straining in the z direction, and are valid for small rotations ($\tan\theta \approx \theta$).

The matrix of direction cosines

$$[T_R] = \begin{bmatrix} L_x & L_y & L_z \\ M_x & M_y & M_z \\ N_x & N_y & N_z \end{bmatrix} \quad (10)$$

of the new shear centre axes in the original x, y, z axis system can be

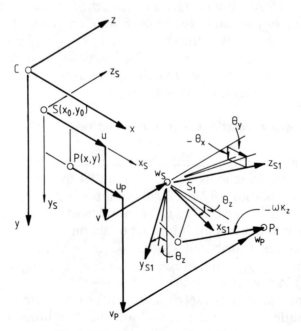

Fig. 3. Displacements and rotations.

obtained by considering a small rotation ($\sin\theta \approx \theta$, $\cos\theta \approx 1 - \frac{1}{2}\theta^2$) of $\theta = \sqrt{(\theta_x^2 + \theta_y^2 + \theta_z^2)}$ about an axis through S_1 whose direction cosines are $\{\theta_x/\theta,\ \theta_y/\theta,\ \theta_z/\theta\}$. This leads to[26-28]

$$[T_R] \approx \begin{bmatrix} (1 - \frac{1}{2}\theta_y^2 - \frac{1}{2}\theta_z^2) & (-\theta_z + \frac{1}{2}\theta_x\theta_y) & (\theta_y + \frac{1}{2}\theta_x\theta_z) \\ (\theta_z + \frac{1}{2}\theta_x\theta_y) & (1 - \frac{1}{2}\theta_x^2 - \frac{1}{2}\theta_z^2) & (-\theta_x + \frac{1}{2}\theta_y\theta_z) \\ (-\theta_y + \frac{1}{2}\theta_x\theta_z) & (\theta_x + \frac{1}{2}\theta_y\theta_z) & (1 - \frac{1}{2}\theta_x^2 - \frac{1}{2}\theta_y^2) \end{bmatrix} \quad (11)$$

Thus, after substituting eqn (9),

$$[T_R] = \begin{bmatrix} (1 - \frac{1}{2}u'^2 - \frac{1}{2}\phi^2) & (-\phi - \frac{1}{2}u'v') & (u' - \frac{1}{2}v'\phi) \\ (\phi - \frac{1}{2}u'v') & (1 - \frac{1}{2}v'^2 - \frac{1}{2}\phi^2) & (v' + \frac{1}{2}u'\phi) \\ (-u' - \frac{1}{2}v'\phi) & (-v' + \frac{1}{2}u'\phi) & (1 - \frac{1}{2}u'^2 - \frac{1}{2}v'^2) \end{bmatrix} \quad (12)$$

It can be seen that $[T_R]$ consists of an antisymmetric first-order component with linear off-diagonal terms involving u', v', and ϕ, and a symmetric second-order component with quadratic off-diagonal terms involving products of u', v', and ϕ.

This result may also be obtained approximately by considering successive rotations about the x, y, z axes corresponding to

$$[T_x] = \begin{bmatrix} 1 & 0 & 0 \\ 0 & \cos\theta_x & -\sin\theta_x \\ 0 & \sin\theta_x & \cos\theta_x \end{bmatrix} \quad (13)$$

$$[T_y] = \begin{bmatrix} \cos\theta_y & 0 & \sin\theta_y \\ 0 & 1 & 0 \\ -\sin\theta_y & 0 & \cos\theta_y \end{bmatrix} \quad (14)$$

$$[T_z] = \begin{bmatrix} \cos\theta_z & -\sin\theta_z & 0 \\ \sin\theta_z & \cos\theta_z & 0 \\ 0 & 0 & 1 \end{bmatrix} \quad (15)$$

Because different sequences of rotations about the x, y, z axes lead to different final results, an average of all possible sequences is assumed, so that

$$[T_R] = \frac{1}{6}([T_x][T_y][T_z] + [T_y][T_z][T_x] + [T_z][T_x][T_y]$$
$$+ [T_z][T_y][T_x] + [T_y][T_x][T_z] + [T_x][T_z][T_y]) \quad (16)$$

which leads to eqn (12).

The curvatures κ_x, κ_y of the deflected shear centre axis and the twist κ_z of the rotated cross-section axes can be obtained[29] from

$$
\begin{Bmatrix} \kappa_x \\ \kappa_y \\ \kappa_z \end{Bmatrix} = \begin{Bmatrix} L'_y L_z + M'_y M_z + N'_y N_z \\ L'_z L_x + M'_z M_x + N'_z N_x \\ L'_x L_y + M'_x M_y + N'_x N_y \end{Bmatrix} \tag{17}
$$

whence

$$
\begin{Bmatrix} \kappa_x \\ \kappa_y \\ \kappa_z \end{Bmatrix} = \begin{Bmatrix} -v'' + \tfrac{1}{2}(u''\phi - u'\phi') \\ u'' + \tfrac{1}{2}(v''\phi - v'\phi') \\ \phi' + \tfrac{1}{2}(u''v' - u'v'') \end{Bmatrix} \tag{18}
$$

The total displacements (u_P, v_P, w_P) of the general point P shown in Fig. 3 are related to the shear centre displacements (u, v, w_s), the axis rotations $(-v', u', \phi)$ and the section warping $\omega\kappa_z$ through

$$
\begin{Bmatrix} u_P \\ v_P \\ w_P \end{Bmatrix} = -\begin{Bmatrix} x - x_0 \\ y - y_0 \\ 0 \end{Bmatrix} + \begin{Bmatrix} u \\ v \\ w_s \end{Bmatrix} + [T_R] \begin{Bmatrix} x - x_0 \\ y - y_0 \\ -\omega\kappa_z \end{Bmatrix} \tag{19}
$$

These may be expressed as linear and quadratic components through

$$
\begin{Bmatrix} u_P \\ v_P \\ w_P \end{Bmatrix} = \begin{Bmatrix} u_L \\ v_L \\ w_L \end{Bmatrix} + \begin{Bmatrix} u_Q \\ v_Q \\ w_Q \end{Bmatrix} \tag{20}
$$

in which

$$
\begin{Bmatrix} u_L \\ v_L \\ w_L \end{Bmatrix} = \begin{Bmatrix} u - (y - y_0)\phi \\ v + (x - x_0)\phi \\ w - xu' - yv' - \omega\phi' \end{Bmatrix} \tag{21}
$$

and

$$
\begin{aligned}
u_Q &= -\tfrac{1}{2}(x - x_0)(u'^2 + \phi^2) - \tfrac{1}{2}(y - y_0)u'v' - \omega u'\phi' \\
v_Q &= -\tfrac{1}{2}(x - x_0)u'v' - \tfrac{1}{2}(y - y_0)(v'^2 + \phi^2) - \omega v'\phi' \\
w_Q &= -\tfrac{1}{2}xv'\phi + \tfrac{1}{2}yu'\phi - \tfrac{1}{2}\omega(u''v' - u'v'')
\end{aligned} \tag{22}
$$

which makes use of the relationship

$$w_s = w - x_0(u' + \tfrac{1}{2}v'\phi) - y_0(v' - \tfrac{1}{2}u'\phi) \tag{23}$$

between the z direction displacements w_s and w of the shear centre and centroid.

2.4 Longitudinal normal strains

The longitudinal normal strain ε_P of an elemental length δz from P parallel to the z axis is given by

$$\varepsilon_P = \varepsilon_{P\delta} - \varepsilon_{P\delta i} + \varepsilon_{Pi} \tag{24}$$

in which $\varepsilon_{P\delta}$ is the strain associated with the total deformations (u, v, w, ϕ) and $\varepsilon_{P\delta i}$ is the strain associated with the initial deformations (u_i, v_i, w_i, ϕ_i). The strain component $\varepsilon_{P\delta}$ may be defined in terms of the rates of change of the deflections u_P, v_P, w_P, along the elements as shown in Fig. 4. The new elemental length is given by

$$(1 + \varepsilon_{P\delta})\delta z = \sqrt{\{(\delta z + w_P'\delta z)^2 + (u_P'\delta z)^2 + (v_P'\delta z)^2\}} \tag{25}$$

so that

$$\varepsilon_{P\delta} \approx w_P' + \tfrac{1}{2}(u_P'^2 + v_P'^2) \tag{26}$$

This 'engineering' definition of strain is based on the original length of the element instead of the current length used in true strain definitions, and omits a small term $\tfrac{1}{2}w_P'^2$ sometimes included in other strain definitions.[30]

Substituting eqns (20)–(22) into eqn (26) and rearranging allows the strain $\varepsilon_{P\delta}$ to be expressed by linear and quadratic components so that

$$\varepsilon_{P\delta} = \varepsilon_{PL} + \varepsilon_{PQ} \tag{27}$$

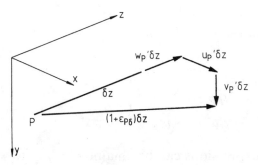

Fig. 4. Longitudinal normal strain.

in which

$$\left\{ \begin{array}{c} \varepsilon_{PL} \\ \varepsilon_{PQ} \end{array} \right\} = \left\{ \begin{array}{c} w'_L \\ w'_Q + \frac{1}{2}(u'^2_L + v'^2_L) \end{array} \right\} \tag{28}$$

so that

$$\varepsilon_{PL} = w' - xu'' - yv'' - \omega\phi'' \tag{29}$$

and

$$\begin{aligned} \varepsilon_{PQ} = {} & \tfrac{1}{2}[u'^2 + v'^2 + (x_0^2 + y_0^2)\phi'^2 - 2x_0v'\phi' + 2y_0u'\phi'] \\ & - \tfrac{1}{2}x(v''\phi - v'\phi' + 2x_0\phi'^2) + \tfrac{1}{2}y(u''\phi - u'\phi' - 2y_0\phi'^2) \\ & - \tfrac{1}{2}\omega(u''v' - u'v'')' + \tfrac{1}{2}(x^2 + y^2)\phi'^2 \end{aligned} \tag{30}$$

Corresponding expressions can be obtained for $\varepsilon_{P\delta i}$ by substituting (u_i, v_i, w_i, ϕ_i) for (u, v, w, ϕ).

2.5 Shear strains

Shear strains in the mid-thickness surface of the thin-walled section are neglected.[5] The shear strain γ_P away from the mid-thickness surface is given by

$$\gamma_P = \gamma_{P\delta} - \gamma_{P\delta i} + \gamma_{Pi} \tag{31}$$

in which $\gamma_{P\delta}$ is the uniform torsion shear strain[5] associated with the total twist κ_z, and $\gamma_{P\delta i}$ is the strain associated with the initial twist κ_{zi}. The uniform torsion shear strain component $\gamma_{P\delta}$ varies with the distance t_P from the mid-thickness surface according to

$$\gamma_{P\delta} = -2t_P\kappa_z \tag{32}$$

so that

$$\gamma_{P\delta} = \gamma_{PL} + \gamma_{PQ} \tag{33}$$

in which

$$\left\{ \begin{array}{c} \gamma_{PL} \\ \gamma_{PQ} \end{array} \right\} = \left\{ \begin{array}{c} -2t_P\phi' \\ -t_P(u''v' - u'v'') \end{array} \right\} \tag{34}$$

Corresponding expressions can be obtained for $\gamma_{P\delta i}$ by substituting (u_i, v_i, ϕ_i) for (u, v, ϕ).

2.6 Strain–displacement relationships

The normal and shear strains given by eqns (29), (30) and (34) can be grouped as

$$\{\varepsilon_P, \gamma_P\}^T = [S]\{\varepsilon - \varepsilon_{\delta i}\} + \{\varepsilon_{Pi}, \gamma_{Pi}\}^T \tag{35}$$

in which

$$\{\varepsilon\} = \begin{Bmatrix} w' \\ -u'' \\ -v'' \\ -\phi'' \\ 0 \\ -\phi' \end{Bmatrix} + \begin{Bmatrix} \frac{1}{2}[u'^2 + v'^2 + (x_0^2 + y_0^2)\phi'^2 - 2x_0v'\phi' + 2y_0u'\phi'] \\ -\frac{1}{2}(v''\phi - v'\phi' + 2x_0\phi'^2) \\ \frac{1}{2}(u''\phi - u'\phi' - 2y_0\phi'^2) \\ -\frac{1}{2}(u''v' - u'v'')' \\ \frac{1}{2}\phi'^2 \\ -\frac{1}{2}(u''v' - u'v'') \end{Bmatrix} \tag{36}$$

$\{\varepsilon_{\delta i}\}$ is given by a corresponding expression with (u_i, v_i, w_i, ϕ_i) substituted for (u, v, w, ϕ), and

$$[S] = \begin{bmatrix} 1 & x & y & \omega & (x^2 + y^2) & 0 \\ 0 & 0 & 0 & 0 & 0 & 2t_P \end{bmatrix} \tag{37}$$

The first component of the generalised strains $\{\varepsilon\}$ consists of linear terms associated with axial straining (w'), curvatures $(-u'', -v'')$ about the y,x axes, a term $(-\phi'')$ associated with warping strains which might be called a 'twistature', and twisting $(-\phi')$. It includes a zero term which is associated with a non-zero quadratic term $\frac{1}{2}\phi'^2$. The second component of $\{\varepsilon\}$ consists of quadratic terms.

Equation (36) can be expressed as

$$\{\varepsilon\} = [B_L + B_Q]\{\Phi\} \tag{38}$$

in which

$$\{\Phi\} = \{u', \quad u'', \quad u''', \quad v', \quad v'', \quad v''', \quad w' \quad \phi, \quad \phi', \quad \phi''\}^T \tag{39}$$

$$[B_L] = \begin{bmatrix} 0 & 0 & 0 & 0 & 0 & 0 & 1 & 0 & 0 & 0 \\ 0 & -1 & 0 & 0 & 0 & 0 & 0 & 0 & 0 & 0 \\ 0 & 0 & 0 & 0 & -1 & 0 & 0 & 0 & 0 & 0 \\ 0 & 0 & 0 & 0 & 0 & 0 & 0 & 0 & 0 & -1 \\ 0 & 0 & 0 & 0 & 0 & 0 & 0 & 0 & 0 & 0 \\ 0 & 0 & 0 & 0 & 0 & 0 & 0 & 0 & -1 & 0 \end{bmatrix} \tag{40}$$

$$[B_Q] = \tfrac{1}{2} \begin{bmatrix} u' + y_0\phi' & 0 & 0 & v' - x_0\phi' & 0 & 0 & 0 & 0 & \begin{matrix}(x_0^2 + y_0^2)\phi' \\ -x_0v' + y_0u'\end{matrix} & 0 \\ 0 & 0 & 0 & \tfrac{1}{2}\phi' & -\tfrac{1}{2}\phi & 0 & 0 & -\tfrac{1}{2}v'' & -2x_0\phi' + \tfrac{1}{2}v' & 0 \\ -\tfrac{1}{2}\phi' & \tfrac{1}{2}\phi & 0 & 0 & 0 & 0 & 0 & \tfrac{1}{2}u'' & -2y_0\phi' - \tfrac{1}{2}u' & 0 \\ \tfrac{1}{2}v''' & 0 & -\tfrac{1}{2}v' & -\tfrac{1}{2}u''' & 0 & \tfrac{1}{2}u' & 0 & 0 & 0 & 0 \\ 0 & 0 & 0 & 0 & 0 & 0 & 0 & 0 & \phi' & 0 \\ \tfrac{1}{2}v'' & -\tfrac{1}{2}v' & 0 & -\tfrac{1}{2}u'' & \tfrac{1}{2}u' & 0 & 0 & 0 & 0 & 0 \end{bmatrix} \quad (41)$$

It can be shown[17] that

$$[\Delta B_Q]\,\{\Phi\} \equiv [B_Q]\,\{\Delta\Phi\} \tag{42}$$

in which Δ is used to indicate a small change in the quantity following.

2.7 Stresses and stress resultants

The longitudinal normal and shear stresses σ_P, τ_P at a point P in the cross-section may be obtained from the strains ε_P, γ_P using

$$\{\sigma_P, \tau_P\}^{\mathrm{T}} = [E]\,\{\varepsilon_P, \gamma_P\}^{\mathrm{T}} \tag{43}$$

and

$$[E] = \begin{bmatrix} E & 0 \\ 0 & G \end{bmatrix} \tag{44}$$

in which E, G are the moduli of elasticity.

The generalised stress resultants $\{\sigma\}$ corresponding to the generalised strains $\{\varepsilon\}$ given by eqn (36) may be defined by

$$\{\mathrm{d}\varepsilon\}^{\mathrm{T}}\{\sigma\} = \int_A \{\mathrm{d}\varepsilon_P, \mathrm{d}\gamma_P\}\,\{\sigma_P, \tau_P\}^{\mathrm{T}}\,\mathrm{d}A \tag{45}$$

Substituting eqns (35) and (43) leads to

$$\{\sigma\} = [D]\,\{\varepsilon - \varepsilon_{\delta \mathrm{i}}\} + \{\sigma_{\sigma \mathrm{i}}\} \tag{46}$$

in which

$$[D] = \int_A [S]^{\mathrm{T}}\,[E]\,[S]\,\mathrm{d}A \tag{47}$$

and

$$\{\sigma_{\sigma \mathrm{i}}\} = \int_A [S]^{\mathrm{T}}\,\{\sigma_{P\mathrm{i}}, \tau_{P\mathrm{i}}\}^{\mathrm{T}}\,\mathrm{d}A \tag{48}$$

The generalised stresses $\{\sigma\} = \{\sigma_1, \sigma_2, \sigma_3, \sigma_4, \sigma_5, \sigma_6\}^{\mathrm{T}}$ have linear and quadratic components, just as do the generalised strains $\{\varepsilon\}$. The linear terms are discussed in Section 3, and shown to correspond to an axial force (σ_1), bending moments (σ_2, σ_3) about the y,x axes, a bimoment (σ_4), a stress resultant (σ_5) which might be called a 'Wagner', and a uniform torque (σ_6).

If the integration of eqn (47) is carried out, then the tangent matrix $[D]$ can be expressed as

$$[D] = \begin{bmatrix} EA & 0 & 0 & 0 & EI_P & 0 \\ 0 & EI_y & 0 & 0 & EI_{Py} & 0 \\ 0 & 0 & EI_x & 0 & EI_{Px} & 0 \\ 0 & 0 & 0 & EI_w & EI_{Pw} & 0 \\ EI_P & EI_{Py} & EI_{Px} & EI_{Pw} & EI_{PP} & 0 \\ 0 & 0 & 0 & 0 & 0 & GJ \end{bmatrix} \tag{49}$$

in which $A, I_y, I_x, I_w, I_P, I_{Py}, I_{Px}, I_{Pw}, I_{PP}$, and J are the section properties defined in Section 2.1.

2.8 Total potential

The total potential[31] of a strained length L of a member and its loading system can be expressed as

$$U_T = U + W \tag{50}$$

in which U is the strain energy stored in the volume V of the member and W is the potential energy of the loading system measured from the straight untwisted position.

The strain energy may be expressed as

$$U = \tfrac{1}{2} \int_V \{\varepsilon_P, \gamma_P\} \{\sigma_P, \tau_P\}^T \, dV \tag{51}$$

and when eqns (35) and (43) are substituted, this becomes

$$U = \tfrac{1}{2} \int_V (\{\varepsilon_{Pi}, \gamma_{Pi}\} + \{\varepsilon - \varepsilon_{\delta i}\}^T [S]^T)$$
$$\times ([E] [S] \{\varepsilon - \varepsilon_{\delta i}\} + \{\sigma_{Pi}, \tau_{Pi}\}^T) \, dV \tag{52}$$

which can be expressed as

$$U = U_{\sigma\varepsilon i} + \int_0^L \{\varepsilon - \varepsilon_{\delta i}\}^T \{\sigma_{\sigma i}\} \, dz + \tfrac{1}{2} \int_0^L \{\varepsilon - \varepsilon_{\delta i}\}^T [D] \{\varepsilon - \varepsilon_{\delta i}\} \, dz \tag{53}$$

in which

$$U_{\sigma\varepsilon i} = \tfrac{1}{2} \int_V \{\varepsilon_{Pi}, \gamma_{Pi}\} \{\sigma_{Pi}, \tau_{Pi}\}^T \, dV \tag{54}$$

The potential energy may be expressed as

$$W = -\int_0^L \{u\}^T \{q\} \, dz - \sum_{1,2} \{u\}^T \{Q\} \tag{55}$$

in which

$$\{q\} = \{q_x, q_y, q_z, m_x, m_y, m_z, b\}^T \tag{56}$$

$$\{Q\} = \{Q_x, Q_y, Q_z, M_x, M_y, M_z, B\}^T \tag{57}$$

and

$$\{u\} = \{u_L\} + \{u_Q\} \tag{58}$$

where

$$\{u_L\} = \left\{ \begin{array}{c} u - (y - y_0)\phi \\ v + (x - x_0)\phi \\ w - xu' - yv' - \omega\phi' \\ -v' - (x - x_0)\phi' \\ u' - (y - y_0)\phi' \\ \phi \\ \phi' \end{array} \right\} \tag{59}$$

and

$$\{u_Q\} = \frac{1}{2} \left\{ \begin{array}{c} -(x - x_0)(u'^2 + \phi^2) - (y - y_0)u'v' - 2\omega u'\phi' \\ -(y - y_0)(v'^2 + \phi^2) - (x - x_0)u'v' - 2\omega v'\phi' \\ -xv'\phi + yu'\phi - \omega(u''v' - u'v'') \\ (y - y_0)(v'^2 + \phi^2)' + (x - x_0)(u'v')' + 2\omega(v'\phi')' \\ -(x - x_0)(u'^2 + \phi^2)' - (y - y_0)(u'v')' - 2\omega(u'\phi')' \\ 0 \\ (u''v' - u'v'') \end{array} \right\} \tag{60}$$

in which the x,y coordinates are those defining the line or plane of action of the corresponding force or moment.

It can be shown that if $\{u_L\}$, $\{u_Q\}$ are expressed as

$$\{u_L\} = [A_L]\{\theta\} \tag{61}$$

and

$$\{u_Q\} = [A_Q]\{\theta\} \tag{62}$$

in which

$$\{\theta\} = \{u, u', u'', v, v', v'', w, \phi, \phi', \phi''\}^T \tag{63}$$

then

$$[\Delta A_Q]\{\theta\} \equiv [A_Q]\{\Delta\theta\} \tag{64}$$

This result is similar to that of eqn (42).

2.9 Virtual displacements and equilibrium

Suppose the member undergoes a set of virtual displacements defined by $\{du, dv, dw, d\phi\}$ from an equilibrium position defined by $\{u, v, w, \phi\}$ while under the action of constant forces and moments. For equilibrium of the position defined by $\{u, v, w, \phi\}$, the principle of virtual work[31] requires that

$$dU_T = 0 \tag{65}$$

for all sets of virtual displacements $\{du, dv, dw, d\phi\}$.

By using eqns (55), (58), (61), and (62), the increment dW can be expressed as

$$dW = -\int_0^L \{du\}^T\{q\}\, dz - \sum_{1,2} \{du\}^T\{Q\} \tag{66}$$

in which

$$\{du\} = [A_L + 2A_Q]\{d\theta\} \tag{67}$$

which makes use of eqn (64). By using eqns (46) and (53), the increment dU can be expressed as

$$dU = \int_0^L \{d\varepsilon\}^T\{\sigma\}\, dz \tag{68}$$

in which

$$\{d\varepsilon\} = [B_L + 2B_Q]\{d\Phi\} \tag{69}$$

which makes use of eqns (38) and (42). Thus eqn (65) becomes

$$\int_0^L (\{d\varepsilon\}^T\{\sigma\} - \{du\}^T\{q\})\, dz - \sum_{1,2} \{du\}^T\{Q\} = 0 \tag{70}$$

It is now assumed that the displacements and twist rotation u, v, w, ϕ can be expressed in the form of

$$\{u, v, w, \phi\}^T = [N]\{\delta\} \tag{71}$$

in which

$$\{\delta\} = \{u_1, u_2, u_1', u_2', v_1, v_2, v_1', v_2', w_1, w_2, \phi_1, \phi_2, \phi_1', \phi_2'\}^T \tag{72}$$

and the elements of $[N]$ are functions of z. In this case $\{\Phi\}, \{\theta\}, \{\theta_1^T, \theta_2^T\}^T$ can be expressed as

$$\{\Phi\} = [N_\sigma]\{\delta\} \tag{73}$$

$$\{\theta\} = [N_q]\{\delta\} \tag{74}$$

$$\{\theta_1^T, \theta_2^T\}^T = [N_Q]\{\delta\} \tag{75}$$

Substituting these relationships and eqns (67) and (69) allows eqn (70) to be expressed as

$$\{d\delta\}^T \left(\int_0^L ([N_\sigma]^T [B_L + 2B_Q]^T \{\sigma\} - [N_q]^T [A_L + 2A_Q]^T \{q\}) \, dz \right.$$

$$\left. - [N_Q]^T [A_{LQ} + 2A_{QQ}]^T \{Q_1^T, Q_2^T\}^T \right) = 0 \tag{76}$$

Since this must hold for all sets of virtual displacements defined by $\{d\delta\}$, then

$$\int_0^L ([N_\sigma]^T [B_L + 2B_Q]^T \{\sigma\} - [N_q]^T [A_L + 2A_Q]^T \{q\}) \, dz$$

$$- [N_Q]^T [A_{LQ} + 2A_{QQ}]^T \{Q_1^T, Q_2^T\}^T = \{0\} \tag{77}$$

which are the non-linear equilibrium equations.

2.10 Neutral equilibrium

For the stability of an equilibrium position defined by $\{u, v, w, \phi\}$ to be neutral,[31]

$$d^2 U_T = 0 \tag{78}$$

for a set of small buckling displacements $\{u_b, v_b, w_b, \phi_b\} = \{du, dv, dw, d\phi\}$ which take place from the equilibrium position under constant forces and moments. In this case, the adjacent buckled position $\{u + u_b, v + v_b, w + w_b, \phi + \phi_b\}$ is also one of equilibrium.

The neutral equilibrium condition of eqn (78) is equivalent to

$$\int_0^L (\{d\varepsilon\}^T \{d\sigma\} + \{d^2\varepsilon\}^T \{\sigma\} - \{d^2u\}^T \{q\}) \, dz$$

$$- \sum_{1,2} \{d^2u\}^T \{Q\} = 0 \tag{79}$$

in which

$$\left.\begin{array}{l} \{d^2\varepsilon\} = [2dB_Q] \{d\Phi\} \\ \{d^2u\} = [2dA_Q] \{d\theta\} \end{array}\right\} \tag{80}$$

Using eqns (73)–(75) with eqns (42), (46) and (64) leads to

$$\{d\delta\}^T [K_T] \{d\delta\} = 0 \tag{81}$$

or

$$\{\delta_b\}^T [K_T] \{\delta_b\} = 0 \tag{82}$$

in which

$$[K_T] = \int_0^L ([N_\sigma]^T ([B_L + 2B_Q]^T [D] [B_L + 2B_Q] + [M_\sigma]) [N_\sigma]$$

$$- [N_q]^T [M_q] [N_q]) \, dz - [N_Q]^T [M_Q] [N_Q] \tag{83}$$

This makes use of the identities

$$\left.\begin{array}{l} [2dB_Q]^T \{\sigma\} \equiv [M_\sigma] \{d\Phi\} \\ [2dA_Q]^T \{q\} \equiv [M_q] \{d\theta\} \\ [2dA_{QQ}]^T \{Q_1^T, Q_2^T\}^T \equiv [M_Q] \{d\theta_1^T, d\theta_2^T\}^T \end{array}\right\} \tag{84}$$

in which the non-zero upper triangle elements of the symmetric matrices $[M_\sigma]$ and $[M_q]$ are given by

$$\left.\begin{array}{rl} M_{\sigma 11} = & M_{\sigma 44} = \sigma_1 \\ M_{\sigma 15} = & -M_{\sigma 24} = \tfrac{1}{2}\sigma_6 \\ M_{\sigma 16} = & -M_{\sigma 34} = \tfrac{1}{2}\sigma_4 \\ M_{\sigma 19} = & \sigma_1 y_0 - \tfrac{1}{2}\sigma_3 \\ M_{\sigma 28} = & \tfrac{1}{2}\sigma_3 \\ M_{\sigma 49} = & -\sigma_1 x_0 + \tfrac{1}{2}\sigma_2 \\ M_{\sigma 58} = & -\tfrac{1}{2}\sigma_2 \\ M_{\sigma 99} = & \sigma_1(x_0^2 + y_0^2) - 2\sigma_2 x_0 - 2\sigma_3 y_0 + \sigma_5 \end{array}\right\} \tag{85}$$

where $\sigma_1, \sigma_2, \sigma_3, \sigma_4, \sigma_5, \sigma_6$ are the elements of $\{\sigma\}$,

$$
\begin{aligned}
M_{q22} &= -q_x(x - x_0) \\
M_{q23} &= -m_y(x - x_0) \\
M_{q25} &= -\tfrac{1}{2}q_x(y - y_0) - \tfrac{1}{2}q_y(x - x_0) \\
M_{q26} &= \tfrac{1}{2}q_z\omega + \tfrac{1}{2}m_x(x - x_0) - \tfrac{1}{2}m_y(y - y_0) - \tfrac{1}{2}b \\
M_{q28} &= \tfrac{1}{2}q_z y \\
M_{q29} &= -q_x\omega \\
M_{q210} &= M_{q39} = -m_y\omega \\
M_{q35} &= -\tfrac{1}{2}q_z\omega + \tfrac{1}{2}m_x(x - x_0) - \tfrac{1}{2}m_y(y - y_0) + \tfrac{1}{2}b \\
M_{q55} &= -q_y(y - y_0) \\
M_{q56} &= m_x(y - y_0) \\
M_{q58} &= -\tfrac{1}{2}q_z x \\
M_{q59} &= -q_y\omega \\
M_{q510} &= M_{q69} = m_x\omega \\
M_{q88} &= -q_x(x - x_0) - q_y(y - y_0) \\
M_{q89} &= m_x(y - y_0) - m_y(x - x_0)
\end{aligned}
\tag{86}
$$

and

$$
[M_Q] = \begin{bmatrix} M_{Q1} & 0 \\ 0 & M_{Q2} \end{bmatrix}
\tag{87}
$$

in which the non-zero upper triangle elements of $[M_{Q1}]$ and $[M_{Q2}]$ are given by equations similar to eqn (86), but with the elements of $\{Q\}$ substituted for the corresponding elements of $\{q\}$.

The neutral equilibrium condition of eqn (82) is satisfied when

$$
|K_T| = 0
\tag{88}
$$

The load sets which satisfy this condition are the buckling load sets.

Because the adjacent buckled position is one of equilibrium, the conditions for neutral equilibrium may also be obtained by using virtual work to analyse the equilibrium of the buckled position. Thus if $\{du, dv, dw, d\phi\}$ are virtual displacements from the buckled position $\{u + u_b, v + v_b, w + w_b, \phi + \phi_b\}$, then

$$
\{d\varepsilon\} = [B_L + 2B_Q + 2B_{Qb}][N_\sigma]\{d\delta\}
\tag{89}
$$

and

$$\{\sigma_b\} = \{\sigma\} + [D][B_L + 2B_Q][N_\sigma]\{\delta_b\} \tag{90}$$

Substituting into the virtual work equilibrium condition of eqn (70) leads to

$$
\begin{aligned}
\{d\delta\}^T \Bigg(&\int_0^L ([N_\sigma]^T[B_L + 2B_Q]\{\sigma\} - [N_q]^T[A_L + 2A_Q]^T\{q\})\,dz \\
&- [N_Q]^T[A_{LQ} + 2A_{QQ}]^T\{Q_1^T, Q_2^T\}^T \\
&+ \int_0^L [N_\sigma]^T([2B_{Qb}]^T\{\sigma\} + [B_L + 2B_Q]^T[D][B_L + 2B_Q][N_\sigma]\{\delta_b\})\,dz \\
&- \int_0^L [N_q]^T[M_q][N_q]\{\delta_b\}\,dz - [N_Q]^T[M_Q][N_Q]\{\delta_b\} \Bigg) = 0 \tag{91}
\end{aligned}
$$

If eqn (77) for the equilibrium of the pre-buckled position is substituted, then this simplifies to

$$\{d\delta\}^T[K_T]\{\delta_b\} = 0 \tag{92}$$

and since this must hold for all sets of virtual displacements $\{d\delta\}$ then

$$[K_T]\{\delta_b\} = \{0\} \tag{93}$$

which are the buckling equilibrium equations.

3 LINEAR BEHAVIOUR THEORY

The simplest approximation to the behaviour of the thin-walled member is given by the linear theory, according to which the deformations $\{u, v, w, \phi\}$ are always proportional to the loads. This theory is obtained by linearising the strain–displacement relationships of eqn (38), by ignoring $[B_Q]$ in comparison to $[B_L]$.

In this case the generalised stresses $\{\sigma\}$ are linearised to

$$
\{\sigma\} =
\begin{Bmatrix}
EAw' \\
-EI_y u'' \\
-EI_x v'' \\
-EI_w \phi'' \\
\sigma_5 \\
-GJ\phi'
\end{Bmatrix}
+
\begin{Bmatrix}
EAw'_i \\
-EI_y u''_i \\
-EI_x v''_i \\
-EI_w \phi''_i \\
\sigma_{5i} \\
-GJ\phi'_i
\end{Bmatrix}
+
\begin{Bmatrix}
\int_A \sigma_{Pi}\,dA \\
\int_A x\sigma_{Pi}\,dA \\
\int_A y\sigma_{Pi}\,dA \\
\int_A \omega\sigma_{Pi}\,dA \\
\int_A (x^2 + y^2)\sigma_{Pi}\,dA \\
\int_A 2t_P \tau_{Pi}\,dA
\end{Bmatrix}
\tag{94}
$$

in which

$$\sigma_5 = EI_P w' - EI_{P_y} u'' - EI_{P_x} v'' - EI_{P_w} \phi'' \tag{95}$$

and

$$\sigma_{5i} = EI_P w_i' - EI_{P_y} u_i'' - EI_{P_x} v_i'' - EI_{P_w} \phi_i'' \tag{96}$$

The first component of the linearised stresses $\{\sigma\}$ consists of terms corresponding to the stress resultants of an axial force ($\sigma_1 = EAw'$), bending moments ($\sigma_2 = -EI_y u''$, $\sigma_3 = -EI_x v''$) about the y,x axes, a bimoment ($\sigma_4 = -EI_w \phi''$), a stress resultant σ_5 which might be called a 'Wagner', and a uniform torque ($\sigma_6 = -GJ\phi'$). Although the 'Wagner' stress resultant σ_5 may exist, it plays no part in the linear behaviour theory, as it does not appear in either the equilibrium equations or the stress equations.

The linearising of eqn (38) by ignoring $[B_Q]$ in comparison to $[B_L]$ leads to other linearisations in which $[A_Q]$ in eqn (58) is ignored in comparison to $[A_L]$, and $[A_{QQ}]$ in comparison to $[A_{LQ}]$. With these linearisations, the total potential U_T (eqn (50)) becomes quadratic in the displacements (u, v, w, ϕ), so that the virtual work equilibrium condition of eqn (65) becomes linear. Thus the non-linear equilibrium condition of eqn (77) simplifies to

$$\int_0^L ([N_\sigma]^T [B_L]^T \{\sigma\} - [N_q]^T [A_L]^T \{q\}) \, dz$$

$$- [N_Q]^T [A_{LQ}]^T \{Q_1^T, Q_2^T\}^T = \{0\} \tag{97}$$

It should be noted that the linearising of eqn (38) causes the left-hand side of the neutral equilibrium condition of eqn (78) to become a non-zero constant, so that this condition cannot be satisfied.

In the special case where the member is initially straight and untwisted and free from residual stresses, then the equilibrium condition of eqn (70), which corresponds to eqn (77) from which eqn (97) was derived, simplifies to

$$\int_0^L (dw' \, EAw' + du'' \, EI_y u'' + dv'' \, EI_x v'' + d\phi'' \, EI_w \phi'' + d\phi' \, GJ\phi'$$

$$- du \, q_x - dv \, q_y - dw \, q_z + dv' \, m_x - du' \, m_y - d\phi \, m_z - d\phi' \, b) \, dz$$

$$- \sum_{1,2} (du \, Q_x + dv \, Q_y + dw \, Q_z - dv' \, M_x + du' \, M_y + d\phi \, M_z + d\phi' \, B)$$

$$= 0 \tag{98}$$

If this is integrated by parts, it can be expressed as

$$\int_0^L [\mathrm{d}u\,\{(EI_yu'')'' - q_x + m_y'\} + \mathrm{d}v\{(EI_xv'')'' - q_y - m_x'\}$$

$$+ \mathrm{d}w\{-(EAw')' - q_z\} + \mathrm{d}\phi\{(EI_w\phi'')'' - (GJ\phi')' - m_z + b'\}]\,\mathrm{d}z$$
$$+ [\{\mathrm{d}u'\,EI_yu'' - \mathrm{d}u(EI_yu'')' - \mathrm{d}u\,m_y\}$$
$$+ \{\mathrm{d}v'\,EI_xv'' - \mathrm{d}v(EI_xv'')' - \mathrm{d}v\,m_x\} + (\mathrm{d}w\,EAw')$$
$$+ \{\mathrm{d}\phi'\,EI_w\phi'' - \mathrm{d}\phi(EI_w\phi'')' + \mathrm{d}\phi\,GJ\phi' - \mathrm{d}\phi\,b\}]_0^L$$

$$- \sum_{1,2}(\mathrm{d}u\,Q_x + \mathrm{d}v\,Q_y + \mathrm{d}w\,Q_z - \mathrm{d}v'\,M_x + \mathrm{d}u'\,M_y + \mathrm{d}\phi\,M_z + \mathrm{d}\phi'\,B)$$

$$= 0 \qquad\qquad (99)$$

Since this must hold for all admissible sets $\{\mathrm{d}u, \mathrm{d}v, \mathrm{d}w, \mathrm{d}\phi\}$ of virtual displacements, then

$$(EI_yu'')'' \qquad\qquad = q_x - m_y' \qquad\qquad (100)$$

$$(EI_xv'')'' \qquad\qquad = q_y + m_x' \qquad\qquad (101)$$

$$-(EAw')' \qquad\qquad = q_z \qquad\qquad (102)$$

$$(EI_w\phi'')'' - (GJ\phi')' = m_z - b' \qquad\qquad (103)$$

These are the linear differential equilibrium equations for bending about the y and x axes, for axial loading and for torsion respectively. Boundary conditions for these equations can also be obtained from eqn (99). The linear nature of these equations demonstrates that the deflections u, v, w and twist rotations ϕ are proportional to the applied loads $\{q\}$ and $\{Q\}$, as shown in Fig. 5. The left-hand sides of these equations include all of the stress resultants $\{\sigma\}$ except the 'Wagner' σ_5.

The stress distribution in the member can be determined from eqns (35), (36) and (43) as

$$\sigma_P = \frac{(EAw')}{A} + \frac{(-EI_yu'')x}{I_y} + \frac{(-EI_xv'')y}{I_x} + \frac{(-EI_w\phi'')\omega}{I_w} \qquad (104)$$

$$\tau_P = (-GJ\phi')2t_P/J \qquad\qquad (105)$$

Again, all of the stress resultants $\{\sigma\}$ except the 'Wagner' σ_5 are included in these equations.

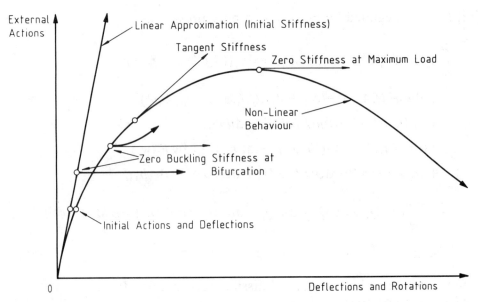

Fig. 5. Non-linear behaviour.

4 BIFURCATION BUCKLING

4.1 General

A special case of neutral equilibrium may arise when the deformations (u, v, w, ϕ) prior to the neutral equilibrium position are independent of the additional deformations (u_b, v_b, w_b, ϕ_b) which initiate at buckling, as shown in Fig. 5. In this case, the equilibrium path is said to bifurcate from the non-linear pre-buckling path to the buckling path, which is initially horizontal. The independence of the pre-buckling and buckling deformations may lead to considerable simplifications, both in the pre-buckling analysis and in the buckling tangent stiffness $[K_T]$ given by eqn (83).

In the classical theories of Timoshenko[7] and Vlasov[5] for bifurcation buckling, further simplifications are made. Firstly, the effects of the buckling deflections (u_b, v_b, w_b, ϕ_b) on both $[B_Q]$ and $\{\sigma\}$ used in eqn (83) are ignored, so that the buckling tangent stiffness matrix becomes independent of the magnitudes of these deformations. This simplification allows the loads at the initiation of buckling to be determined, but prevents any investigation of the post-buckling behaviour at finite displacements.

Secondly, the stress resultants $\{\sigma\}$ used in the geometric matrix $[M_\sigma]$

given by eqn (85) are linearised. This linearisation will generally lead to quite accurate predictions of the buckling loads, except when the pre-buckling behaviour is sufficiently non-linear to cause substantial changes from the linearised stress resultants. It should be noted that the 'Wagner' stress resultant σ_5, which plays no part in the linear theory, now is included through the term $M_{\sigma 99}$ in eqn (85).

Thirdly, the matrix $[B_Q]$ appearing in eqn (83) for the buckling tangent stiffness $[K_T]$ is ignored in comparison with $[B_L]$. This may sometimes lead to inaccurate predictions of the buckling loads, even when the pre-buckling behaviour is very linear.[32]

Two examples of bifurcation buckling are illustrated in the following sub-sections.

4.2 Flexural–torsional buckling of columns

When an initially straight, untwisted, and stress-free column is loaded only by centroidal axial end forces $Q_{z1} = -Q_{z2} = -P$, then it will first deform $\{0, 0, w, 0\}$ with non-zero stress resultants $\sigma_1 = -P$ and $\sigma_5 = -PI_P/A$. When neutral equilibrium is reached, the column may bifurcate into an adjacent equilibrium position defined by $\{u_b, v_b, 0, \phi_b\}$.

If the non-linear term $[B_Q]$ of eqn (83) is ignored, then eqn (82) may be expressed (after division throughout by 2) as

$$\frac{1}{2} \int_0^L [\{EI_y(u_b'')^2 + EI_x(v_b'')^2 + EI_w(\phi_b'')^2 + GJ(\phi_b')^2\}$$
$$- P\{(u_b')^2 + (v_b')^2 + (I_P/A + x_0^2 + y_0^2)(\phi_b')^2$$
$$+ 2y_0 u_b' \phi_b' - 2x_0 v_b' \phi_b'\}] \, dz = 0 \qquad (106)$$

which is commonly referred to as the energy equation for column buckling, with the first group of terms representing the additional strain energy stored during buckling, and the second group representing the work done by the end loads P during buckling.

Alternatively, eqn (92) can be expressed as

$$\int_0^L [\{du'' \, EI_y u_b'' + dv'' \, EI_x v_b'' + d\phi'' \, EI_w \phi_b'' + d\phi' \, GJ\phi_b'\}$$
$$- P\{du' \, u_b' + dv' \, v_b' + d\phi' \, (I_P/A + x_0^2 + y_0^2)\phi_b'$$
$$+ du' \, y_0\phi_b' + d\phi' \, y_0 u_b' - dv' \, x_0\phi_b' - d\phi' \, x_0 v_b'\}] \, dz = 0 \qquad (107)$$

If this is integrated by parts, it can be expressed as

$$\int_0^L [du\{(EI_y u_b'')'' + (Pu_b')' + (Py_0\phi_b')''\}$$

$$+ dv\{(EI_x v_b'')'' + (Pv_b')' - (Px_0\phi_b')'\}$$

$$+ d\phi\{(EI_w\phi_b'')'' - (GJ\phi_b')' + (P(I_P/A + x_0^2 + y_0^2)\phi_b')'$$

$$+ (Py_0 u_b')' - (Px_0 v_b')'\}] \, dz + \text{constants} = 0 \tag{108}$$

Since this must hold for all admissible sets of virtual displacements $\{du, dv, 0, d\phi\}$, then

$$(EI_y u_b'')'' + (Pu_b')' + (Py_0\phi_b')' = 0 \tag{109}$$

$$(EI_x v_b'')'' + (Pv_b')' - (Px_0\phi_b')' = 0 \tag{110}$$

$$(EI_w\phi_b'')'' - (GJ\phi_b')' + (P(I_P/A + x_0^2 + y_0^2)\phi_b')' + (Py_0 u_b')'$$

$$- (Px_0 v_b')' = 0 \tag{111}$$

which are commonly used as the differential equilibrium equations. Boundary conditions for these equations may be obtained from appropriate groups of the constants of eqn (108).

In the case of a simply supported column, the buckled shapes are defined by

$$\frac{u_b}{u_c} = \frac{v_b}{v_c} = \frac{\phi_b}{\phi_c} = \sin\frac{\pi z}{L} \tag{112}$$

If these are substituted into eqn (106), it becomes

$$\frac{1}{2}\frac{\pi^2}{2L} \begin{Bmatrix} u_c \\ v_c \\ \phi_c \end{Bmatrix}^T \begin{bmatrix} (P_y - P) & 0 & -Py_0 \\ 0 & (P_x - P) & Px_0 \\ -Py_0 & Px_0 & r_2^2(P_z - P) \end{bmatrix} \begin{Bmatrix} u_c \\ v_c \\ \phi_c \end{Bmatrix} = 0 \tag{113}$$

in which

$$P_x = \pi^2 EI_x/L^2 \tag{114}$$

$$P_y = \pi^2 EI_y/L^2 \tag{115}$$

$$r_2^2 P_z = GJ + \pi^2 EI_w/L^2 \tag{116}$$

$$r_2^2 = I_P/A + x_0^2 + y_0^2 \tag{117}$$

Equation (113) is the widely quoted[7] equation used to obtain the flexural–torsional column buckling loads. These loads can also be obtained by substituting eqn (112) into eqns (109)–(111).

4.3 Out-of-plane buckling of beam-columns

When an initially straight, untwisted, and stress-free monosymmetric beam-column is loaded only in the plane of symmetry with end forces $Q_{z1} = -Q_{z2} = -P$ and moments $M_{x1} = -M_{x2} = -M$, then initially it will deform $\{0, v, w, 0\}$ in the plane of symmetry with non-zero stress resultants $\sigma_1 = -P$, $\sigma_3 = M$, $\sigma_5 = -PI_P/A + MI_{Px}/I_x$.

When neutral equilibrium is reached, the beam-column may bifurcate into a buckled position defined by $\{u_b, 0, 0, \phi_b\}$. If the non-linear term $[B_Q]$ of eqn (83) is ignored, then eqn (82) can be expressed (after division throughout by 2) as

$$\frac{1}{2}\int_0^L [\{EI_y(u_b'')^2 + EI_w(\phi_b'')^2 + GJ(\phi_b')^2\}$$

$$- P\{(u_b')^2 + (I_P/A + y_0^2)(\phi_b')^2 + 2y_0 u_b'\phi_b'\}$$

$$+ M\{-u_b'\phi_b' + u_b''\phi_b + (I_{Px}/I_x - 2y_0)(\phi_b')^2\}] \, dz = 0 \qquad (118)$$

which is similar to most common versions[7] of what is referred to as the energy equation for beam-column buckling, with the first group of terms representing the additional strain energy stored during buckling, and the second and third groups representing the work done by the end loads P and moments M during buckling.

The only difference between eqn (118) and that of Timoshenko and Gere[7] is their use of $\int_0^L Mu_b''\phi_b \, dz$ for $-\int_0^L Mu_b'\phi_b' \, dz$, which only differ by the constants of integration $-[Mu_b'\phi_b]_0^L$. These are zero in this case and in many others.

The form of eqn (118) may be preferred because of the physical interpretations that can be given for the terms $-Mu_b'\phi_b'$ and $Mu_b''\phi_b$. The quantity of Mu_b' is the torque component about the z axis of the moment M, and so the work done by this on an element δz which undergoes a differential twist $\phi_b'\delta z$ is equal to $-\frac{1}{2}(Mu_b')(\phi_b'\delta z)$. Similarly, the quantity $-M\phi$ is the moment component about the y axis of the moment M, and so the work done by this on an element δz which undergoes a differential rotation $u_b''\delta z$ is equal to $-\frac{1}{2}(M\phi_b)(u_b''\delta z)$.

The buckling differential equilibrium equations may be obtained in the same way as that used in Section 4.2 for column buckling, whence

$$(EI_y u_b'')'' + (Pu_b')' + (Py_0\phi_b')' + (M\phi_b)'' = 0 \qquad (119)$$

$$(EI_w\phi_b'')'' - (GJ\phi_b')' + [P(I_P/A + y_0^2)\phi_b']' + (Py_0 u_b')' + (Mu_b')'$$

$$- [M(I_{Px}/I_x - 2y_0)\phi_b']' = 0 \qquad (120)$$

In the case of a simply supported beam-column, the buckled shapes are defined by

$$\frac{u_b}{u_c} = \frac{\phi_b}{\phi_c} = \sin\frac{\pi z}{L} \tag{121}$$

If these are substituted into eqn (118), it becomes

$$\frac{1}{2}\frac{\pi^2}{2L}\begin{Bmatrix} u_c \\ \phi_c \end{Bmatrix}^T \begin{bmatrix} (P_y - P) & -(Py_0 + M) \\ -(Py_0 + M) & (r_1^2(P_z - P) + M\beta_x) \end{bmatrix} \begin{Bmatrix} u_c \\ \phi_c \end{Bmatrix} = 0 \tag{122}$$

in which

$$\beta_x = I_{Px}/I_x - 2y_0 \tag{123}$$

$$r_1^2 = I_P/A + y_0^2 \tag{124}$$

Equation (122) has a widely quoted[8] solution

$$M = (P_y\beta_x/2) \pm \sqrt{\{(P_y\beta_x/2)^2 + r_1^2 P_y P_z\}} \tag{125}$$

for the elastic buckling moment of a monosymmetric beam $(P = 0)$.

It may be noted that this solution ignores the effects[32] of the pre-buckling deflections v, which increase the buckling moment above the value given by eqn (125). This effect was omitted with the non-linear term $[B_Q]$ of eqn (83), which gives rise to additional terms associated with v' and v'' (see eqn (41)).

5 NON-LINEAR BEHAVIOUR

5.1 Tangent modulus method of solution

The elastic non-linear behaviour of a thin-walled member is shown diagrammatically in Figs 5 and 6 by the relationship between the external applied actions

$$\{F_E\} = \int_0^L [N_q]^T [A_L]^T \{q\}\, dz + [N_Q]^T [A_{LQ}]^T \{Q_1^T, Q_2^T\}^T \tag{126}$$

and the displacements $\{\delta\}$. These are related by

$$\{F_E\} = \{F_I(\{\delta\})\} \tag{127}$$

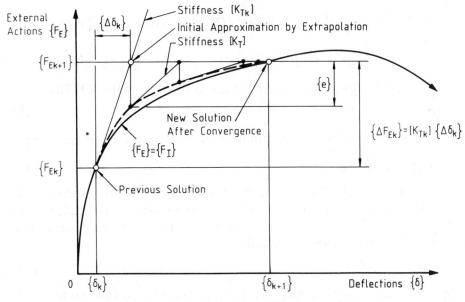

Fig. 6. Solution of non-linear equilibrium equations.

in which the equivalent internal resistances

$$\{F_I\} = \int_0^L ([N_\sigma]^T [B_L + 2B_Q]^T \{\sigma\} - [N_q]^T [2A_Q]^T \{q\}) \, dz$$

$$- [N_Q]^T [2A_{QQ}]^T \{Q_1^T, Q_2^T\}^T \tag{128}$$

include the non-linear components of the external actions. A comparison of these equations with eqn (77) demonstrates that eqn (127) is a restatement of the equilibrium conditions.

Because the equilibrium equations (eqns (77) and (127)) are non-linear, they must be solved iteratively. This may be done by beginning from an initial approximation based on an extrapolation from a previously determined solution $\{F_{Ek}\}, \{\delta_k\}$ of the equilibrium equations. Thus if the external actions are to be increased by $\{\Delta F_E\}$, the corresponding initial deflection increments $\{\Delta \delta\}$ can be approximated by considering

$$\{dF_I\} = \int_0^L ([N_\sigma]^T [B_L + 2B_Q]^T \{d\sigma\} + [N_\sigma]^T [2dB_Q]^T \{\sigma\}$$

$$- [N_q]^T [2dA_Q]^T \{q\}) \, dz - [N_Q]^T [2dA_{QQ}]^T \{Q_1^T, Q_2^T\}^T \tag{129}$$

Using eqns (42), (64), (69) and (73)–(75), this becomes

$$\{dF_I\} = \int_0^L ([N_\sigma]^T ([B_L + 2B_Q]^T [D] [B_L + 2B_Q] + [M_\sigma]) [N_\sigma]$$

$$- [N_q]^T [M_q] [N_q]) \{d\delta\} \, dz - [N_Q]^T [M_Q] [N_Q] \{d\delta\} \qquad (130)$$

in which $[M_\sigma]$, $[M_q]$, and $[M_Q]$ are given by eqns (85)–(87). Thus

$$\{dF_I\} = [K_T] \{d\delta\} \qquad (131)$$

in which the tangent stiffness matrix $[K_T]$ is given by eqn (83). Thus

$$[K_T] \{\Delta\delta\} = \{\Delta F_E\} \qquad (132)$$

which may be solved to obtain the initial deflection increments $\{\Delta\delta\}$.

Equation (132) for the tangent stiffness behaviour is similar to the buckling equilibrium equations of eqn (92) for neutral equilibrium. They become identical when the condition

$$\{\Delta F_E\} = \{0\} \qquad (133)$$

for constant applied actions is enforced, and $\{\Delta\delta\}$ is interpreted as the vector $\{\delta_b\}$ of the buckling displacements. However, the equations

$$[K_T] \{\Delta\delta\} = \{0\} \qquad (134)$$

also define the maximum load condition for non-linear behaviour, as shown in Fig. 5.

The new values of $\{\delta\}$ and $\{F_E\}$ obtained from the extrapolation described above will usually not satisfy the equilibrium equations (eqn (127)) exactly, but will lead to a set of errors

$$\{e\} = \{F_E\} - \{F_I\} \qquad (135)$$

These errors may be changed by

$$\{\Delta e\} = -\{\Delta F_I\} \qquad (136)$$

or

$$\{\Delta e\} = -[K_T] \{\Delta\delta\} \qquad (137)$$

by making changes $\{\Delta\delta\}$ in the deflections. Thus the errors $\{e\}$ may be approximately reduced to zero by introducing changes

$$\{\Delta e\} = -\{e\} \qquad (138)$$

through deflection increments $\{\Delta\delta\}$ which satisfy

$$[K_T] \{\Delta\delta\} = \{e\} \qquad (139)$$

This iteration process is shown diagrammatically in Fig. 6 for the case in which the tangent stiffness matrix $[K_T]$ corresponds to the current values of $\{F_E\}$ and $\{\delta\}$.

5.2 Finite element method of implementation

The non-linear equilibrium equations (eqns (77) and (127)), and the tangent stiffness equations (eqns (132) and (139)) used to solve them, are too complicated to allow closed-form solutions to be obtained by hand for all but the simplest of problems, unless the equations are considerably simplified by assuming that many terms are unimportant and can be omitted. In general, only numerical solutions can be obtained, and the effort required is prohibitive without the use of a computer.

On the other hand, the equilibrium and tangent stiffness equations are already in suitable forms for a matrix method of computer solution, such as the finite element method.[16-19]

For this method, the member length is divided into a number of finite elements, and the variations of the displacements and twist rotation $\{u, v, w, \phi\}$ along the element length L may be approximated by polynomials of the type

$$u = \{z\}^T \{\alpha\} \tag{140}$$

in which

$$\{z\}^T = \{z^0, z^1, z^2, \ldots, z^n\} \tag{141}$$

$$\{\alpha\} = \{\alpha_0, \alpha_1, \alpha_2, \ldots, \alpha_n\}^T \tag{142}$$

and the values of n depend on the orders of polynomial approximation. They are, however, expressed in the alternative form of

$$u = \{N_u\}^T \{\delta_u\} \tag{143}$$

in which

$$\{N_u\}^T = \{z\}^T [a] \tag{144}$$

$$\{\delta_u\} = \{u_i, u_j, u_i', u_j', u_i'', u_j'', \ldots\}^T \tag{145}$$

and $[a]$ is a matrix which depends on the length of the element ij, and the order of the approximation chosen. In the lowest order of approximation used

$$(n_{u, v, w, \phi}) = (3, 3, 1, 3) \tag{146}$$

corresponding to the 14 nodal degrees of freedom $\{\delta\}$ defined by eqn (72), associated with cubic ($n = 3$) polynomials for u, v, ϕ and a linear ($n = 1$) polynomial for w.

More accurate approximations can be obtained by using higher order elements,[33] such as that defined by

$$(n_{u, v, w, \phi}) = (5, 5, 3, 5) \tag{147}$$

which has additional degrees of freedom

$$\{\delta_{E2}\} = \{u_i'', u_j'', v_i'', v_j'', w_i'', w_j'', \phi_i'', \phi_j''\}^T \tag{148}$$

or that defined by

$$(n_{u,v,w,\phi}) = (7, 7, 5, 7) \tag{149}$$

which has a second set of additional degrees of freedom

$$\{\delta_{E3}\} = \{u_i''', u_j''', v_i''', v_j''', w_i''', w_j''', \phi_i''', \phi_j'''\}^T \tag{150}$$

While the degrees of freedom $\{\delta\}$ used with the lowest order element have physical significance with respect to geometrical continuity between adjacent elements, the additional degrees of freedom $\{\delta_{E2}\}, \{\delta_{E3}\}$ introduced with the higher order elements have no such significance. Because of this, these additional degrees of freedom are eliminated by condensation[16, 17] after the element stiffness matrices are obtained and before their assembly into the structure stiffness matrices.

The integrations along the element length required for the equilibrium and tangent stiffness equations are made by Gauss quadrature,[17] by using the values of the integrands at the Gauss points.

The modified Newton–Raphson technique[17, 34] may be used to find the equilibrium position under variable arc-length constraint.[35-38] Alternatively, the method of Powell and Simons[39] may be used.

5.3 In-plane bending

Approximate solutions for the non-linear in-plane bending may be obtained for special cases. If the member is initially straight and unstressed, and then moments M_x and loads Q_y, q_y at the shear centre, and Q_z, q_z at the centroid are applied, then eqn (76) becomes

$$\int_0^L (dv'v'\sigma_1 - dv''\sigma_3 + dw'\sigma_1 - dv\, q_y - dw\, q_z)\, dz$$

$$- (dv_1 Q_{y1} + dv_2 Q_{y2} - dv_1' M_{x1} - dv_2' M_{x2}$$

$$+ dw_1 Q_{z1} + dw_2 Q_{z2}) = 0 \tag{151}$$

in which

$$\{\sigma_1, \sigma_3\}^T = \{EAw' + \tfrac{1}{2}EAv'^2, -EI_x v''\}^T \tag{152}$$

This may be simplified by approximating σ_1 by the linear term EAw'. Integration by parts then leads to

$$\int_0^L [dv\{(-EAw'v')' + (EI_x v'')'' - q_y\}$$

$$+ dw\{-(EAw')' - q_z\}] \, dz + \text{constants} = 0 \qquad (153)$$

Since this must hold for all admissible sets of virtual displacements $\{dv, dw\}$, then

$$-(EAw'v')' + (EI_x v'')'' - q_y = 0 \qquad (154)$$

$$-(EAw')' - q_z \qquad\qquad = 0 \qquad (155)$$

which are commonly used as the differential equilibrium equations. The boundary conditions for these equations obtained from appropriate groups of the constants of eqn (153) are given by

$$\left.\begin{array}{rcl}
M_{x1} &=& EI_x v_1'' \\[4pt]
M_{x2} &=& -EI_x v_2'' \\[4pt]
Q_{y1}' &=& -EAw_1' v_1' - (EI_x v_1'')' \\[4pt]
Q_{y2}' &=& EAw_2' v_2' - (EI_x v_2'')' \\[4pt]
Q_{z1} &=& -EAw_1' \\[4pt]
Q_{z2} &=& EAw_2'
\end{array}\right\} \qquad (156)$$

These equations are non-linear, in that they include deformation products $w'v'$. These are associated with terms of the type $\sigma_1 v'$, which may be interpreted as the transverse shear force components of the axial stress resultant σ_1 caused by the rotation v' of the member. These components are equivalent to the rates of change of the bending moment components $\sigma_1 v$ caused by the displacements v of the member when the axial stress resultant σ_1 is constant ($q_z = 0$).

5.4 Biaxial bending and torsion

Approximate solutions for the non-linear biaxial bending and torsion behaviour may be obtained for special cases. If the member is doubly symmetric ($x_0 = y_0 = 0$), initially straight and untwisted, and loaded along the centroidal axis, then eqn (76) becomes

$$\int_0^L [(du')(\sigma_1 u' - \tfrac{1}{2}\sigma_3\phi' + \tfrac{1}{2}\sigma_4 v'' + \tfrac{1}{2}\sigma_6 v'')$$

$$+ (du'')(-\sigma_2 + \tfrac{1}{2}\sigma_3\phi - \tfrac{1}{2}\sigma_6 v') + (du'')(-\tfrac{1}{2}\sigma_4 v')$$

$$+ (dv') (\sigma_1 v' + \tfrac{1}{2}\sigma_2\phi' - \tfrac{1}{2}\sigma_4 u'' - \tfrac{1}{2}\sigma_6 u'')$$
$$+ (dv'') (-\tfrac{1}{2}\sigma_2\phi - \sigma_3 + \tfrac{1}{2}\sigma_6 u') + (dv'') (\tfrac{1}{2}\sigma_4 u')$$
$$+ (dw') (\sigma_1) + (d\phi) (-\tfrac{1}{2}\sigma_2 v'' + \tfrac{1}{2}\sigma_3 u'')$$
$$+ (d\phi') (\tfrac{1}{2}\sigma_2 v' - \tfrac{1}{2}\sigma_3 u' + \sigma_5\phi' - \sigma_6)$$
$$+ (d\phi'') (-\sigma_4) - (du) (q_x) - (du') (m_y - \tfrac{1}{2}bv'')$$
$$- (du'') (\tfrac{1}{2}bv') - (dv) (q_y) - (dv') (-m_x + \tfrac{1}{2}bu'')$$
$$+ (dv'') (\tfrac{1}{2}bu') - (dw) (q_z) - (d\phi) (m_z) - (d\phi') (b)] \, dz$$
$$+ \text{constants} = 0 \tag{157}$$

If this is integrated by parts, then the conditions that the resulting equation must hold for all admissible sets of virtual displacements $\{du, dv, dw, d\phi\}$ can be expressed as

$$q_x - m_y' + \sigma_2'' \quad = \; -(\sigma_1 u')' + (\tfrac{1}{2}\sigma_3\phi')' + (\tfrac{1}{2}\sigma_3\phi)'' - (\tfrac{1}{2}\sigma_4 v'')'$$
$$+ (\tfrac{1}{2}\sigma_4 v')'' - (\tfrac{1}{2}\sigma_6 v'')' - (\tfrac{1}{2}\sigma_6 v')'' - (\tfrac{1}{2}bv'')'$$
$$- (\tfrac{1}{2}bv')'' \tag{158}$$

$$q_y + m_x' + \sigma_3'' \quad = \; -(\sigma_1 v')' - (\tfrac{1}{2}\sigma_2\phi')' - (\tfrac{1}{2}\sigma_2\phi)'' + (\tfrac{1}{2}\sigma_4 u'')'$$
$$- (\tfrac{1}{2}\sigma_4 u')'' + (\tfrac{1}{2}\sigma_6 u'')' + (\tfrac{1}{2}\sigma_6 u')'' + (\tfrac{1}{2}bu'')'$$
$$+ (\tfrac{1}{2}bu')'' \tag{159}$$

$$q_z + \sigma_1' \quad = \; 0 \tag{160}$$

$$m_z - b' + \sigma_4'' - \sigma_6' = \; -\tfrac{1}{2}\sigma_2 v'' - (\tfrac{1}{2}\sigma_2 v')' + \tfrac{1}{2}\sigma_3 u'' + (\tfrac{1}{2}\sigma_3 u')'$$
$$- (\sigma_5\phi')' \tag{161}$$

in which

$$\sigma_5 \qquad\qquad \approx \sigma_1 I_P/A \tag{162}$$

which are the non-linear equilibrium equations.

These equations are sometimes simplified for members with $I_x \gg I_y$ by assuming that the deflections v are very small, and that $\sigma_1, \sigma_3 \gg \sigma_2, \sigma_4, \sigma_6$. In this case, the equilibrium equations become

$$\left.\begin{aligned}
q_x - m_y' + \sigma_2'' &= \; -(\sigma_1 u')' + (\tfrac{1}{2}\sigma_3\phi')' + (\tfrac{1}{2}\sigma_3\phi)'' \\
q_y + m_x' + \sigma_3'' &= \; -(\sigma_1 v')' + (\tfrac{1}{2}bu'')' + (\tfrac{1}{2}bu')'' \\
q_z + \sigma_1' &= \; 0 \\
m_z - b' + \sigma_4'' - \sigma_6' &= \; -[\sigma_1(I_P/A)\phi']' + \tfrac{1}{2}\sigma_3 u'' + (\tfrac{1}{2}\sigma_3 u')'
\end{aligned}\right\} \tag{163}$$

6 CONCLUSIONS

A restatement has been made of the theory of non-linear elastic biaxial bending and torsion of thin-walled open section members. This restatement is made by developing the non-linear relationships between the member strains and displacements, and using these to derive the non-linear equilibrium and tangent stiffness equations in forms which are suitable for computer solution.

Such a treatment is independent of the historical processes used to extend progressively the theories of structural member behaviour, starting initially from the linear engineering theory of bending. It therefore provides an independent check of the currently generally accepted theories derived by Timoshenko, Vlasov, and others. A comparison of these two approaches has revealed that many small terms are missing from the currently accepted theories, which must therefore be regarded as approximate.

The restatement of the theory made in this paper produces equations which are too complex for hand solution, and so numerical methods of computer solution must be used, such as the finite element method. Such a method is capable of giving solutions of high accuracy within the limitations imposed by the assumptions made.

Future restatements of the theory should address such problems as the effects of moderate rotations, shear straining, and cross-section distortion.

ACKNOWLEDGEMENTS

This work was supported by a research grant made available by the Australian Research Grants Scheme, and by a Feodor–Lynen Fellowship awarded by the Alexander von Humboldt Foundation of the Federal Republic of Germany.

The authors are grateful for the advice and assistance freely given by Prof. J. M. Rotter and Associate Professor G. J. Hancock, and for the preparation of the manuscript by Mrs J. Whittle.

REFERENCES

1. Euler, L., Sur la force des colonnes, *Mem. Acad. Berlin,* **13** (1759), translated by Van den Broek, J. A., *American Journal of Physics* (1947) 309.
2. Saint-Venant, Mémoire sur la torsion des prismes, *Mémoires des Savants Etrangers,* **XIV** (1855) 233–560.

3. Timoshenko, S. P., Einige Stabilitaetsprobleme der Elastizitaetstheorie, in *Collected Papers of Stephen P. Timoshenko*, McGraw-Hill, New York, 1953, 1–50.

4. Timoshenko, S. P., Sur la stabilité des systèmes élastiques, in *Collected Papers of Stephen P. Timoshenko*, McGraw-Hill, New York, 1953, 92–224.

5. Vlasov, V. Z., *Thin-Walled Elastic Beams*, 2nd ed., Israel Program for Scientific Translation, Jerusalem, 1961.

6. Timoshenko, S. P., Theory of bending, torsion, and buckling of thin-walled members of open cross-section, in *Collected Papers of Stephen P. Timoshenko*, McGraw-Hill, New York, 1953, 559–609.

7. Timoshenko, S. P. & Gere, J. M., *Theory of Elastic Stability*, 2nd ed., McGraw-Hill, New York, 1961.

8. Trahair, N. S. & Bradford, M. A., *The Behaviour and Design of Steel Structures*, 2nd ed., Chapman and Hall, London, 1988.

9. Murray, N. W., *Introduction to the Theory of Thin-Walled Structures*, Oxford University Press, Oxford, UK, 1984.

10. Michell, A. G. M., Elastic stability of long beams under transverse forces, *Phil. Mag.,* **48** (1899) 298–309.

11. Prandtl, L., *Kipperscheinungen*, Thesis, Munich, 1899.

12. Wagner, H., *Verdrehung und Knickung von offenen Profilen* (Torsion and buckling of open sections), NACA TM 807, 1936.

13. Horne, M. R., The stanchion problem in frame structures designed according to ultimate carrying capacity, *Proc. Inst. Civ. Engrs,* **5**(1) (1956) 105–46.

14. Kitipornchai, S., Wang, C. M. & Trahair, N. S., Closure to discussion by Ojalvo, M., on Buckling of monosymmetric I-beams under moment gradient, *J. Struct. Engng, ASCE,* **113**(6) (1987) 1391–5.

15. Papangelis, J. P. & Trahair, N. S., Flexural–torsional buckling of mono-symmetric arches, *J. Struct. Engng, ASCE,* **113**(10) (1987) 2271–88.

16. Desai, C. S. & Abel, J. F., *Introduction to the Finite Element Method*, Van Nostrand Reinhold, New York, 1972.

17. Zienkiewicz, O. C., *The Finite Element Method*, 3rd ed., McGraw-Hill, London, 1977.

18. Hinton, E. & Owen, D. R. J., *Finite Element Programming*, Academic Press, London, 1977.

19. Bathe, K.-J., *Finite Element Procedures in Engineering Analysis*, Prentice-Hall, Englewood Cliffs, New Jersey, 1982.

20. Roberts, T. M., Instability, geometric non-linearity and collapse of thin-walled beams, in *Beams and Beam-Columns. Stability and Strength*, ed. R. Narayanan, Applied Science Publishers, London, 1983, 135–60.

21. Rajasekaran, S., Finite element method for plastic beam-columns, in *Theory of Beam-Columns, Vol. 2, Space Behaviour and Design*, ed. W. F. Chen and T. Atsuta, McGraw-Hill, New York, 1977, 539–608.

22. Hasegawa, A., Liyanage, K. K. & Nishino, F., Spatial instability and nonlinear finite displacement analysis of thin-walled members and frames, *J. Fac. Engng, Univ. Tokyo,* **38**(4) (1986) 19–78.

23. Yang, Y.-B. & McGuire, W., Stiffness matrix for geometric nonlinear analysis, *J. Struct. Engng, ASCE,* **112**(4) (1986) 853–77.

24. Attard, M. A., Nonlinear theory of non-uniform torsion of thin-walled open beams, *Thin-Walled Structures,* **4** (1986) 101–34.
25. Attard, M. A. & Somervaille, I. J., Non-linear analysis of thin-walled, open beams, *Comput. Struct.,* **25**(3) (1987) 437–43.
26. Whittaker, E. T., *A Treatise on the Analytical Dynamics of Particles and Rigid Bodies,* 4th ed., Cambridge University Press, London, 1937.
27. Donald, G. S. & Kleeman, P. W., A stiffness matrix for the large deflection analysis of space frames, *Proc. 3rd Australasian Conference on the Mechanics of Structures and Materials,* University of Auckland, New Zealand, 1971.
28. Hancock, G. J., *The behaviour of structures composed of thin-walled members,* PhD Thesis, University of Sydney, 1975.
29. Love, A. E. H., *A Treatise on the Mathematical Theory of Elasticity,* 4th ed., Dover, New York, 1944.
30. Wittrick, W. H., Some observations on the dynamic equations of prismatic members in compression, *Int. J. Mech. Sci.,* **27** (1985) 375–82.
31. Langhaar, H. L., *Energy Methods in Applied Mechanics,* John Wiley & Sons, New York, 1972.
32. Vacharajittiphan, P., Woolcock, S. T. & Trahair, N. S., Effect of in-plane deformation on lateral buckling, *J. Struct. Mech.,* **3**(1) (1974) 29–60.
33. Roik, K., Carl, J. & Lindner, J., *Biegetorsionsprobleme Gerader Duennwandiger Staebe,* Wilhelm Ernst & Sohn, Berlin, 1972.
34. Owen, D. R. J. & Hinton, E., *Finite Elements in Plasticity,* Pineridge Press, Swansea, UK, 1980.
35. Riks, E., An incremental approach to the solution of snapping and buckling problems, *Int. J. Sol. Struct.,* **15** (1979) 529–51.
36. Ramm, E., Strategies for tracing the nonlinear response near limit points, in *Nonlinear Finite Element Analysis in Structural Mechanics,* ed. W. Wunderlich, E. Stein and K.-J. Bathe, Springer–Verlag, Berlin, 1981, 68–89.
37. Crisfield, M. A., A fast incremental/iterative solution procedure that handles snap-through, *Comput. Struct.,* **13** (1981) 55–62.
38. Crisfield, M. A., An arc-length method including line searches and accelerations, *Int. J. Numer. Methods Eng.,* **19** (1983) 1269–89.
39. Powell, G. & Simons, J., Improved iteration strategy for non-linear structures, *Int. J. Numer. Methods Eng.,* **17** (1981) 1455–67.

Thin-Walled Structures **9** (1990) 309–338

Recent Developments in the Buckling and Nonlinear Analysis of Thin-Walled Structural Members

Gregory J. Hancock,[a] Andrew J. Davids,[b] Peter W. Key,[a]*
Sammy C. W. Lau,[c] & Kim J. R. Rasmussen[a]

[a]School of Civil and Mining Engineering, University of Sydney, Sydney,
New South Wales 2006, Australia
[b]Wargon Chapman Partners, Consulting Engineers, Sydney, New South Wales, Australia
[c]Ove Arup and Partners, Consulting Engineers, Sydney, New South Wales, Australia

ABSTRACT

This paper describes recent work performed at the University of Sydney to develop buckling and nonlinear analyses of thin-walled structural members undergoing local, distortional and overall buckling. The analyses are based on the finite strip method of structural analysis and include elastic and inelastic buckling and the full nonlinear response with both post-local buckling and plasticity. Two variations of the finite strip method have been used, these being the semi-analytical and spline finite strip methods. A nonlinear beam-column analysis based on the influence coefficient method for including the local buckling behaviour in the overall member response is also described.

The analytical methods are compared with tests performed at the University of Sydney on cold-formed rectangular hollow sections, welded I-sections, welded channel sections and cold-formed channel sections. Spatial plastic collapse mechanisms developed for the welded sections described above are also compared with the post-ultimate response of the test sections.

NOTATION

b	Width of strip
e	Specimen axial shortening

*Present address: Starch International Limited, Melbourne, Victoria, Australia.

Thin-Walled Structures 0263-8231/90/$03·50 © 1990 Elsevier Science Publishers Ltd, England. Printed in Great Britain

e_0	Loading eccentricity
E_p, G_p	Plastic moduli
f_u, f_v, f_w	Polynomial functions of y alone
h	Knot spacing in spline analysis
$[K], [G]$	Stiffness and stability matrices
$[K_T]$	Tangent stiffness matrix
L	Length of strip
L_t	Length of column between pinned ends
n, m	Primary and secondary displacement harmonic numbers
P	Axial load
P_{lE}, P_{lR}	Experimental and theoretical local buckling loads
u, v, w	Displacements in x, y, z directions respectively
v_R	Rigid body displacement in y direction
w_0	Plate geometric imperfection in z direction
$\{w\}$	Nodal line force vector
x, y, z	Cartesian coordinates
X, Y, Z	Global coordinates
α_i	Spline coefficient
γ_{xy}	Shear strain in x, y plane
$_m\gamma_{xy}$	Membrane shear strain in x, y plane
$\{\delta\}$	Nodal line displacement vector
$\varepsilon_x, \varepsilon_y$	Strain in x, y directions
$_m\varepsilon_x, {}_m\varepsilon_y$	Membrane strain in x, y directions
$\Delta\varepsilon_{xp}, \Delta\varepsilon_{yp}, \Delta\gamma_{xyp}$	Plastic strain increment
ε_Y	Yield strain
$\varepsilon_1, \varepsilon_2$	Nodal line strains
λ	Plastic strain proportionality constant or eigenvalue
v	Poisson's ratio
ρ	Applied strain gradient
σ_{cr}	Elastic or inelastic buckling stress
σ_e	von Mises effective stress
σ_m	Mean compressive stress or hydrostatic stress
σ_{max}	Ultimate strength determined in test
$\sigma_x, \sigma_y, \sigma_z$	Longitudinal stress in x, y, z directions
σ_L	Longitudinal applied stress
σ_T	Transverse applied stress
σ_Y	Yield stress
τ	Applied shear stress
τ_{xy}	Shear stress in x, y plane
$\psi_i, \bar{\psi}_i$	B_3-spline and amended spline

Subscripts

H, P, S	Hookean, primary or secondary displacement
p	Plastic straining
u, v, w	Quantities refer to u, v, w displacements

Superscript

'	Plastic strain deviator

1 INTRODUCTION

The buckling and nonlinear analysis of thin-walled structural members including plasticity requires considerable computing effort to achieve solutions. It was decided by the first author approximately 12 years ago that to investigate accurately thin-walled structural member behaviour without recourse to very large computer systems, the finite strip method of analysis developed by Cheung[1] would be useful. This paper summarises the finite strip buckling and nonlinear analysis methods developed at the University of Sydney since 1976 and relates the work to concurrent results by other researchers including the substantial contributions of Professor Noel Murray.

The finite strip method has several advantages over finite element methods when applied to thin-walled members. These include the greatly reduced number of degrees of freedom for a given structural system, and the simple conformability of membrane and flexural displacements at plate junctions. However, end boundary conditions other than simple supports may be difficult to account for when using the finite strip method. For local buckling phenomena, the boundary conditions at the ends of the member do not play a large part in the behaviour of local buckles distant from the ends. Hence the semi-analytical finite strip method, which uses harmonic functions longitudinally, can be used to predict accurately the behaviour of short wavelength buckling modes. However, for longer wavelength modes, the end boundary conditions become important. To overcome this problem, two different approaches have been developed. In cases where local and overall buckling interact, the semi-analytical finite strip method has been used to describe the nonlinear local buckling behaviour only, and a beam-column analysis has been used in conjunction to describe the nonlinear beam-column behaviour. For modes such as distortional buckling, where membrane and flexural deformations occur over wavelengths comparable with the section length, the spline finite strip method[2] has been used. This latter method can accurately account for end boundary conditions other than simple supports, although a considerably larger number of degrees of freedom is required in the spline finite strip analysis compared with the semi-analytical finite strip analysis.

The semi-analytical finite strip method was first developed for buckling modes involving only flexural deformations by Przemieniecki,[3] and both flexural and membrane deformations by Plank and Wittrick.[4] Murray and Thierauf[5] first applied the method to stiffened plates and investigated modes which involved local, overall and stiffener buckling with combined flexural and membrane deformations. Similar studies were performed on I-section beams[6] and channel section columns[7] where distortional modes of buckling were investigated. Mahendran and Murray[8] more recently applied the method to study shear buckling modes including combined compression and shear in stiffened box-section columns.

The semi-analytical finite strip method was first developed to study the elastic post-local buckling behaviour of plate assemblies by Graves-Smith and Sridharan[9] and the nonlinear local buckling response of plate assemblies by Hancock.[10] The nonlinear analysis was also applied to study the interaction between local and overall buckling of columns[11] and of beams and the elastic stress redistribution after local buckling of thin-walled I-sections in bending[13] and compression. The incorporation of the nonlinear local buckling analysis into a beam-column analysis using the Influence Coefficient Method[15, 16] was performed by Davids and Hancock[17] to investigate the effect of local buckling deformations on the bending of thin-walled columns and beam-columns.

The flow theory of plasticity[18] was first incorporated in the semi-analytical method by Mofflin.[19] Mofflin adopted Little's[20] live energy formulation in a nonlinear finite strip analysis and studied the inelastic behaviour of stiffened plates and columns composed of both steel and aluminium. Key and Hancock[21] developed an inelastic analysis similar to that of Mofflin except that the solution procedure was based on the Newton–Raphson technique rather than the live energy method described by Little.

The spline finite strip method was first applied to elastic buckling problems by Lau and Hancock[22] who also recently extended the method to the inelastic buckling range[23] using the deformation theory of plasticity. Work is currently underway to extend the spline method to the nonlinear elastic range.

The main purpose of this paper is to summarise the displacement functions, strain–displacement relationships and plasticity models used in the different analyses referenced above. Comparisons are also provided of these analyses with test results produced at the University of Sydney for a range of thin-walled section types including welded I-sections and channel sections, and cold-formed channel and square hollow sections.

2 FINITE STRIP METHOD

2.1 General

The finite strip procedure, in which a prismatic member is discretised into a number of strips which are joined at longitudinal nodal lines as shown in Fig. 1, is a variation of the more general finite element technique.[24] While the finite element technique uses polynomial displacement functions in both directions, the finite strip procedure uses harmonic functions or spline functions in the longitudinal direction and a relatively simple polynomial function in the transverse direction. The longitudinal functions are chosen to satisfy the end boundary conditions and the transverse polynomial functions normally give compatibility between strips. For buckling of thin-walled sections with simply supported ends, the harmonic longitudinal functions used in the finite strip analysis match the longitudinal variation of the buckling modes as derived from an analytical buckling solution. Hence the use of the name 'semi-analytical finite strip method' when a harmonic series is chosen.

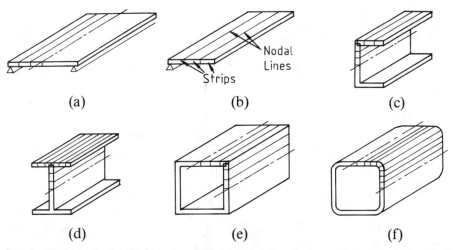

Fig. 1. Typical member finite strip subdivision. (a) Simply-supported plate; (b) outstand; (c) channel section; (d) I-section; (e) fabricated hollow section; (f) cold-formed hollow section.

2.2 Displacement functions

2.2.1 Semi-analytical finite strip method

A typical strip and its Lagrangian coordinate system are shown in Fig. 2. The strip is assumed to be compressed between rigid frictionless platens which produce applied strains ε_1 and ε_2 on nodal lines 1 and 2 respectively as shown in Fig. 2. The resulting total displacements are given by

$$u = u_H + u_P + u_S \tag{1a}$$

$$v = v_H + v_P + v_S \tag{1b}$$

$$w = w_H + w_P + w_S \tag{1c}$$

where subscript H refers to the prebuckling (Hookean) deformations and the subscripts P and S refer to primary and secondary buckling deformations. The membrane displacements corresponding to the Hookean deformations are given by (see Fig. 2)

$$u_H = (\rho y - \varepsilon_1)(x - L/2) \tag{2a}$$

$$v_H = v_R + v(\varepsilon_1 y - \rho y^2/2) + \rho x(L - x)/2 \tag{2b}$$

where $\rho = (\varepsilon_1 - \varepsilon_2)/b$ and v_R is a rigid body displacement.

The prebuckling displacements allow uniform compression and curvature of each strip. The flexural deformations (w_H) resulting from prebuckling displacements are usually small and are assumed to be zero.

The primary (buckling) displacements are given by

$$u_P = \sum_n f_u^{(n)} \cos(n\pi x/L) \tag{3a}$$

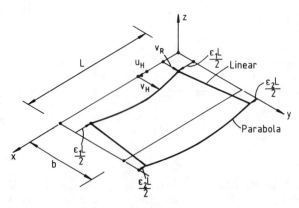

Fig. 2. Finite strip coordinate system and prebuckling displacement field.

$$v_P = \sum_n f_v^{(n)} \sin(n\pi x/L) \tag{3b}$$

$$w_P = \sum_n f_w^{(n)} \sin(n\pi x/L) \tag{3c}$$

for $n = 1, 3, 5, 7, \ldots$, where $f_u^{(n)}, f_v^{(n)}$ are linear functions of y alone and $f_w^{(n)}$ is a cubic function of y alone.

The secondary (post-buckling) displacements are given by

$$u_S = \sum_m f_u^{(m)} \sin(m\pi x/L) \tag{4a}$$

$$v_S = \sum_m f_v^{(m)} \cos(m\pi x/L) \tag{4b}$$

$$w_S = \sum_m f_w^{(m)} \cos(m\pi x/L) \tag{4c}$$

for $m = 0, 2, 4, 6, \ldots$, where $f_u^{(m)}, f_v^{(m)}$ are linear functions of y alone and $f_w^{(m)}$ is a cubic function of y alone. The functions of y are expressed in terms of degrees of freedom to be determined by the analysis. The particular terms chosen from eqns (1)–(4) for a specific problem depend upon the end boundary conditions defined in the problem. The choice of appropriate functions is discussed in detail for the specific problems described in Sections 4 and 5.

2.2.2 Spline finite strip method

As for the semi-analytical finite strip method, a thin-walled structural member is subdivided transversely into a number of strips using nodal lines as shown in Fig. 1. However, it is further subdivided longitudinally into m sections using $(m + 3)$ section knots. The nodal lines and section knots for one strip are shown in Fig. 3(a). The two additional section knots on each nodal line outside the length of the strip are required to fully define the spline function over the length of the strip.

The spline function chosen to represent the displacements along the length of a structural member is the B_3-spline of equal section length. The displacement function describing the longitudinal variation is taken as the summation of $(m + 3)$ local B_3-splines by

$$f(x) = \sum_{i=-1}^{m+1} \alpha_i \, \psi_i(x) \tag{5}$$

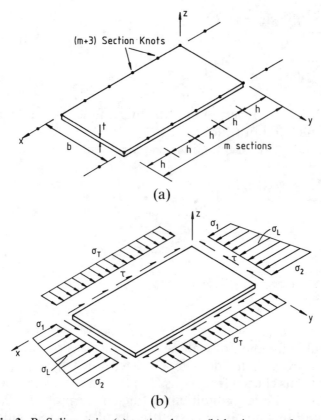

Fig. 3. B_3-Spline strip: (a) section knots; (b) basic state of stress.

where $\psi_i(x)$ is a local B_3-spline as shown in Fig. 4(a) and α_i is a coefficient to be determined in the analysis. A linear combination of local B_3-splines is shown in Fig. 4(b).

A local B_3-spline function is a piecewise polynomial function which is twice continuously differentiable. A standard local B_3-spline of equal section length (Fig. 4(a)) is defined by

$$
\psi_i(x) = \frac{1}{6h^3}
\begin{bmatrix}
(x - x_{i-2})^3 & \text{for } x_{i-2} \leqslant x \leqslant x_{i-1} \\[2mm]
\begin{aligned}
& h^3 + 3h^2(x - x_{i-1}) \\
& + 3h(x - x_{i-1})^2 \\
& - 3(x - x_{i-1})^3
\end{aligned} & \text{for } x_{i-1} \leqslant x \leqslant x_i \\[2mm]
\begin{aligned}
& h^3 + 3h^3(x_{i+1} - x) \\
& + 3h(x_{i+1} - x)^2 \\
& - 3(x_{i+1} - x)^3
\end{aligned} & \text{for } x_i \leqslant x \leqslant x_{i+1} \\[2mm]
(x_{i+2} - x)^3 & \text{for } x_{i+1} \leqslant x \leqslant x_{i+2} \\[2mm]
0 & \text{otherwise}
\end{bmatrix}
\tag{6}
$$

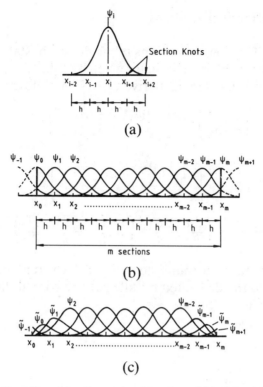

Fig. 4. (a) A local B_3-spline, (b) a linear combination of local B_3-splines, (c) amended boundary local splines.

There are many different methods to modify the local boundary splines in order to satisfy the prescribed boundary conditions. A set of splines amended for particular boundary conditions is shown in Fig. 4(c). The amended local boundary splines $\bar{\psi}$ satisfy appropriate displacement and slope boundary conditions. For example, a built-in end will have zero displacement and slope so the amended splines should be chosen to satisfy these constraints. Full details are set out in Refs 25 and 26.

The spline finite strip analysis described in this paper only applies to elastic and inelastic buckling problems. Hence only the primary (buckling) displacements are described. The primary displacements are given by

$$u_P = f_u(y)\, f(x) \tag{7a}$$

$$v_P = f_v(y)\, f(x) \tag{7b}$$

$$w_P = f_w(y)\, f(x) \tag{7c}$$

where $f_u(y)$, $f_v(y)$ are linear functions of y alone and $f_w(y)$ is a cubic function of y alone; $f(x)$ is given by eqn (5).

2.3 Strain-displacement relations

The strain–displacement equations relate the strain state at any position in the plate to the displacement fields given by eqns (1)–(7). The strains in the plate at mid-thickness, as derived by Novozhilov,[27] are given by

$$
_m\varepsilon_x = \frac{\partial u}{\partial x} + \left[\frac{1}{2}\left(\frac{\partial u}{\partial x}\right)^2 + \frac{1}{2}\left(\frac{\partial v}{\partial x}\right)^2 + \frac{1}{2}\left(\frac{\partial w}{\partial x}\right)^2 \right] \tag{8a}
$$

$$
_m\varepsilon_y = \frac{\partial v}{\partial y} + \left[\frac{1}{2}\left(\frac{\partial u}{\partial y}\right)^2 + \frac{1}{2}\left(\frac{\partial v}{\partial y}\right)^2 + \frac{1}{2}\left(\frac{\partial w}{\partial y}\right)^2 \right] \tag{8b}
$$

$$
_m\gamma_{xy} = \frac{\partial u}{\partial y} + \frac{\partial v}{\partial x} + \left[\frac{\partial u}{\partial y}\cdot\frac{\partial u}{\partial x} + \frac{\partial v}{\partial y}\cdot\frac{\partial v}{\partial x} + \frac{\partial w}{\partial y}\cdot\frac{\partial w}{\partial x} \right] \tag{8c}
$$

It is assumed that normals to the surface remain straight and perpendicular to the deformed middle surface so that the strains at any point x, y, z are given by

$$
\varepsilon_x = {}_m\varepsilon_x - z\frac{\partial^2 w}{\partial x^2} \tag{9a}
$$

$$
\varepsilon_y = {}_m\varepsilon_y - z\frac{\partial^2 w}{\partial y^2} \tag{9b}
$$

$$
\gamma_{xy} = {}_m\gamma_{xy} - 2z\frac{\partial^2 w}{\partial x\,\partial y} \tag{9c}
$$

2.4 Elastic and plastic stress–strain relations

2.4.1 Flow theory

An increment of strain is in general composed of an elastic component and a plastic component. Up to the point of yield, strain increments are entirely elastic and the stress is related to strain through the conventional elastic constitutive relationships given by Timoshenko and Woinowsky-Krieger.[28] Once yielding begins, the Prandtl–Reuss flow rule[18] governs the proportion of the total strain increment that occurs plastically, as given by

$$
\frac{\Delta\varepsilon_{xp}}{S_x} = \frac{\Delta\varepsilon_{yp}}{S_y} = \frac{\Delta\gamma_{xyp}}{S_{xy}} = \lambda \tag{10}
$$

where the stress deviators are $S_x = \sigma_x - \sigma_m$, $S_y = \sigma_y - \sigma_m$ and $S_{xy} = 2\tau_{xy}$, λ is a positive scalar, and

$$\sigma_m = \frac{\sigma_x + \sigma_y + \sigma_z}{3} \tag{11}$$

The through-thickness normal stress σ_z is assumed to be zero. The von Mises yield criterion[18] given by eqn (12) is used to relate yield occurring under a state of biaxial stress to the yield stress in simple tension or compression:

$$\sigma_e = (\sigma_x^2 + \sigma_y^2 - \sigma_x\sigma_y + 3\tau_{xy}^2)^{1/2} \tag{12}$$

Yielding will begin when the von Mises effective stress σ_e reaches the uniaxial yield stress. The plasticity model adopted assumes the yield stress is equal in tension and compression and the material strain hardens isotropically.

2.4.2 Deformation theory
As for the flow theory, an increment of strain is in general composed of an elastic component and a plastic component, where the elastic component is given by the elastic constitutive relationships of Timoshenko and Woinowsky–Krieger.[28] In the plastic range, Bijlaard[29] assumed that for pure compression, there exists a relation between the stress σ and the plastic strain ε_p such that

$$\sigma = E_p \varepsilon_p \tag{13}$$

and that the plastic strain deviators $(\varepsilon_{xp}', \varepsilon_{yp}', \gamma_{xyp}')$ are related directly to the plastic stress deviators by

$$\varepsilon_{xp}' = \varepsilon_{xp} - \varepsilon_{mp} = \frac{S_x}{2G_p} \tag{14a}$$

$$\varepsilon_{yp}' = \varepsilon_{yp} - \varepsilon_{mp} = \frac{S_y}{2G_p} \tag{14b}$$

$$\gamma_{xyp}' = \gamma_{xyp} = \frac{S_{xy}}{2G_p} \tag{14c}$$

where

$$\varepsilon_{mp} = (\varepsilon_{xp} + \varepsilon_{yp} + \varepsilon_{zp})/3 = 0 \tag{14d}$$

and

$$G_p = E_p/3 \tag{14e}$$

The definitions of S_x, S_y and S_{xy} are the same as for the flow theory. The plastic strain is the same as the plastic strain deviator since plastic deformations do not cause a change in volume and ε_{mp} is zero. As for the flow theory model, yielding begins when the von Mises effective stress σ_e reaches the uniaxial yield stress.

2.5 Formulation and solution of stiffness equations

2.5.1 Buckling analyses
Buckling analyses are based on the primary buckling displacements (u_P, v_P, w_P) alone. The choice of appropriate functions for u_P, v_P, w_P for particular boundary conditions is discussed in detail in Section 4.1 following.

The increase in the flexural strain energy (U_F) associated with the flexural buckling deformations (w_P) can be computed using conventional finite element/strip techniques.[1, 24] The increase in the potential energy (W_F) of the membrane stresses $(\sigma_L, \sigma_T, \tau$ shown in Fig. 3(b)) resulting from flexural deformations has been taken to be the same as that used by Plank and Wittrick,[4] and is given by

$$W_F = -\frac{1}{2} \int_0^L \int_0^b \left\{ \sigma_L \left(\frac{\partial w}{\partial x} \right)^2 + \sigma_T \left(\frac{\partial w}{\partial y} \right)^2 + 2\tau \frac{\partial w}{\partial x} \cdot \frac{\partial w}{\partial y} \right\} t \, dx \, dy \quad (15)$$

where $\sigma_L = \sigma_1 + (\sigma_2 - \sigma_1) y/b$ and t is the plate thickness.

The terms in eqn (15) are based on the product of the stresses shown in Fig. 3(b) with the nonlinear terms in eqns (8) which involve plate flexural displacements.

The increase in the membrane strain energy (U_M) associated with the membrane buckling deformations (u_P, v_P) can be computed using conventional finite element/strip techniques.[1, 24] The increase in the potential energy (W_M) of the membrane stresses $(\sigma_L$ shown in Fig. 3(b)) resulting from membrane deformations has been taken to be the same as that used by Plank and Wittrick,[4] and is given by

$$W_M = -\frac{1}{2} \int_0^L \int_0^b \left\{ \sigma_L \left(\frac{\partial u}{\partial x} \right)^2 + \sigma_L \left(\frac{\partial v}{\partial x} \right)^2 \right\} t \, dx \, dy \quad (16)$$

The terms in eqn (16) are based on the product of the longitudinal stress (σ_L) in Fig. 3(a) with the nonlinear terms in eqn (8a) which involve inplane displacements. Plank and Wittrick did not believe that the tranverse stresses (σ_T) or shear stresses (τ) could produce membrane modes of buckling.

At a point of neutral equilibrium, it can be shown that the total potential energy $(U_F + U_M + W_F + W_M)$ resulting from infinitestimal buckling deformations is constant. Application of the Ritz principle[30] to the total potential energy leads to an eigenvalue problem expressed by

$$([K] - \lambda [G]) \{\delta_P\} = (0) \tag{17}$$

where $\{\delta_P\}$ is the vector of primary (buckling) displacements. The eigenvalue problem is solved for the smallest buckling load factor λ, and the corresponding eigenvector of primary buckling displacements $\{\delta_P\}$.

2.5.2 Equilibrium equations for nonlinear analyses

The total equilibrium equation provides a relationship between the stress state in a strip and its current deformed shape. The principle of virtual displacements, which is applicable irrespective of the material behaviour, can be used to formulate the total equilibrium equation for use in nonlinear analyses in terms of the total strip nodal line displacements. The total equilibrium equation is given by

$$\int_V d\varepsilon_i \, \sigma_i \, dV = \{d\delta\}^T \{w\} \tag{18}$$

in which the repeated indices imply summation. The σ_i are the components σ_x, σ_y, τ_{xy} of the internal stress distribution in equilibrium with the external load system $\{w\}$ and the $d\varepsilon_i$ are the variations in the strain components ε_x, ε_y, γ_{xy} resulting from the virtual nodal line displacements $\{d\delta\}$. The strain ε_i and its increment $d\varepsilon_i$ can be expressed as functions of the nodal line displacements using eqns (1)–(4), (8) and (9). As a consequence of plasticity, the current stress state σ_i at any point within the strip is a function of the strain history and cannot be uniquely defined in terms of the total strain. The elastic–plastic stress–strain relations are used to update the current stress as increments of load are applied.

The solution procedure for the total equilibrium equation requires a relationship between the increments of applied load and the resultant incremental displacements which is valid for the current material and deformation state of the structure. If two neighbouring equilibrium states are considered, each of which can be expressed in the form of eqn (18), the difference between the two provides the incremental equilibrium equation, given by eqn (19):

$$[k_T] \{\Delta\delta\} = \{\Delta w\} \tag{19}$$

$[k_T]$ is the tangent stiffness matrix for a single strip in its local coordinate system and relates the increment of nodal load $\{\Delta w\}$ to the resultant incremental displacement $\{\Delta\delta\}$. The total and incremental equilibrium equations, evaluated for a strip in its local x, y, z coordinate system, must be transformed to the global axis system X, Y, Z when assembling the tangent stiffness matrix $[K_T]$ for the whole section.

2.5.3 Solution procedure for nonlinear analyses

The combined material and geometric nonlinear finite strip analysis detailed in this paper uses a modified Newton–Raphson solution procedure in which the tangent stiffness matrix is updated at the beginning of the load increment and also at stages during the iteration procedure, depending on the rate of convergence or possible divergence. Equilibrium is checked using eqn (18), which calculates an out-of-balance load vector for subsequent use with the tangent stiffness equations to estimate the incremental deflection. Convergence is firstly achieved based on a fixed level of plasticity. The yield criterion is then checked and adjustments made to the stresses which have either reached yield during the current increment, exceeded the stress on the yield surface or elastically unloaded from the yield surface. Equilibrium is re-established using the Newton–Raphson procedure and the process repeated until the convergence criteria are satisfied.

As a consequence of the strain history dependent nature of the flow rules of plasticity, the stresses, σ_x, σ_y and τ_{xy}, and the von Mises effective stress σ_e are stored at monitoring points distributed in the plate as shown in Fig. 5. Using only the stresses at the monitoring points, the integration is performed by employing Gaussian quadrature longitudinally in each strip to obtain maximum efficiency from a minimum number of monitoring stations (shown as n_2 in Fig. 5). Laterally, integration is performed using simple summation with n_1 monitoring stations, while Simpson's rule integration is used through the thickness with n_3 layer points as shown in Fig. 5.

3 NONLINEAR ANALYSIS FOR BEAM-COLUMNS

Under the action of compressive load, a thin-walled prismatic plate assembly may locally buckle into a number of half-waves between nodal planes as depicted in Fig. 6. The length of section between nodal planes and equal to a half-wavelength has been called a 'locally buckled cell'. Each locally buckled cell can be analysed independently and the behaviour of the full member modelled as a synthesis of the locally buckled cells as described by Davids and Hancock.[17]

The influence coefficient method of analysis as described by Chen and Atsuta[15] and Han and Chen[16] has been used to model the elastic nonlinear response of an isolated beam-column bending in one plane, as

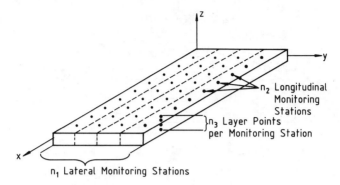

Fig. 5. Finite strip integration terminology.

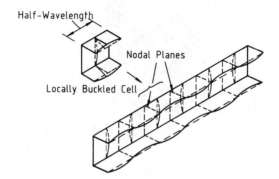

Fig. 6. Locally buckled member.

shown in Fig. 7a. In this finite difference method, the continuous beam-column is modelled as a series of nodes for which equilibrium equations can be written in a matrix format. The formulation and solution procedure are ideally suited to follow reliably the beam-column behaviour which may contain load and displacement limit points. The influence coefficient analysis includes the effects of arbitrary initial overall geometric imperfection, end load eccentricity, transverse loading and general end conditions.

Each node of the beam-column is assumed to be located at the mid-length of a locally buckled cell. The nonlinear local buckling analysis described later in Section 5.1 can be used to obtain the response of each locally buckled cell to the prescribed curvature and axial load. The nonlinear local buckling analysis includes the effects of local geometric imperfections and residual stresses. A typical locally buckled cell is shown in Fig. 7b.

The combination of the finite strip elastic nonlinear analysis of locally

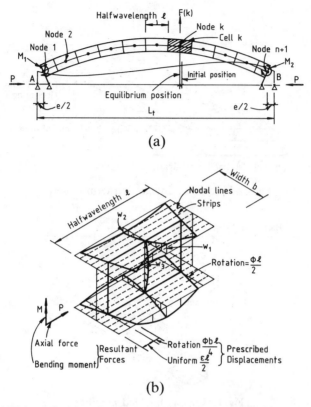

Fig. 7. (a) Thin-walled beam-column. (b) Locally buckled thin-walled section.

buckled thin-walled sections with the influence coefficient method of analysis of beam-columns requires certain assumptions. These are:

(1) The beam-column can be replaced by a series of cells each of length equal to the half-wavelength of a local buckle as shown in Fig. 7a.

(2) The moment and axial force resisted by a cell which is subjected to defined values of curvature and axial strain, can be determined for each cell (see Fig. 7b) in isolation using the finite strip elastic nonlinear analysis as described in Section 5.1 below.

(3) The average values of moment and axial force along a cell can be used to describe that cell in the nonlinear analysis of the beam-column.

(4) The only interaction between the cells is by way of equilibrium of the section stress resultants of moment, shear and axial force, as well as compatibility of centreline displacements of adjacent cells.

(5) The effect of section shear on the local buckling response of a cell is ignored.

The complete details of the method are given in Ref. 17.

4 BUCKLING STUDIES

4.1 Elastic buckling

The semi-analytical buckling analysis has been based on the primary (buckling) displacement functions given by eqn (3) together with the strain energy defined by Cheung[1] and the potential energy of membrane forces resulting from longitudinal stress (σ_L) and defined by eqns (15) and (16). The displacement functions given by eqn (3) assume a member which has ends free to rotate about both axes perpendicular to the axis of the member; longitudinal end warping displacements are unrestrained but no sectional distortions are allowed at the ends. Solutions to a wide range of problems have been given, including I-beams[6], channel section columns as used for storage racks (Hancock[7]), purlin sections[31] and unlipped channel sections.[32]

Mahendran and Murray[8] further extended eqn (3) to include the full Fourier series with both sine and cosine terms so that shear buckling modes could be studied where there was a phase shift in the buckling mode across the width of the strip. This approach is similar in some ways to that of Plank and Wittrick[4] where complex functions were used for the displacements.

The spline buckling analysis was based on the primary (buckling) displacements given by eqn (7) together with the strain energy defined by Fan and Cheung[2] and the potential energy of the membrane forces defined by eqns (15) and (16). A range of plate problems, including both simply supported and built-in ends, was presented in Ref. 22 to verify the accuracy of the method. A problem of a stiffened plate of finite length subjected to combined compression and shear was also studied to demonstrate the economy of the method when compared with a finite element analysis.

4.2 Inelastic buckling

An inelastic buckling analysis using the spline method has recently been presented by Lau and Hancock.[23] The inelastic buckling analysis uses the displacement functions given by eqn (7), the strain energy given by

Fan and Cheung[2] and potential energy terms as in Section 4.1. However, for members which have yielded in compression, the deformation theory presented in Section 2.4.2 above has been used to describe the material properties in the inelastic range. The deformation theory was used since it is well known that it provides the best estimate of inelastic buckling loads.[23]

Tests of 68 channel section columns of different section sizes, shapes, thicknesses and steel grades have been performed at the University of Sydney for comparison with the inelastic buckling analysis. The test sections were brake-pressed from steel strips and were tested in fix-ended condition under uniform compression. Full details of the tests including section dimensions, yield strengths and specimen lengths are given in Ref. 33. The specimen lengths ranged from 300 mm stub columns to 1900 mm long columns and the modes of failure ranged from local, through distortional, to flexural–torsional.

The cross-sectional shape of one of these sections, which is commonly used as uprights in steel storage racks, is shown in Fig. 8(a). The theoretical inelastic buckling mode computed for the specimen RA17-1900[34] is shown in Fig. 8 at eight sections along a half-length of the column. This mode of buckling has been called distortional[7] because it involves both flexural and membrane deformations of the component plates but does not involve torsional deformation of the whole section.

A comparison of the theoretical elastic and inelastic buckling stresses with the test results for a range of section lengths is shown in Fig. 9 for

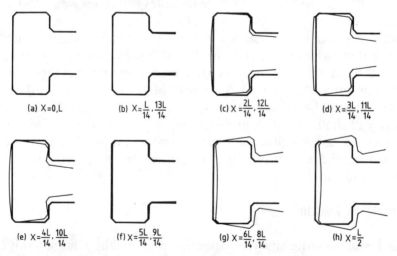

(a) $X = 0, L$ (b) $X = \frac{L}{14}, \frac{13L}{14}$ (c) $X = \frac{2L}{14}, \frac{12L}{14}$ (d) $X = \frac{3L}{14}, \frac{11L}{14}$

(e) $X = \frac{4L}{14}, \frac{10L}{14}$ (f) $X = \frac{5L}{14}, \frac{9L}{14}$ (g) $X = \frac{6L}{14}, \frac{8L}{14}$ (h) $X = \frac{L}{2}$

Fig. 8. Distortional buckling mode of specimen RA17–1900 using inelastic spline buckling analysis.

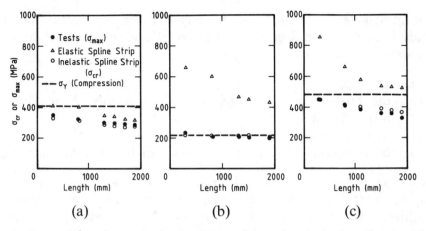

Fig. 9. Comparison of test results for RA sections using inelastic spline buckling analysis. (a) RA17, (b) RA20, (c) RA24.

three different plate thicknesses. The RA17 section was 1·7 mm thick and had a mean compressive yield strength of 406 MPa for the flat material, the RA20 section was 2·0 mm thick and had a mean compressive yield strength of 217 MPa for the flat material, and the RA24 section was 2·4 mm thick and had a mean compressive yield strength of 479 MPa for the flat material. The yield strengths are shown by the dashed lines in Fig. 9.

The elastic buckling stresses are well above the test strengths, especially for the RA20 section. However, the inelastic buckling stresses closely approximate the test strengths for all three steel grades and thicknesses. The inelastic spline buckling analysis has thus been verified for these sections with fairly small geometric imperfections for which the buckling load was indicative of the column strength and which did not fail in the post-buckling range. For sections where the yield stress substantially exceeds the theoretical elastic buckling stress, an alternative analysis including post-buckling would be necessary to determine theoretically the ultimate load.

5 NONLINEAR LOCAL BUCKLING STUDIES

5.1 Elastic

The elastic nonlinear local buckling analysis assumes that a length of section equal to the local buckle half-wavelength is compressed between rigid frictionless platens. The local buckle half-wavelength is normally determined before the nonlinear analysis using the elastic buckling analysis described in Section 4.1. The boundary conditions at the rigid frictionless platens are assumed to be:

(a) no in-plane shear strain;
(b) the cross-section remains undistorted implying no flexural displacements;
(c) plate flexural moments are unrestrained;
(d) no longitudinal displacements other than the applied compression.

Based on these boundary conditions, only certain terms from the displacement functions set out in eqns (1)–(4) have been used for the nonlinear local buckling analysis. Sridharan and Graves-Smith[35] have shown that if $n = 1$ is selected for the primary (buckling) displacements, then $m = 0, 2$ should be used for the secondary (post-buckling) displacements. The finite strip post-local buckling analysis described by Graves-Smith and Sridharan[9] and the nonlinear analysis described by Hancock[13] employed a subset of eqns (3) and (4) given by eqns (4a) and (4b) describing membrane deformations and eqn (3c) describing flexural deformations. The subset satisfies the end boundary conditions summarised above.

The strain–displacement relations used in these analyses are the same as those given in eqns (8) and (9) except that:

(a) only those nonlinear terms involving the plate flexural displacement (w) have been included since the analysis is only a local buckling analysis;
(b) the plate geometric imperfections (w_0) have been included in the analysis by subtracting from eqns (8) and (9) terms equal to those involving w but with w_0 replacing w.

The nonlinear equations were formulated using the procedures set out in Section 2.5.2. The solution procedures were the same as those set out in Section 2.5.3 except that exact integration was used rather than numerical integration.

The nonlinear analysis has been used for the elastic post-local buckling analyses used in the interaction of local and lateral buckling of I-beams,[12] the stress redistribution of locally buckled I-beams,[13] and the stress redistribution in locally buckled I-columns.[14] The boundary conditions at plate junctions which are not coplanar are not completely compatible in these analyses and have been summarised in detail by Hancock.[13]

5.2 Inelastic

A nonlinear local buckling analysis including plasticity has recently been described by Key and Hancock.[21] It is based on the boundary conditions and displacement functions described in Section 5.1 and the flow theory of plasticity described in Section 2.4.1. The formulation and solution of the equilibrium equation are as described in Sections 2.5.2 and 2.5.3 respectively.

The analysis has been used to study cold-formed square hollow sections (SHS) subjected to compression. The cold-formed sections were analysed over a length equal to 0·8 times the elastic buckling half-wavelength. This value was found from analytical studies to produce the minimum ultimate load. The section was modelled as a quarter of a box between the centrelines of adjacent faces. Each half face was modelled using five coplanar strips with the 5th strip narrower than the other four and representing the corners of the section with enhanced yield strength and a rounded stress–strain curve. The stress–strain curves used were modelled analytically from the experimentally measured curves described

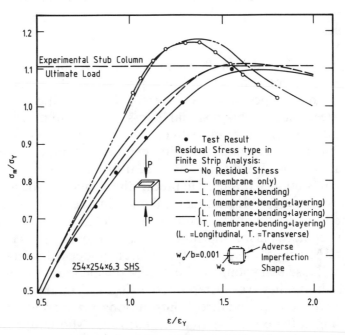

Fig. 10. Stress versus axial strain, 254 × 254 × 6·3 SHS stub column: influence of residual stress.

in Ref. 36. The local geometric imperfections were taken as $w_0/b = 0{\cdot}001$ in the adverse mode as shown in Fig. 10.

The finite strip analysis with 13 layer points through the plate thickness was used to investigate the nonlinear response of the four different-sized SHS sections described in Ref. 36. The influence of the various components of residual stress was investigated by progressive inclusion of the components in the analysis. The average stress versus axial strain has been plotted for the 254 × 254 × 6·3 SHS in Fig. 10. The results have been non-dimensionalised with respect to the nominal yield stress (σ_Y) of 350 MPa and the corresponding yield strain (ε_Y).

The influence of the different components of the residual stress is quite clear in the figure. In particular, the longitudinal bending component of residual stress and the transverse residual stresses each have a significant influence on the nonlinear behaviour of the section. The curve including all components of residual stress is quite close to the test points and justifies the care taken to include all components of residual stress in the analysis.

6 NONLINEAR BEAM-COLUMN BEHAVIOUR

6.1 General

Tests of pin-ended thin-walled fabricated I-section columns[37] and channel section columns[38] have been performed at the University of Sydney. Each test specimen was fabricated by welding of three high strength steel plates, and residual stresses, local imperfections and overall imperfections were measured.

The behaviour was simulated using two distinct but complementary theoretical models. Firstly, the nonlinear beam-column analysis, as described in Section 3, was used to predict the elastic nonlinear response to compressive loading including local buckling, residual stresses, local and overall imperfections and end loading eccentricities. Secondly, the theory for spatial plastic mechanisms, as presented by Murray and Khoo[39] and Murray,[40] was used to formulate a model to describe the post-ultimate collapse behaviour. In the spatial plastic mechanism analysis, the axial shortening was determined using the model proposed by Davids[41] which comprised three contributions, viz. a shortening due to plate folding at the central spatial mechanism, a shortening due to the lateral deflection at the centre, and an elastic axial compression of the parts of the column away from the central spatial mechanism.

6.2 I-sections

Comparison of the experimental load versus axial shortening and load versus lateral deflection of test specimen 240–4200–A[37] with different theoretical models is shown in Fig. 11. The test was controlled by prescribing the axial shortening, and the test readings are marked with small circles. The specimen was analysed as an overall geometrically perfect eccentrically loaded pin-ended column, of length equal to the test specimen length plus the bearing length to the rotational pins of the test

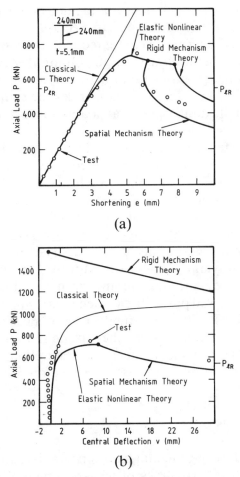

Fig. 11. Comparison of theoretical and experimental response for I-section specimen 240–4200–A. (a) Load versus specimen shortening curves; (b) load versus central deflection curves.

rig (450 mm). Details of the cross-section are shown in Fig. 11(a). At loads less than the local buckling load during the test, the initial eccentricity of loading about the minor principal axis, at the mid-length, was determined to be 0·7 mm. This value was used as a uniform initial load eccentricity in the subsequent analysis. The nonlinear analysis included a local imperfection in the shape of the local buckling mode of magnitude equal to 0·05 mm, and a residual stress distribution as shown in Ref. 37. The theoretical local buckling load (P_{lR}), as obtained from an elastic finite strip buckling analysis including the effect of residual stress, is also shown in Fig. 11.

The elastic theoretical response predicted by classical Timoshenko beam-column theory[42] which does not include cross-section distortion, and the nonlinear theory described in Section 3, which includes the effect of local buckling, can be compared with the test results up to the test ultimate load. The nonlinear beam-column theory closely predicts the experimental observations up to the point of the theoretical elastic maximum strength, and clearly demonstrates the significant reduction of the axial and flexural rigidity at loads above the local buckling load (P_{lR}).

The post-ultimate response predicted by a spatial plastic mechanism theory and a rigid section mechanism theory are also shown in Fig. 11. The spatial plastic mechanism analysis allowed for a short section at the specimen mid-length to be grossly distorted, whereas the rigid section mechanism analysis assumed that a simple plastic hinge formed at the specimen mid-length, and excluded cross-section distortions. Full details of the spatial plastic mechanism analysis based on the theory described by Murray and Khoo[39] and Murray[40] are given in Ref. 41.

The spatial plastic mechanism theory more closely predicts the experimentally observed post-ultimate behaviour with regard to strength and rate of collapse than the rigid section mechanism theory. In conclusion, the combination of the elastic nonlinear and spatial mechanism theories provides an accurate description of the response of the locally buckled thin-walled I-section column to compression and bending.

6.3 Channel sections

Comparisons of the experimental load versus axial shortening and load versus lateral deflections curves of test specimens S2L2700E + 2 and S2L4500C[38] with different theoretical models are shown in Figs 12 and 13 respectively. The test readings are marked with triangles which have been connected with straight lines. The tests were controlled by

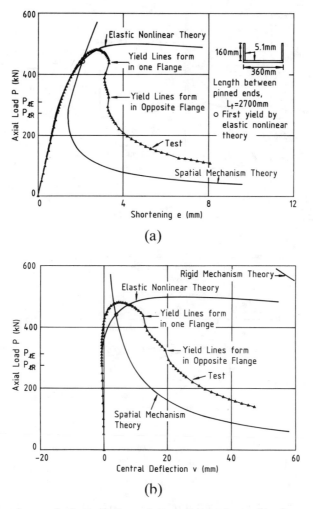

Fig. 12. Comparison of theoretical and experimental results for test specimen S2L2700E + 2. (a) Load versus specimen shortening curves; (b) load versus central deflection curves.

specifying the lateral deflection (v) rather than the axial shortening, thus allowing the full loading range behaviour to be obtained experimentally, including the decrease in axial shortening which occurred when yield lines formed across the flanges, as shown in Fig. 12. However, in the test of specimen S2L4500C, the formation of yield lines was associated with an instability in the control loop, which caused the specimen to fail suddenly, as shown in Fig. 13. As also shown in Fig. 13, the specimen was reloaded after the sudden collapse to obtain the loading curve of the grossly deformed specimen. The experimental local buckling load (P_{IE})

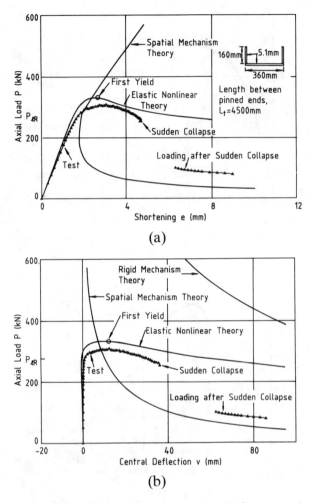

Fig. 13. Comparison of theoretical and experimental results for test specimens S2L4500C. (a) Load versus specimen shortening curves; (b) load versus central deflection curves.

under uniform compression was obtained for specimen S2L2700E + 2 in a separate test, as described in Rasmussen and Hancock,[38] and has been included in Fig. 12.

The specimens were analysed as geometrically imperfect eccentrically loaded pin-ended columns. The cross-section and column lengths analysed are shown in Figs. 12(a) and 13(a). The specimens were nearly straight as their overall geometric imperfections were measured to be less than 1/10 000 of their length, and were analysed using end loading eccentricities (e_0) equal to 5·4 mm and 1·2 mm for specimens S2L2700E + 2 and S2L4500C respectively. The eccentricities were assumed positive towards the web, and were in agreement with those used in the tests. The analysis included a local imperfection in the shape of the local buckling mode of magnitude 0·17 mm and a residual stress distribution as shown in Fig. 4 of Ref. 38. The theoretical local buckling loads, including the effect of residual stress (P_{1R}), are shown in Figs 12 and 13, as obtained from a finite strip buckling analysis based on a local buckling half-wavelength equal to 425 mm. The point where first yield occurred according to the elastic nonlinear analysis is marked with a circle in Figs 12 and 13.

The spatial plastic mechanism curves shown in Figs 12 and 13 were obtained by use of the Type 5 spatial plastic mechanism, as described in Table 1 of Ref. 39. In addition, Figs 12(b) and 13(b) show the rigid section mechanism curve which was obtained by assuming that a simple plastic hinge formed at the centre of the column, and excluded cross-section distortions. The load versus axial shortening spatial mechanism curves shown in Figs 12(a) and 13(a) were obtained using the model described in Section 6.1.

The test results for specimen S2L2700E + 2, as given in Fig. 12(b), show that the specimen deformed initially towards the flanges as a result of the eccentricity used in the test. However, the stress redistribution associated with local buckling deformations induced overall bending towards the web which caused the lateral deflection to change direction. The elastic nonlinear analysis describes this behaviour, as shown in Fig. 12(b), and also predicts the reduction in axial stiffness after local buckling, as shown in Fig. 12(a). Furthermore, the shape of the curves predicted by the nonlinear analysis for specimen S2L4500C closely resembles the test points in the range of elastic behaviour as shown in Fig 13.

The theoretical overall to local buckling load ratios were equal to 9·8 and 3·5 for specimens S2L2700E + 2 and S2L4500C respectively, and so the overall deflections shown in Figs 12(b) and 13(b) were initiated by local buckling rather than overall instability. This dependency of the overall deflection on the local buckling load demonstrates that short fabricated channel section columns loaded between pinned ends are highly sensitive to the local buckling load and consequently on the level of compressive residual stress.

The spatial plastic mechanism analysis conservatively predicts the post-ultimate strength as shown in Figs 12 and 13. The shape of the curves is in close agreement with the experimental results. By comparison, the spatial plastic mechanism curves are in much closer agreement with the test points than are the rigid section mechanism curves.

7 CONCLUSIONS

A consistent theoretical approach to the buckling and nonlinear analysis of thin-walled structural members, including local buckling and section distortion, has been described. The methods of analysis are based mainly on the finite strip method of structural analysis which has proved itself very valuable for accurately studying the local, distortional and overall modes of buckling of thin-walled members including the interaction between buckling modes.

For members with boundary conditions other than simple supports and including yielding, a version of the spline finite strip method, including the deformation theory of plasticity, has been proved from tests at the University of Sydney to be accurate and efficient for predicting the inelastic buckling loads, including distortional modes, of thin-walled channel sections. Further extensions into the post-buckling range are currently underway.

For cold-formed members with stockier plate elements which undergo substantial yielding before local buckling, a nonlinear local buckling analysis, including the flow theory of plasticity, has proved itself to be accurate. Comparisons of this analysis with tests performed at the University of Sydney on tubular section columns with residual stresses produced by the cold-forming process have shown the importance of considering all types of residual stresses in the analysis, including the through-thickness variation and transverse residual stresses.

For beam-columns which undergo combined local buckling and overall compression and bending, a method of analysis combining the influence coefficient method for beam-columns and a nonlinear local buckling analysis has proved itself to be accurate and reliable. Comparisons with tests on thin-walled I-section and channel section columns have proved the method for predicting the nonlinear elastic response.

The combination of the nonlinear elastic theory and the spatial plastic mechanism theory has been shown to provide a description of the behaviour of thin-walled columns both before and after the ultimate load. This approach follows closely the ideas and concepts presented by Murray[43] for stiffened plates.

REFERENCES

1. Cheung, Y. K., *Finite Strip Method in Structural Analysis*, Pergamon Press, New York, 1976.

2. Fan, S. C. & Cheung, Y. K., Analysis of shallow shells by spline finite strip method, *Engineering Structures,* **5**(4) (1983) 255–63.
3. Przemieniecki, J. S., Finite element structural analysis of local instability, *J. Am. Inst. Aeronautics and Astronautics,* **11**(2) (1974) 33–9.
4. Plank, R. J. & Wittrick, W. H., Buckling under combined loading of thin flat-walled structures by a complex finite strip method, *Int. J. Numer. Methods Engng,* **8**(2) (1974) 323–39.
5. Murray, N. W. & Thierauf, G., *Tables for the Design and Analysis of Stiffened Steel Plates,* Vieweg, Braunschweig, FRG, 1981.
6. Hancock, G. J., Local distortional and lateral buckling of I-beams, *J. Struct. Div., ASCE,* **104**(ST11) (Nov.) (1978) 1787–98.
7. Hancock, G. J., Distortional buckling of steel storage rack columns, *J. Struct. Engng, ASCE,* **111**(12) (Dec.) (1985) 2770–83.
8. Mahendran, M. & Murray, N. W., Elastic buckling analysis of ideal thin-walled structures under combined loading using a finite strip method, *Thin-Walled Structures,* **4**(5) (1986) 329–62.
9. Graves-Smith, T. R. & Sridharan, S., A finite strip method for the post-locally buckled analysis of plate structures, *Int. J. Mech. Sci.,* **20** (1978) 833–42.
10. Hancock, G. J., Nonlinear analysis of thin sections in compression, *J. Struct. Div., ASCE,* **107**(ST3) (March) 455–71.
11. Hancock, G. J., Interaction buckling in I-section columns, *J. Struct. Div., ASCE,* **107**(ST1) (Jan.) (1981) 165–79.
12. Bradford, M. A. & Hancock, G. J., Elastic interaction of local and lateral buckling in beams, *Thin-Walled Structures,* **2**(1) (1984) 1–25.
13. Hancock, G. J., Nonlinear analysis of thin-walled I-sections in bending, in *Aspects of the Analysis of Plate Structures,* ed. D. J. Dawe, R. W. Horsington, A. G. Kamtekar and G. H. Little, Oxford University Press, Oxford, UK, 1985, Chapter 14.
14. Davids, A. J. & Hancock, G. J., Compression tests of short welded I-sections, *J. Struct. Engng, ASCE,* **112**(5) (May) (1986) 960–76.
15. Chen, W. F. & Atsuta, T., Theory of beam-columns, **2**, in *Space Behaviour and Design,* McGraw-Hill, New York, 1977.
16. Han, D. J. & Chen, W. F., Buckling and cyclic inelastic analysis of steel tubular beam-columns, *Engineering Structures,* **5** (April) (1983) 119–32.
17. Davids, A. J. & Hancock, G. J., Nonlinear elastic response of locally buckled thin-walled beam-columns, *Thin-Walled Structures,* **5**(3) (1987) 211–26.
18. Mendelson, A., *Plasticity: Theory and Application,* Macmillan, New York, 1968.
19. Mofflin, D. S., *Plate buckling in steel and aluminium,* PhD Thesis, University of Cambridge, Cambridge, UK, August 1983.
20. Little, G. H., Rapid analysis of plate collapse by live-energy minimisation, *Int. J. Mech, Sci.,* **19** (1977) 725–44.
21. Key, P. W. & Hancock, G. J., Nonlinear analysis of cold-formed sections using the finite strip method, *Proc. Ninth Int. Spec. Conf. on Cold-Formed Steel Structures,* St Louis, Missouri, November 1988.
22. Lau, S. C. W. & Hancock, G. J., Buckling of thin flat-walled structures by a spline finite strip method, *Thin-Walled Structures,* **4**(4) (1986) 269–94.
23. Lau, S. C. W. & Hancock, G. J., Inelastic buckling analyses of beams,

columns and plates using the spline finite strip method, *Thin-Walled Structures,* 7(1989) 213–38.

24. Zienkiewicz, O. C., *The Finite Element Method,* McGraw-Hill, London, 1977.
25. Fan,. S. C., *Spline finite strip in structural analysis,* PhD Thesis, University of Hong Kong, 1982.
26. Lau, S. C. W. & Hancock, G. J., *Buckling of thin flat-walled structures by a spline finite strip method,* Research Report, School of Civil and Mining Engineering, University of Sydney, R487, May 1985.
27. Novozhilov, V. V., *Foundations of the Nonlinear Theory of Elasticity,* Graylock Press, Rochester, NY, 1953.
28. Timoshenko, S. P. & Woinowsky-Krieger, S., *Theory of Plates and Shells,* McGraw-Hill, New York, 1959.
29. Bijlaard, P. P., Theory and tests on the plastic stability of plates and shells, *J. Aero. Sci.,* **16** (1949) 529–41.
30. Langhaar, H. L., *Energy Methods in Applied Mechanics,* John Wiley, New York, 1962.
31. Hancock, G. J., The behaviour and design of cold-formed purlins, *J. Austr. Inst. Steel Constr.,* **15**(3) (1981).
32. Hancock, G. J., The behaviour and design of cold-formed channels in compression, *J. Austr. Inst. Steel Constr.,* **17**(3) (1983).
33. Lau, S. C. W. & Hancock, G. J., *Inelastic buckling of channel columns in the distortional mode,* Research Report, School of Civil and Mining Engineering, University of Sydney, R578, August 1988.
34. Lau, S. C. W. & Hancock, G. J., Distortional buckling tests of cold-formed channel sections, *Proc. Ninth Int. Spec. Conf. on Cold-Formed Steel Structures,* St Louis, Missouri, November 1988.
35. Sridharan, S. & Graves-Smith, T. R., Postbuckling analysis with finite strips, *J. Eng. Mech. Div., ASCE,* **107** (Oct.) (1981) 869–88.
36. Key, P. W., Hasan, S. W. & Hancock, G. J., Column behaviour of cold-formed hollow sections, *J. Struct. Engng, ASCE,* **114**(ST2) (Feb.) (1988) 390–407.
37. Davids, A. J. & Hancock, G. J., Compression tests of long welded I-section columns, *J. Struct. Engng, ASCE,* **112**(10) (Oct.) (1986) 2281–98.
38. Rasmussen, K. J. R. & Hancock, G. J., Compression tests of welded channel section columns, *J. Struct. Engng, ASCE,* **115**(4) (April 1989) 789–808.
39. Murray, N. W. & Khoo, P. S., Some basic plastic mechanisms in the local buckling of thin-walled steel structures, *Int. J. Mech. Sci.,* **23**(12) (1981).
40. Murray, N. W., *Introduction to the Theory of Thin-Walled Structures,* Oxford University Press, 1984.
41. Davids, A. J., *The behaviour of thin-walled I-section columns,* PhD Thesis, University of Sydney, 1987.
42. Timoshenko, S. P. & Gere, J. M., *Theory of Elastic Stability,* McGraw-Hill, New York, 1961.
43. Murray, N. W., Buckling of stiffened panels loaded axially and in bending, *Structural Engineer,* **51**(8) (August) (1973) 285–301.

Thin-Walled Structures **9** (1990) 339–350

Distortional Buckling Strength of Elastically Restrained Monosymmetric I-Beams

M. A. Bradford

School of Civil Engineering, The University of New South Wales, Kensington,
New South Wales 2033, Australia

ABSTRACT

An inelastic method of analysis of the distortional buckling of monosymmetric I-beams is augmented to include the effects of elastic restraints against translation, minor axis rotation, torsion and warping. The method is validated for problems for which inelastic, distortional and restraint solutions are known. A study is made of a monosymmetric beam with separate translational, rotational and torsional restraints, and conclusions are made regarding the strength of the beam when the cross-section is free to distort.

NOTATION

The dimensions of the beam are shown in Fig. 1 and the restraints are shown in Fig. 2. Other principal notation is as below:

E, E_{st}	Young's modulus and strain hardening modulus respectively
$[g]$	Stability matrix
G	Shear modulus
h'	Strain hardening modular ratio
J	Torsion constant
$[k]$	Stiffness matrix
$[k_r]$	Restraint stiffness matrix
M_{Id}	Inelastic distortional buckling moment
M_{Ir}	Inelastic lateral buckling moment

Thin-Walled Structures 0263-8231/90/$03·50 © 1990 Elsevier Science Publishers Ltd, England, Printed in Great Britain

M_{od} Elastic distortional buckling moment
M_{or} Elastic lateral buckling moment
M_P Full plastic moment
P_y Euler buckling load
$\{q\}$ Vector of maximum displacements
u_T, u_B Top and bottom flange lateral displacements respectively
U Strain energy stored during buckling
U_r Strain energy stored in restraints
V Work done during buckling

λ Buckling load factor
λ_d Distortional buckling slenderness
λ_r Flexural–torsional buckling slenderness
ν Poisson's ratio
σ_Y Yield stress
ϕ_T, ϕ_B Top and bottom flange twists respectively

1 INTRODUCTION

In a steel framed structure, the component members are often restrained against overall buckling by other connected members or by external cladding. The accurate calculation of the buckling strength of these component members therefore requires incorporation of the effects of the restraints in the analysis. Such an accurate calculation will lead to more efficient structures.

It has been shown[1] that when a beam with a slender web is subjected to continuous elastic restraints, the elastic buckling mode may be distortional instead of flexural–torsional, characterised by out-of-plane flexure or distortion of the flexible web of the beam. This is particularly true of composite girders of steel and concrete in negative bending,[2-4] where the top flange is restrained by the slab, and where lateral movement of the bottom flange is restrained only by the flexibility of the web. Whilst the flexural–torsional buckling of restrained beams has been well documented, it is only recently that distortional buckling of restrained beams has been studied.[1, 3, 5]

In this paper, an inelastic method of analysis of the distortional buckling of monosymmetric steel I-beams[6] is augmented to include the effects of continuous elastic restraints. The inelastic theory is reviewed briefly, and a model of elastic restraining actions appropriate to the chosen displacement fields is introduced.[1] The method is then applied to inelastic distortional buckling of monosymmetric beams with elastic translational, rotational and torsional restraints, and conclusions are made regarding the strength of such members for the overall buckling limit state.

2 THEORY

Using recently developed theory,[7] it is assumed that the top and bottom flanges of the member displace and twist sinusoidally in a number of half-wavelengths during buckling. It is also assumed that the flanges displace and twist as rigid bodies, while the web plate buckles out-of-plane as a cubic curve. This allows for easy development and assembly of the stiffness and stability matrices for the monosymmetric beam.

The geometry of the monosymmetric beam, which is assumed to be loaded in uniform bending, is shown in Fig. 1. The stress–strain curve for

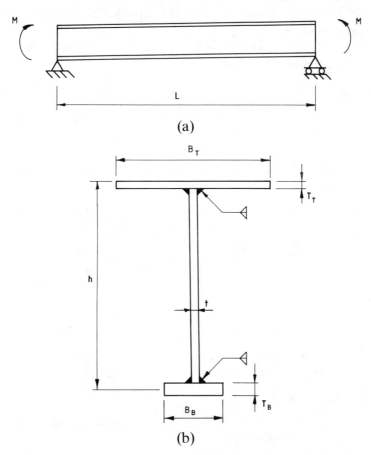

Fig. 1. Monosymmetric beam: (a) loading; (b) cross-section.

the steel is taken as a trilinear idealisation, with yield stress σ_Y, elastic Young's modulus E, constant yield plateau, strain hardening modulus $E_{st} = E/h'$ and a strain of 10 times the yield strain at the onset of strain hardening. This model has been discussed elsewhere.[8, 9]

Residual stresses appropriate for monosymmetric beams fabricated by welding three plates are adopted. These are based on a model developed at Cambridge University over many years,[10] and recently summarised.[11] For this, tension blocks stressed to σ_Y are assumed at the welds, juxtaposed by compressive stress blocks in the flanges and central portion of the web such that equilibrium of the unloaded beam is maintained.

The continuous elastic restraints which act on the monosymmetric beam, and their positions, are shown in Fig. 2. These are translational restraints k_{tT} and k_{tB}, rotational restraints k_{ryT} and k_{ryB}, torsional restraints k_{rzT} and k_{rzB}, and warping restraints k_{zzT} and k_{zzB}, where the subscripts T and B denote the restraint applied to the top or bottom flange respectively.

It has been shown[1] that the strain energy stored in the restraints when the beam buckles is given by

$$U_r = \tfrac{1}{2}\{q\}^T [k_r] \{q\} \tag{1}$$

where $\{q\}$ is the vector of the amplitudes of the deformations u_T, u_B, ϕ_T,

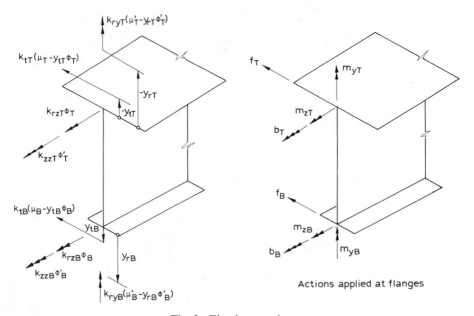

Fig. 2. Elastic restraints.

ϕ_B, and $[k_r]$ is the restraint stiffness matrix developed from the restraint stiffnesses and their positions.

In the incremental and iterative solution for the critical moment, an initial curvature ρ is applied to the section, and this is increased monotonically by a load factor λ. At each value of λ, the strain energy

$$U = \tfrac{1}{2}\{q\}^T ([k(\lambda)] + [k_r]) \{q\} \tag{2}$$

is calculated, as well as the work done

$$V = \tfrac{1}{2}\{q\}^T [g(\lambda)] \{q\} \tag{3}$$

The stiffness matrix $[k]$ and stability matrix $[g]$ are both functions of λ, and derivations have been published.[6]

The stability condition

$$|[k] + [k_r] - [g]| = 0 \tag{4}$$

is tested at the monotonically increasing values of λ, until the determinant changes sign. When this occurs, the method of bisections[12] is used to converge on the critical curvature $\lambda_{cr}\rho$. The eigenvector is then extracted to obtain a representation of the buckled shape, whilst the critical moment is obtained by numerical integration over the cross-section[6] using a trapezoidal rule,[12] and using the constitutive relationship for the structural steel.

3 ACCURACY OF MODEL

The accuracy of the 'nonlinear' inelastic stiffness matrices $[k]$ and $[g]$ in the prediction of inelastic distortional buckling has been demonstrated elsewhere.[6] Elastic distortional buckling of unrestrained beams was validated,[6] whilst predictions in agreement with those of Kitipornchai and Wong-Chung[11] were obtained for inelastic flexural–torsional buckling of unrestrained monosymmetric beams.

When the restraints are included, the accuracy of the matrix $[k_r]$ has been verified by flexural–torsional buckling comparisons with the solutions of Trahair[13] for elastically restrained monosymmetric beams. For this, the yield stress σ_Y was made very large to simulate elastic behaviour, while the strain energy corresponding to web out-of-plane flexure was increased in order to simulate flexural–torsional (rigid web) buckling.[7] The elastic solutions for restrained flexural–torsional buckling were identical to those previously obtained.[1]

The inelastic flexural–torsional buckling of restrained monosymmetric I-beams was validated against a computer model.[14] The restrained beam that was compared with Trahair's study was used, except that residual stresses and yielding were introduced. It was found that the inelastic solutions were identical to those of Bradford[14] when distortion of the web was suppressed.

4 PARAMETRIC STUDY OF INELASTIC BUCKLING

4.1 General

A monosymmetric beam with the dimensions shown in Fig. 3 was analysed with translational, rotational and torsional restraints on the bottom (tension) flange. It has been shown elastically[1] that translational, rotational and torsional restrains applied to the tension flange exemplify greater the effects of web distortion on overall buckling.

In modelling the residual stresses, the tension blocks stressed to σ_Y were assumed to have a width of 20 mm. A yield stress σ_Y of 250 MPa was

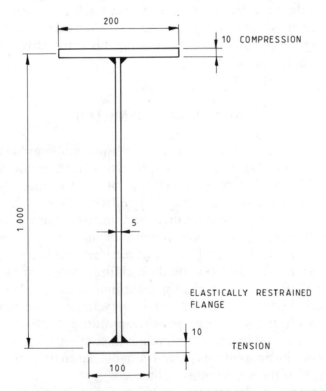

Fig. 3. Section analysed parametrically. $E = 200\,000$ MPa, $\sigma_Y = 250$ MPa, $h' = 33$, $\nu = 0\cdot3$.

used, whilst a strain hardening modular ratio h' of 33 was employed in the modelling of the constitutive relationship for the structural steel.

4.2 Translational restraints

Dimensionless buckling moments M/M_P were determined for various values of the dimensionless beam length L/h and the dimensionless restraint value $k_t L^2/\pi^2 P_y$ used in Trahair's study,[13] where k_t is the restraint stiffness applied to the bottom flange, P_y is the Euler buckling load of the beam, and M_P is the plastic moment. The results shown in Fig. 4 illustrate that the elastic rigid-web flexural–torsional buckling

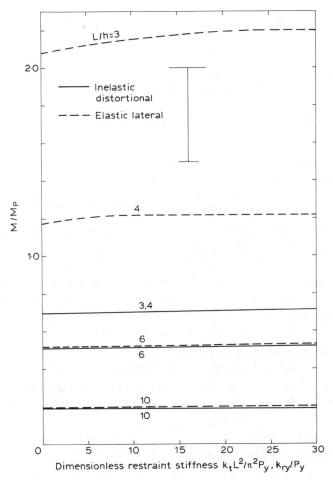

Fig. 4. Buckling of beam with translational and rotational restraints.

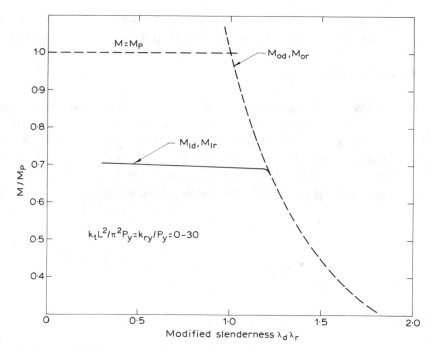

Fig. 5. Relationship between strength and slenderness.

moments M_{or} decrease as L/h increases, but remain relatively independent of the modified restraint stiffness, as was confirmed in Trahair.[13] On the other hand, the inelastic distortional buckling moments M_{Id} are independent of the length for $L/h = 3$ and 4, but for longer lengths approach the elastic rigid web lateral buckling moment M_{or} as the effects of inelasticity and distortion decrease.

Figure 5 shows the relationship between strength and slenderness, where the inelastic distortional buckling moment M_{Id} is plotted against the modified slenderness $\lambda_d = \sqrt{M_P/M_{od}}$, and the rigid-web inelastic buckling moment M_{Ir} is plotted against the modified slenderness $\lambda_r = \sqrt{M_P/M_{or}}$, where M_{od} and M_{or} are the elastic distortional and elastic flexural–torsional buckling moments for the restrained beam respectively. It can be seen that, over the range of restraint values $k_t L^2/\pi^2 P_y$ from 0 to 30 represented in the figure, the relationship between inelastic buckling and elastic slenderness (λ_d and λ_r) is identical for distortional and rigid-web flexural–distortional buckling.

4.3 Minor axis rotational restraints

The dimensionless buckling moments M/M_P were determined as a function of the dimensionless modified minor axis restraint k_{ry}/P_y

applied at the tension flange for the same values of L/h used in the translational restraint study, where k_{ry} is the minor axis rotational stiffness. When plotted in this way, Trahair[13] showed that the elastic buckling solutions for flexural–torsional buckling of beams with the same modified translational and rotational restraints were identical. This was also shown to be true for elastic distortional buckling.[1]

This relationship was studied inelastically, and it was found that inelastic distortional and flexural–torsional buckling solutions for the monosymmetric beam restrained rotationally were almost identical to the beam restrained translationally (within 0·1%) when the parameters $k_t L^2/\pi^2 P_y$ and k_{ry}/P_y are selected to have the same values. Because of this, Figs 4 and 5 apply to beams restrained rotationally as well as to beams restrained translationally.

4.4 Torsional restraints

Dimensionless buckling moments M/M_P were computed for a range of dimensionless torsional restraints $k_{rz} L^2/\pi^2 GJ$ applied to the tension flange, where k_{rz} is the value of the torsional restraint. These are plotted in Fig. 6 for values of L/h of 3, 4, 6 and 10. The figure shows that in the predominantly inelastic range of distortional buckling ($L/h = 3$ and 4), the distortional buckling moment M_{Id} remains constant at the same value found for translational and rotational restraint, and approaches the elastic flexural–torsional value M_{or} for smaller values of $k_{rz} L^2/\pi^2 GJ$ as the beam becomes longer. However, the distortional buckling moment for the beam more highly restrained against torsion does not follow the lateral buckling solution, as was demonstrated elastically by Bradford.[1]

A plot of the relationship between the strengths M_{Id} and M_{Ir} and slenderness $\lambda_d = \sqrt{M_P/M_{od}}$ and $\lambda_r = \sqrt{M_P/M_{or}}$ was constructed for the beam with torsional restraint over the range of $k_{rz} L^2/\pi^2 GJ$ from 1 to 10^4. Although the values of M_{od} and M_{or} vary significantly for larger values of the modified restraint, it was found that the relationship between strength and slenderness was very close to that of Fig. 5 for both distortional and flexural–torsional buckling of torsionally restrained beams.

Figure 7 shows the eigenmodes or buckled shapes for the mono-symmetric beam with $L/h = 4$ whose bottom flange is restrained elastically against torsion. It is interesting to note that while the inelastic and elastic distortional buckling moments differ significantly for this beam over the range of torsional restraints considered, the buckled shapes are almost identical, with significant distortion being displayed, particularly for the more highly restrained beams.

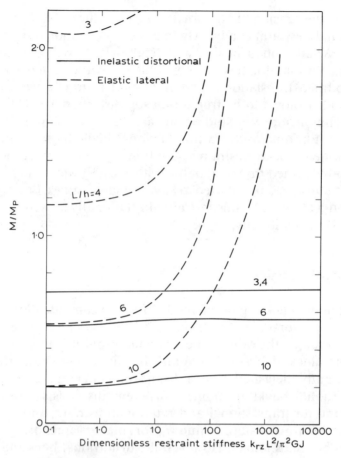

Fig. 6. Buckling of beam with torsional restraints.

5 CONCLUSIONS

An inelastic method of analysis of distortional buckling of mono-symmetric I-beams developed elsewhere[6] has been augmented to include the effects of elastic restraints against translation, minor axis rotation, torsion and warping.[1] It was shown that inelastic flexural–torsional buckling of fabricated monosymmetric beams and elastic distortional buckling of monosymmetric I-beams predicted by the computer model agreed with established solutions.

The inelastic distortional buckling moments were almost identical for translational restraints and minor axis rotational restraints on the smaller tension flange for the same values of $k_t L^2/\pi^2 P_y$ (translation) and k_{ry}/P_y (rotation). This conclusion extends the already demonstrated

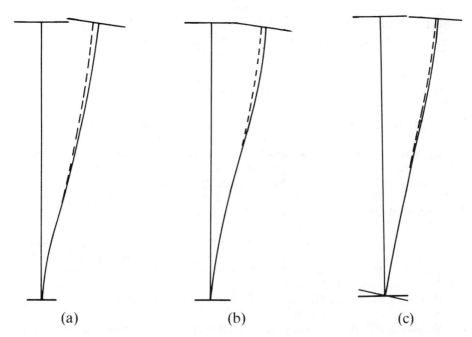

Fig. 7. Buckling mode for beam with torsional restraints ($L/h = 4$). ————, Inelastic distortional; — — —, elastic distortional; $(k_{rz}L^2)/(\pi^2\,GJ)$ is (a) 1000, (b) 1·0, and (c) 0.

behaviour for elastic flexural–torsional buckling,[13] and for elastic distortional buckling.[1] For both translational and rotational restraints, the relationship between the inelastic flexural–torsional buckling moment M_{Ir} and the modified slenderness $\lambda_r = \sqrt{M_P/M_{\mathrm{or}}}$ was the same as that between the inelastic distortional buckling moment M_{Id} and the modified slenderness $\lambda_d = \sqrt{M_P/M_{\mathrm{od}}}$.

The behaviour of monosymmetric beams restrained against torsion was similar to that of beams restrained against translation and rotation, except that long beams exhibited a near constant distortional buckling moment[1] when highly restrained. This contrasts with the flexural–torsional buckling solutions[13] for beams restrained torsionally. Although the inelastic flexural–torsional and distortional buckling moments of short beams restrained torsionally were almost identical, the eigenmode of the beam for which distortion was free to take place inelastically indicated substantial web deformation.

Finally, in the inelastic buckling range of short monosymmetric beams with translational, rotational and torsional restraints on their tension flanges, the inelastic flexural–torsional buckling moment is nearly the same as the inelastic distortional buckling moment. This is because the buckling of short beams is predominated by plasticity, so that the severe elastic web distortion that occurs for these short beams if yielding is ignored[15] has little effect on their strength.

REFERENCES

1. Bradford, M. A., Buckling of elastically restrained beams with web distortions, *Thin-Walled Structures,* **6** (1988) 287–304.
2. Johnson, R. P., & Bradford, M. A., Distortional lateral buckling of continuous composite bridge girders, *Proc. Conf. on Instability and Plastic Collapse of Steel Structures,* Manchester, 1983, 569–80.
3. Bradford, M. A., & Johnson, R. P., Inelastic buckling of composite bridge girders near internal supports, *Proc. Inst. Civ. Engrs,* Part 2, **83** (1987) 143–59.
4. Svensson, S. E., Lateral buckling of beams analysed as elastically supported columns subject to a varying axial force, *J. Const. Steel Res.,* **5** (1985) 179–93.
5. Bradford, M. A. & Trahair, N. S., Distortional buckling of I-beams, *J. Struct. Div., ASCE,* **107** (ST2) (1981) 355–70.
6. Bradford, M. A., Buckling strength of deformable monosymmetric I-beams, *Engng Structs,* **10** (1988) 167–73.
7. Bradford, M. A. & Waters, S. W., Distortional instability of fabricated, monosymmetric I-beams, *Comput. Struct.,* **29**(4) (1988) 715–24.
8. Dawe, J. L., & Kulak, G. L., Plate instability of W shapes, *J. Struct. Engng, ASCE,* **109**(6) (1983) 1278–91.
9. Bradford, M. A. & Trahair, N. S., Inelastic buckling of beam-columns with unequal end moments, *J. Const. Steel Res.,* **5** (1985) 195–212.
10. Dwight, J. B., The effect of residual stresses on structural stability. In *Residual Stresses and their Effects,* The Welding Institute, London, 1981, Chapter 5, 21–7.
11. Kitipornchai, S. & Wong-Chung, A. D., Inelastic buckling of welded monosymmetric I-beams, *J. Struct. Engng, ASCE,* **113**(4) (1987) 740–56.
12. Hornbeck, R. W., *Numerical Methods,* Quantum Publishers, New York, 1975.
13. Trahair, N. S., Elastic lateral buckling of continuously restrained beam-columns. In *The Profession of a Civil Engineer,* Sydney University Press, Sydney, 1979, 61–73.
14. Bradford, M. A., Inelastic buckling of tapered, monosymmetric I-beams, *Engng Structs,* **11**(2) (1989) 119–26.
15. Hancock, G. J., Bradford, M. A. & Trahair, N. S., Web distortion and flexural–torsional buckling, *J. Struct. Div., ASCE,* **106**(ST7) (1980) 1557–71.

SESSION 6

Thin-Walled Structures **9** (1990) 351–376

Fatigue Cracking in Damaged Cylinders Subjected to Cyclic Compressive Loading

A. C. Walker & M. K. Kwok

Department of Mechanical Engineering, University of Surrey, Guildford, Surrey GU2 5XH, UK

ABSTRACT

This paper presents the results of analytical and experimental investigations of the occurrence of cracking in thin-walled structures which are damaged and subjected to axial compressive loading with cyclically varying magnitude. The experimental investigation comprised nine test specimens, namely three plain cylinders, three plain ring stiffened and three T-ring stiffened cylinders. The paper describes the method whereby damage was inflicted on the cylinders and describes test results, including strain gauge data.

The analysis was performed using a commercial finite element program which incorporated non-linearities in the strain–displacement and stress–strain relationships. The results of the analysis were found to be in good agreement with the test results, and the occurrence of cracking was noted to be dependent on the combined levels of tensile residual stresses due to the damage and to the levels of compressive stresses due to the imposed loading.

1 INTRODUCTION

The research reported in this paper is the latest in a number of investigations into the behaviour of shells having geometries and loading similar to those encountered in offshore practice. The research has been sponsored over a number of years at a number of centres by the UK Department of Energy, and the Science and Engineering Research Council Marine Technology Directorate. The earlier work[1-4] concentrated on providing the means with which engineers could evaluate the strength

351

Thin-Walled Structures 0263–8231/90/$03·50 © 1990 Elsevier Science Publishers Ltd, England, Printed in Great Britain

of ring and stringer stiffened shells subjected to combined axial and pressure loading. The validity of the various forms of analysis — finite element, finite difference, etc. — was proved using the results from tests performed on small-scale test shells. A major achievement of that work was the development of fabrication techniques with which the shells could be welded from thin sheet steel having properties similar to that used in full-scale shells. The techniques provided shells with geometric defects and welding residual stresses of a magnitude similar to those found in practice. Thus the analysis and testing have provided a good basis for design.

It was appreciated some time ago that the collision of supply vessels with platforms is by no means a rare event[5] and that for very thin-walled cylindrical shells the damage inflicted during such collisions could result in a serious deterioration of the shell's strength. Research was commissioned to determine the degree of this deterioration and to provide engineers with guidance to aid in the assessment of the effects of damage of various types. Results of that research[6,7] showed that for the type of damage investigated, i.e. a localised dent to the skin of the shell, the loss of strength was less than had been anticipated for shells loaded primarily in axial compression. Indeed, a simple relationship could be derived for small levels of damage, which predominates in practice, relating the loss of strength to the proportional area of shell damaged in the impact to that remaining undamaged. The behaviour of damaged shells when subjected to predominantly pressure loading was found to be more complex.

Thus it appears that for small levels of damage an axially compressed shell will suffer only a small loss of strength and can remain in service, at least until repair can most conveniently be performed. However, during the period when the damaged shell is in service it will be subjected to cyclic variations in the applied loading, due to wave and wind loading on the structure as a whole. There is little information on the behaviour of shells subjected to such loading and it was to provide some insight and engineering information that the present research was initiated. Fatigue of structures is a complex subject and when combined with the non-linear characteristics of damaged shells it is obvious that a research programme of limited scope, such as this one, will not provide all the answers. Indeed, the research reported here should be regarded as a pilot project aimed at establishing if a phenomenon exists and investigating in a preliminary manner the factors which have greatest effect.

It is important, from a practical viewpoint, to appreciate two factors central to the interpretation of the research results. One relates to the use of small-scale test models in the experimental investigation. Although such models have a complete validity for the determination of strain patterns in the damaged condition and can provide results which may be directly related to full-scale tests, the same cannot yet be said of their validity for the study of the onset of fatigue cracking. Thus the tests described in this report were primarily aimed at establishing the strain distributions in the test models and correlating them with theoretical predictions. The inferences made with regard to the initiation of fatigue cracking in the small-scale models is as yet tentative. The second factor relates to the type of damage inflicted on the test shells. In the present research this took the form of a straight-edged dent, usually mid-way between the ends of the shell. Of course, there are other forms of damage which can occur in practice and thus the results of this research must be interpreted cautiously when they are to be applied to practical shells with other forms of damage. Nevertheless, despite the inherent limitations due to these two factors, the results of this programme of research have provided insight into the phenomenon of fatigue cracking in thin-walled shells and to the factors which most influence the development of the cracks.

2 TEST PROGRAMME

The testing involved the use of small-scale shells specially fabricated from sheet steel. The method of fabrication to ensure the test specimens had geometric imperfections representative of those in practical-sized shells has been developed over a number of years and used successfully in previous research.[1, 3, 6] Essentially, the skin of the shell was rolled to the specified radius and seam welded. The stiffeners were prepared from sheet, and in the case of the T-ring stiffeners machined to size. They were then clamped to the skin by copper faced jigs, and hand welded using a micro TIG technique to form the complete shell. The copper forms a very effective heat sink which minimises the thermal distortion. The whole shell is heat treated, together with specimens of the skin and stiffener material, to eliminate residual stresses and normalise the sheet material.

A total of nine test specimens were fabricated, namely three plain shells, V1–V3; three shells with plain ring stiffeners, V4–V6; and three with T-ring stiffeners, V7–V9. Details of the geometries of all the specimens are shown in Fig. 1. Each shell was welded to rigid end-rings which facilitated mounting on the testing machine. Each shell was surveyed after fabrication and attachment to the end-rings by rotating the shell relative to a fixed displacement transducer. Measurements were made at 1° intervals around the shell and at 5 mm intervals along

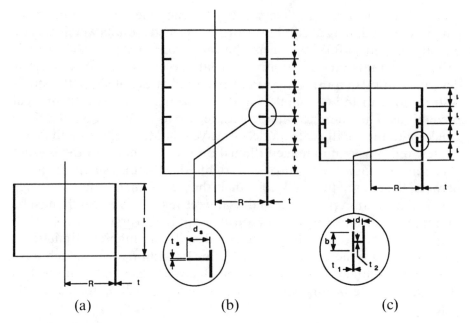

Fig. 1. Geometries of test specimens. (a) Unstiffened model (V1–V3): $R = 160$, $t = 0.84$, $l = 96$, $l/R = 0.6$, $R/t = 190.5$. (b) Plain ring stiffened model (V4–V6): $R = 160$, $t = 0.6$, $l = 40$, $d_s = 4.8$, $t_s = 0.6$, $l/R = 0.25$, $R/t = 267$, $d_s/t_s = 8$. (c) T-ring stiffened model (V7–V9): $R = 160$, $l = 24$, $d = 3$, $b = 6$, $t = 0.6$, $t_1 = 0.84$, $t_2 = 0.6$, $l/R = 0.15$, $R/t = 267$, $b/t_1 = 7.14$, $d/t_2 = 5$.

its length. The measurements were recorded in digital form and subsequently processed statistically to provide the best mean-fit cylinder and the deviations from that surface. Typical of the results are those shown in Fig. 2, in which the initial deformations are shown in pictorial form and also as components of a Fourier series. The numerical values of these Fourier components for all the shells are presented in Sridharan and Walker.[1]

Each shell was subjected to simulated damage in the form of a dent imposed radially and at right angles to the axis of the shell. The dent was imposed using the equipment shown in Fig. 3 and was such that a controlled load could be applied at a very slow rate. Both the load and the displacement of the indenter were measured and recorded. Figure 4 exemplifies the results of the indenting process and it may be seen that periodically the load was removed, thus facilitating the measurement of the permanent, i.e. residual, dent depth corresponding to a specified applied load. Example results of the relationship between the loading and the residual depths are presented.

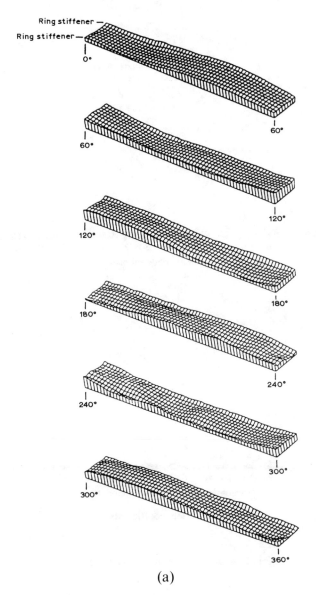

(a)

Fig. 2. Typical output of an imperfection survey for shell V6. (a) Plot of initial imperfection at mid-panel of model V6.

Subsequent to the imposition of the dent the shells were mounted in a hyperbaric test facility which permitted the simultaneous application of pressure and axial compressive loading. The loading patterns applied to the shells are shown in Table 1, which also shows the corresponding dent depths. It may be noted that some shells were subjected to various ranges of axial loading; typically the test procedure was to subject a shell to a

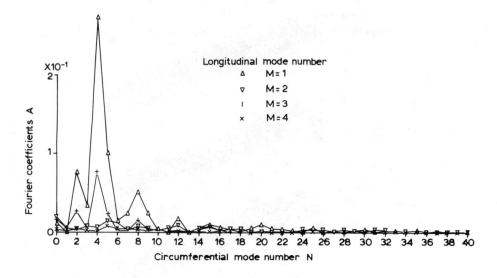

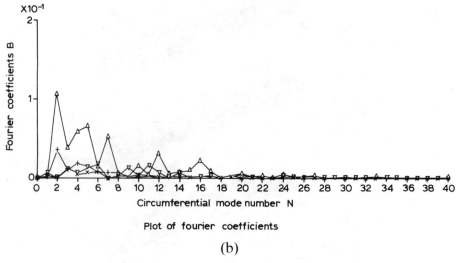

Plot of fourier coefficients

(b)

Fig. 2.—*contd.* (b) Plot of Fourier coefficients.

cyclically varying axial load at a specified range either until a crack was observed or until approximately 3×10^6 cycles had elapsed. If no cracking had occurred the amplitude of the loading was increased and the load cycling continued. The loading amplitudes varied in a sinusoidal manner at a rate of 10 Hz.

A major objective of the research reported here was to determine how well a finite element program could predict the strains, stresses and deformations during the denting process and the subsequent loading

Fig. 3. Equipment to impose damage.

phase. A further objective was to investigate if the occurrence of fatigue cracking could be predicted from the finite element results. In order to achieve these results a precise knowledge of the material characteristics was important. A large number of dynamic and quasi-static tests were performed. Figure 5 shows the results from the dynamic loading in which sinusoidally varying loads, at different amplitudes, were applied to specimens of thin sheet steel, the geometry of which is shown in the figure. A very small hole was drilled in the shell to act as a crack initiator

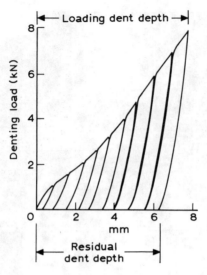

Fig. 4. Typical output of denting test (model V9).

TABLE 1
Loading Applied to Test Specimens

Shell	Residual dent depth (mm)	Hydrostatic pressure (N/mm^2)	Cyclic axial loading (kN)
V1	4·15	—	50 ± 50
V2	1·89	—	50 ± 50
V3	0·80	—	50 ± 50
V4	5·9	—	37 ± 37
V5	1·87	0·25	18·75 ± 18·7
	3·05	0·25	18·75 ± 18·7
V6	3·58	0·25	18·75 ± 18·75
			35 ± 35
V7	3·00	0·25	30 ± 30
			47·6 ± 47·6
V8	4·21	0·25	40 ± 40
			45 ± 45
			50 ± 50
V9	6·47	0·25	20 ± 20
			25 ± 25
			30 ± 30
			35 ± 35
			40 ± 40

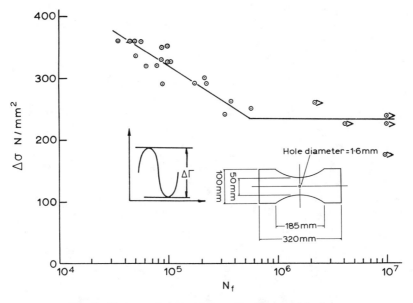

Fig. 5. Fatigue characteristics of 0·6 mm thick sheet.

and the figure relates the magnitude of the cyclic stress range at mid-length of the specimen to the number of cycles at which an observable crack was induced. Figure 6 shows a typical result for a specimen tested in quasi-static conditions. It may be seen that the sheet material had a very distinct yield point and an extensive yield plateau. Values of the material properties averaged over a number of specimens are shown in Table 2; the maximum deviation from these average values was less than 5%.

3 NUMERICAL ANALYSIS

As stated above, a primary objective of the research was to determine how well a finite element program could predict the strains and deformations in a highly deformed shell, which incorporated non-linear strain–displacement and stress–strain relationships. The analysis reported here was performed using LUSAS, a commercially available finite element program developed by Finite Element Analysis Ltd (FEAL). LUSAS had already been subjected to a series of non-linear benchmark tests which had engendered some confidence in the program's capacity to cope with non-linear requirements in the present project. It is worth noting here, however, that the application of LUSAS to these non-linear

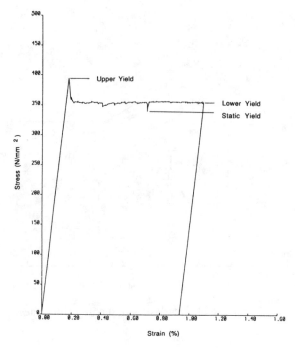

Fig. 6. Tensile characteristics of stress-relieved sheet steel.

TABLE 2
Material Properties of Stress-Relieved Sheet Steel

	Yield stress σ_0 (N/mm²)	Elastic modulus E (kN/mm²)	Poisson's ratio ν
0·6 mm Thick sheet steel	387	208	0·28
0·84 mm Thick sheet steel	313	202	0·3
Plain ring stiffeners	387	207	
T-Ring stiffeners	366	205	

shell analyses was not a straightforward matter. The analyses required significant understanding on the part of the research team of the physics of the shell behaviour to be able to arrive at the results presented here and in Walker and Kwok.[8]

The analyses performed using LUSAS were essentially quasi-static with no truly dynamic effects being considered. This corresponded fairly accurately to the physical test conditions in which the cyclic loading rate was quite low. The analysis process was performed in two stages; the first stage was the simulation of the generation of the damage to the shell, followed by the second stage which was to replicate the effects of applying pressure and axial loading to the damaged shell. Computer space and time was reduced by employing symmetry conditions such that only one eighth of the shell surface was modelled in the finite element mesh. The mesh geometries for the various types of shells are shown in Figs 7–9. The element formulation used was an isoparametric shell element with eight nodes. The stiffeners were also modelled using that shell element. The non-linear geometric deformations were accommodated by a total Lagrangian formulation and the non-linear material properties were modelled by the von Mises yield criterion and the Hencky flow rule.

The first stage in the analysis proved to be difficult and time-consuming since LUSAS does not incorporate an efficient contact element. The effect of the indenter bar impinging on the skin of the shell was simulated in the manner shown schematically in Fig. 10. Essentially, an applied radial displacement was prescribed for node A and the amplitude increased until the dent depth attained the value at which node B was contacted. The radial displacement was then prescribed equally for nodes A and B and increased in amplitude until node C would be contacted, and so on. In the event this proved to be fairly successful in simulating the application of the denting load. The unloading process was essentially a reverse of the loading process. However, considerable difficulty was experienced in achieving a set of prescribed displacements which ensured zero loads on all the nodes

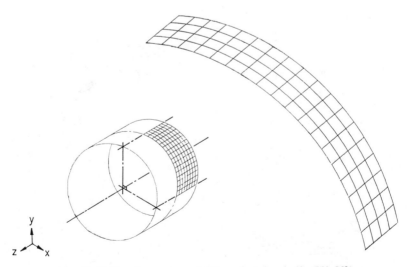

Fig. 7. Finite element modelling of plain shells (V1–V3).

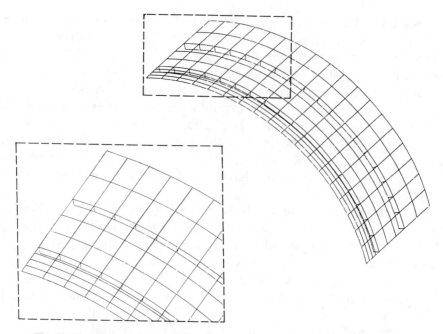

Fig. 8. Finite element modelling of plane ring stiffened shells (V4–V6).

involved in the deformations. This required a trial-and-error process which, although successful, required considerable computer time.

The application of simulated external loading to the damaged shell modelled on the computer was fairly straightforward.

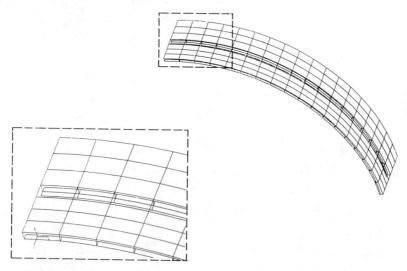

Fig. 9. Finite element modelling of T-ring stiffened shells (V7–V9).

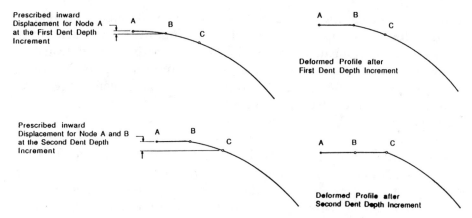

Fig. 10. Finite element simulation of denting test.

4 TEST RESULTS

This section presents briefly the results of the tests and comparisons with the corresponding computer results. Unfortunately, because of space restrictions it is only possible to report on selected results; details of all results are presented in Walker and Kwok.[8]

4.1 Plain shells (V1–V3)

These shells were tested at the outset of the programme to determine if indeed cracks could develop in the region of the damage. Compared to the ring stiffened shells the plain specimens had very little instrumentation. Nevertheless, some strain gauges were attached to model V2 to obtain a measure of the non-linearity of the strains in the region of the dent. The loading magnitude was arranged such that the maximum was less than 50% of the shells' collapse capacity. An undamaged but otherwise nominally identical shell had been tested previously and had collapsed at a quasi-static value of purely longitudinal compression of 208 kN.[5] Thus the maximum load used in the present tests is less than half this value and about 80% of the design load according to accepted offshore design codes.

Figure 11 shows results from the denting tests on shells V1–V3; it is evident that the results from all three shells were fairly consistent and that there is reasonable agreement with analytical predictions. A plastic mechanism analysis has been developed[9] to provide an engineering approach to the energy absorption of a plain shell subject to a slow impact. That simplified analysis makes assumptions with regard to the form of the damage and considers the remainder of the shell to be rigid. A plastic mechanism approach, in which the boundaries of the mechanism were modelled as plastic hinges, was followed to arrive at a relationship between the applied indenter load and the corresponding residual dent depth. The predictions of this simplified approach are seen in Fig. 11 to be in good agreement with the corresponding results from LUSAS and the tests.

Shell V1 was dented to a depth of 4·15 mm, i.e. five times the skin thickness, and subjected to cyclic loading with amplitude varying between 0 kN and 100 kN, compressive. After about 3.0×10^6 cycles of loading, cracks were observed on the outside of the shell at the ends of the dent. These cracks extended rapidly with continuation of the cyclic loading until at 3.8×10^6 cycles they had extended substantially across the dent.

Shell V2 was dented to a depth of 1·9 mm, and then subjected to cyclic loading. Substantial cracking developed in the shell after about 3×10^6 cycles. A view of the exterior of V2 showing the cracking is given in Fig. 12. The cracks extended through the thickness of the shell. Six strain gauges had been attached to the shell, three inside and three outside, as shown in Fig. 13, all aligned to measure longitudinal strains. The strains were found to diminish very rapidly from the end of the dent region into the undamaged portion of the shell, but it may be seen from Fig. 13 that at position 1, very near to the end of the dent, there was very substantial

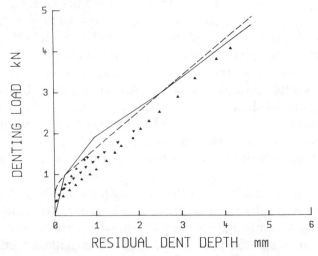

Fig. 11. Plot of denting load vs residual dent depth of models V1–V3. ▲, V1 (4·15 mm); ▼, V2 (1·89); +, V3 (0·80 mm); ———, LUSAS's result; — — —, plastic analysis.

Fig. 12. Exterior view of cracked model V2.

bending, with the membrane strain deviating only very gradually from the nominal value as the loading was increased. The comparison of the test results with the corresponding LUSAS values is shown in Fig. 14, which indicates a reasonable agreement except very close to the dent, where the measured strain is greater than that predicted.

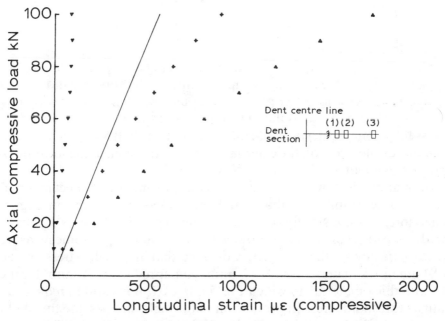

Fig. 13. Plot of axial compressive load versus longitudinal strain at position no. 1 on model V2. ▲, External; ▲, internal, +, membrane; ———, nominal.

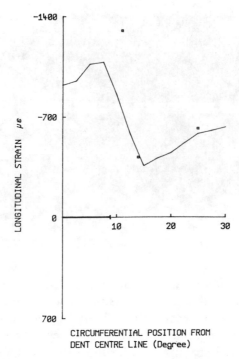

Fig. 14. Exterior surface strain of model V2: axial load = 100 kN. □, Model V2; ————, LUSAS's result.

All the measured strains due to the applied loading were compressive in nature and not likely to cause fatigue cracking at the number of cycles applied in this test. Therefore, we must consider the superposition of the residual stresses and the applied stresses as a mechanism for widening cracking. Figure 15 shows theoretical values of the longitudinal residual stress for a dent depth similar to that imposed on shell V2. It may be seen that the tensile stress on the external surface of the shell at the location of gauge 1 is about 190 N/mm².

No material tests were carried out on the 0·84 mm thick sheet material in a manner similar to that which generated the results in Fig. 5. Therefore, it is not strictly possible to interrogate the analysis results to predict the onset of cracking. However, it is possible to get some measure of the efficacy of the analysis. Consider that the yield stress of the 0·84 mm thick material was 310 N/mm² comapred to 385 N/mm² for the 0·6 mm thick material, to which Fig. 5 relates. If it is valid to reduce the fatigue threshold stress in proportion to the yield stresses, the threshold stress for the 0·84 mm thick material would have been about 180 N/mm². Of course, this is a somewhat naïve and oversimplified approach and

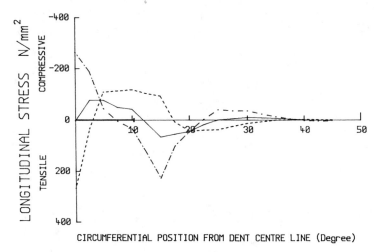

Fig. 15. Longitudinal residual stress at residual dent depth of 2·60 mm for shell V2.
———, Membrane; — · — ·, exterior surface; — — —, interior surface.

fatigue tests should be performed on the material. Nevertheless, the above approach may give some insight to the value of the analysis results. Thus, shell V2 was found to have a tensile stress range of zero to 190 N/mm^2 which, in comparison with the surmised material fatigue threshold of 180 N/mm^2, would indicate that cracking should occur, and indeed cracking was observed in the test.

The numerical results showed that increasing the dent depth did not significantly increase the magnitude of the maximum residual stress. On the other hand if the residual stress magnitudes decreased significantly and at a dent depth similar to that imposed on **Shell V3**, i.e. 0·8 mm, the maximum tensile residual stress was about 100 N/mm^2, which is below the threshold at which fatigue cracking would be induced in the sheet material used in the test shells. Indeed, even after 3·5 × 10^6 cycles of loading no fatigue cracking was observed in shell V3.

4.2 Plain ring stiffened shells (V4–V6)

All the shells in this series had the same geometry and were all dented prior to fatigue loading. With the exception of shell V4, the cyclic compressive loading was applied in conjunction with external pressure which was constant throughout the test.

The results of the denting tests on all these shells are presented in Fig. 16, where it may be seen that the comparison with the LUSAS and the plastic mechanism analyses is very good. It may also be noted here that

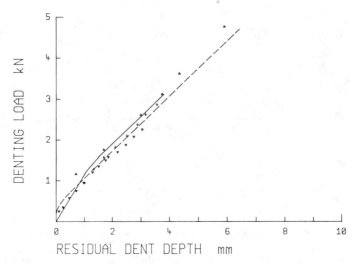

Fig. 16. Plot of denting loading versus residual dent depth of models V4–V6. ▲, V4 (5·90 mm); ▼, V5 (3·05 mm); +, V6 (3·58 mm); ————, LUSAS's result; — — —, plastic analysis.

the LUSAS analysis shows that at a dent depth of 1·2 mm, or greater, the dent form seems to be established and the stiffness of the shell against further penetration is constant.

Shell V4 was essentially a preliminary test to establish that the presence of plain ring stiffeners would not inhibit the development of cracking at the damage zone. The shell was dented to a residual depth of 5·9 mm, and the shell loaded cyclically in compression varying sinusoidally between 0 kN and 74 kN. The first sign of cracking occurred at about $3·6 \times 10^4$ cycles with a rapid rate of increase so that by $9·6 \times 10^4$ cycles the cracks were 20 mm long.

Shell V5 was strain gauged as shown in Fig. 17, and Fig. 18 shows a typical result of the residual strains measured during the denting test. The comparison of test and LUSAS results are good and engender confidence in the efficacy of the finite element method at large strain levels. The corresponding stress results are shown in Fig. 19, where it can be seen that a significant level of tensile residual stress has been induced in the shell surface. Thus on the basis of the argument presented above, even if the applied loads induce compressive stresses there is a possibility of fatigue cracking occurring. The shell was subjected to a pressure of $0·25 \text{ N/mm}^2$ and a cyclic loading varying between 0 kN and 37·5 kN. This loading was observed to induce a maximum compressive stress at the edge of the dent of about 190 N/mm^2, i.e. less than that which in combination with the tensile residual stress would result in fatigue

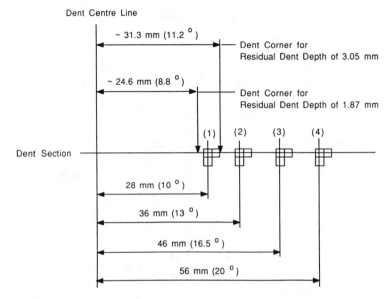

Fig. 17. Layout of strain gauges on model V5.

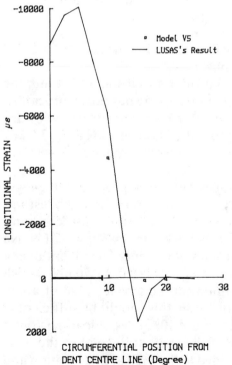

Fig. 18. Residual strain on exterior surface of model V5: residual dent depth = 1·87 mm. □, Model V5; ———, LUSAS's result.

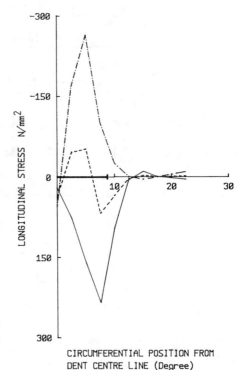

Fig. 19. Residual stresses of model V5: residual dent depth = 1·87 mm. ———, Exterior surface; —·—·, interior surface; — — —, membrane.

CIRCUMFERENTIAL POSITION FROM DENT CENTRE LINE (Degree)

cracking. Indeed, even when the shell had been subjected to $1·5 \times 10^6$ cycles of loading, no cracking was observed.

The dent depth was increased to 3·05 mm and it was noted that the maximum tensile residual stress increased slightly but not significantly. The shell was then subjected simultaneously to a pressure of 0·25 N/mm^2 and a compressive load varying sinusoidally between 0 kN and 37·5 kN. After 3×10^6 cycles of loading no cracks were observed and the test was discontinued.

Shell V6 was fitted with strain gauges and crack propagation gauges subsequent to being dented to a depth of 3·6 mm. A preliminary test was performed in which the shell was loaded to a pressure of 0·25 N/mm^2 and a compressive cyclic loading varying between 0 kN and 37 kN. No cracking was induced after 1×10^6 cycles of loading. The magnitude of the maximum compressive loading was increased to 70 kN, which theoretically should induce a maximum cyclic tensile value of about 270 N/mm^2. According to the data in Fig. 6, this should be sufficient to induce cracking and indeed after about 1×10^6 cycles of loading cracks were observed on the outer surface of the shell at the end of the dent. Crack detection gauges had been bonded to the shell at that location and

Fig. 20 shows the rate of development of the crack in which each step increase in resistance marks the progress of the crack through the strands of the gauge. The mean propagation rate was calculated from Fig. 20 to be 1.25×10^{-5} mm/cycle of loading. An exterior view of shell V6 in its cracked state is shown in Fig. 21.

4.3 T-Ring stiffened cylinders

All the shells in this series had the same geometry and were subjected to the same pressure loading, viz. 0.25 N/mm^2.

The comparison of example theoretical and test results obtained during the denting procedure is shown in Fig. 22. It is evident that LUSAS predicts quite well the deformations for specified loading for dent depths greater than about 2·5 mm. The marked change in the slope of the line predicted by LUSAS is caused by the T-ring stiffeners yielding and then buckling locally. Since the computer program does not incorporate any form of imperfection in the shape of the stiffeners, it is probable that the deviation between the test and theoretical predictions for small dent depths is due to non-linear buckling of the stiffeners. The correspondence between the strain gauge results and the theoretical values, shown in Fig. 23, is generally very good, even in the regions with very large strains.

A test was performed in which the compressive cyclic loading varied

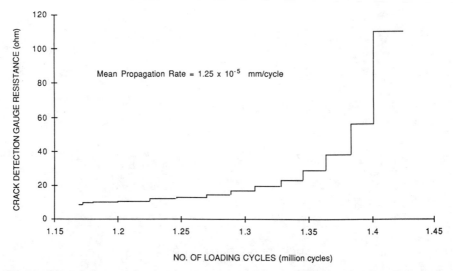

Fig. 20. Plot of change of resistance versus number of loading cycles of crack detection gauge on model V6.

Fig. 21. Exterior view of cracked model V6.

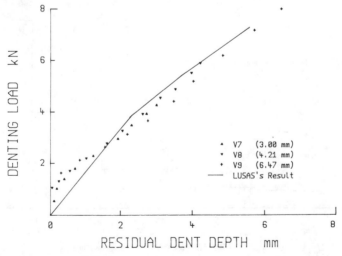

Fig. 22. Plot of denting load versus residual dent depth of models V7–V9. ▲, V7 (3·00 mm); ▼, V8 (4·21 mm); +, V9 (6·47 mm); ————, LUSAS's result.

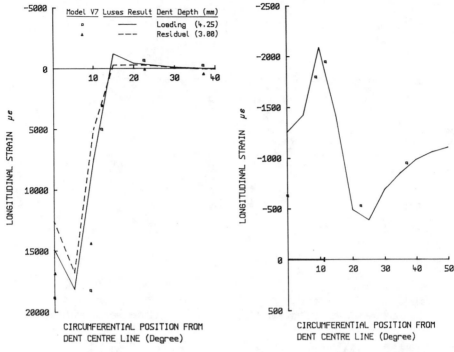

Fig. 23. Interior surface strain on model V7 during denting test.

Fig. 24. Exterior surface strain of model V7: combine loading pressure = 0·25 N/mm + axial load = 95 kN. □, Model V7; ———, LUSAS's result.

between 0 kN and 60 kN in addition to the applied pressure. After 3×10^6 cycles of loading no cracking was observed. The maximum cyclic load was increased to 95 kN with a similar result. The shell collapsed prematurely at 100 kN when a further increase in loading was attempted. A comparison between an example theoretical result for **Shell V7** and the corresponding strain gauge values is shown in Fig. 24.

Theoretical predictions for the variation of the residual stresses and the maximum applied stresses around the shell are shown in Fig. 25. It may be inferred that the maximum tensile stress induced in the shell by the cyclically varying loading is 210 N/mm² which is below the threshold at which fatigue cracking would be induced. Hence the absence of fatigue cracks in the test specimens is understandable.

Shells V8 and **V9** were dented to greater depths and subjected to similar ranges of cyclic loading, as shown in Table 1. In neither of these shells was any cracking observed at the damage zone. Analysis predicted that at the maximum intensity of applied compressive cyclic loading the

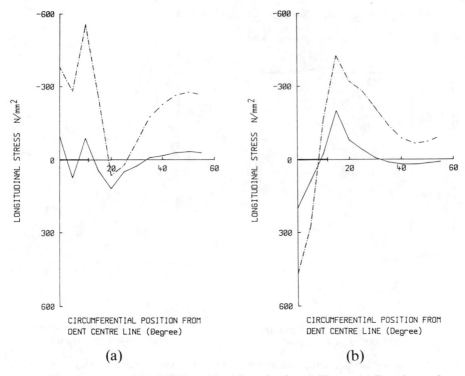

Fig. 25. Surface stress of model V7: residual dent depth = 3·00 mm. (a) Exterior surface; (b) interior surface. ————, Residual; — · — ·, total.

maximum tensile stress induced in the shell by the combination of the applied compressive loading and the tensile residual stresses was from zero to 183 N/mm² for shell V8 and from zero to 184 N/mm² for shell V9. Both these values were below the threshold value necessary to induce fatigue cracking.

5 COMMENTS AND CONCLUSIONS

The primary purpose of this research was to investigate the possible incidence of fatigue-induced cracking in thin-walled cylinders which have suffered a form of damage and then been subjected to pressure and axial compressive loading, the amplitude of the latter varying between zero and a specified value. Attention was focussed on determining the stresses induced in the shell near the damaged area, during both the damage process and the subsequent loading. The determination of the stress distribution in these shells was also the subject of finite element analysis, using a commercially available program.

Observations during the tests, and subsequent interpretation of strain gauge results, showed that cracks will be induced in damaged cylinders due to cyclically varying compressive stresses being induced by the applied loading at a location of adequately intense tensile residual stresses. If the dent depth is small the level of the tensile stresses is not sufficient to exceed the fatigue threshold stress for the material. On the other hand, if the dent is adequately deep to develop a sufficiently high level of tensile stresses, a fatigue crack will develop only if the compressive stresses induced by the applied loading are also of sufficient magnitude.

Tests on plain and plain ring stiffened shells showed that if the dent depth was greater than about 1·5–2 times the shell thickness and if the maximum applied compressive load exceeded 50% of the failure load of an undamaged counterpart, the conditions were theoretically appropriate for the initiation of a fatigue crack, and indeed such through-thickness cracks were observed in the test specimens. It was also noted that provided the dent was greater than the minimum depth, the level of the tensile residual stresses did not increase significantly with increases in the dent depth. The tests on the T-ring stiffened cylinders showed that the denting process induced tensile stresses of a more than sufficient level. However, perhaps because of the greater stiffness of the T-ring stiffeners compared to their plain counterparts, it was not possible for sustainable levels of compressive loading to generate stresses in the shell of an adequate magnitude to cause cracking, and indeed no cracks were observed in the T-ring stiffened test models.

The numerical analysis provided results which were in remarkably good agreement with the corresponding test results, given the extremely non-linear nature of the shell behaviour in the region of the dent. However, the analyses consumed very considerable resources in manpower and computing facilities due to this non-linear behaviour. Another significant difficulty encountered in the numerical work followed from the need to treat the damage process in a step-by-step manner, as described in Section 3. In reality, the imposition of damage by an indenter is a continuously varying contact problem, and although some programs, including LUSAS, incorporate contact elements, experience has shown that they are not efficient when dealing with structurally non-linear systems. Contact elements introduce another level of non-linearity, and in many practical instances the calculation routines fail to converge. Nevertheless, it may be concluded that the finite element analyses provided accurate and valuable predictions of the stresses and deformations in the region of the dent, during both the damage process and the subsequent stages of applied loading.

This programme of research should be viewed as preliminary and care should be taken in interpreting the results from the specific form of damage considered here to other forms which may occur in practice. Particularly, there is a need to test shells at a greater scale than here, to corroborate the initial results of this programme and to provide a greater base of data for the guidance of engineers.

ACKNOWLEDGEMENTS

The authors would like to acknowledge the financial support of the UK Department of Energy and the SERC Marine Technology Directorate. They also gratefully acknowledge the input of Stuart McCall to this programme and the contribution of his skill and ingenuity in facilitating the performance of the tests.

REFERENCES

1. Sridharan, S. & Walker, A. C., Experimental investigation of the buckling behaviour of stiffened cylindrical shells. Department of Energy, Report No. OT-R-7835, London, February 1980.
2. Galletley, G. D. & Pemsing, K., Interactive buckling tests on cylindrical shells subjected to axial compression and external pressure — a comparison of experiments, theory and various codes. *Proc. Inst. Mech. Engrs,* **99**(C4) (1985) 259–80.
3. Walker, A. C. & McCall, S., Buckling tests on stringer stiffened cylinder models subjected to load combinations. Det norske Veritas, Report 82-0299, 1982.
4. Nelson, H. M., Green, D. R. & Phillips, D. V., Buckling studies of large diameter stiffened tubes — pilot test. University of Glasgow, Civil Engineering Department, June 1978.
5. Ellinas, C. P. & Valsgaard, S., Collisions and damage of offshore structures — a state of the art. *J. Energy Resources Technology,* **107** (1985) 297–314.
6. Kwok, M. K., McCall, S. & Walker, A. C., The behaviour of damaged cylindrical shells subjected to static and dynamic loading. In *Advances in Solid Mechanics — 2,* Elsevier Applied Science, London, 1987.
7. Onofriou, A. & Harding, J. E., Residual strength of damaged ring-stiffened cylinders. *Proc. OMAE Conf.,* Dallas, Texas, February 1985.
8. Walker, A. C. & Kwok, M. K., Fatigue characteristics of damaged cylinders. Report to Department of Energy, London, 1988.
9. Walker, A. C. & Kwok, M. K., Process of damage in thin-walled cylindrical shells. In *Advances in Marine Structures,* Elsevier Applied Science, London, 1987.

Thin-Walled Structures **9** (1990) 377–387

On the Use of Bubble Functions in Stability Analysis

R. Lawther

School of Civil Engineering, The University of New South Wales, Kensington, New South Wales 2033, Australia

ABSTRACT

Bubble functions are finite element modes that are located entirely within a single element. Elements with such modes have an added complexity, and are generally not favoured in linear analysis. This is because the extra element complexity is not rewarded with a commensurate improvement in performance. The use of bubble elements in buckling analysis is examined, taking frame elements as a starting point. Two formulations are presented, and the greatly improved performance of these is demonstrated. The results indicate that the efficiency of bubble formulations needs to be re-thought.

1 INTRODUCTION

One of the underlying characteristics of thin-walled structures is that they are prone to buckling, and consequently buckling (and post-buckling) is a very important phenomenon in their analysis. This paper is concerned directly with buckling, and begins an investigation into the part that bubble function formulations can play in such analyses. Here the concentration is on the elastic buckling of plane frames, although the extension to three-dimensional frames follows directly, and the principles can be applied to finite elements for the buckling analysis of any structures. The results show a greatly improved performance for a small increase in complexity. It is also shown that the bubble elements can be defined and assembled in such a way that the structure stiffness and stability matrices require very little storage space above that required by the usual minimal elements.

Thin-Walled Structures 0263-8231/90/$03·50 © 1990 Elsevier Science Publishers Ltd, England. Printed in Great Britain

2 BUBBLE FUNCTIONS

In finite element analysis the term *bubble function* refers to a mode which has non-zero values in the interior of an element but has zero values on the boundary. The name is derived from the obvious analogy to the displacements of a soap bubble. Bubbles can be written in terms of displacements, stresses or any parameters that define the element, but this work will concentrate on buckling analysis using displacement field elements, so here *bubble* will mean a displacement bubble, that is, a displacement mode that admits non-zero displacements in the interior of an element but is zero at all nodal freedoms where the element connects to an adjacent one.

A bubble function represents a displacement mode of the element beyond the minimal configuration of modes needed to give a compatible assembly. An element with bubble displacements is therefore more complex than is required, and its use must be justified in terms of superior performance. It is the old problem of balancing element complexity against mesh complexity. In linear analysis it is usually found that a greater improvement in accuracy will come from refining a mesh of minimal elements rather than using the more complex bubble elements.

The usual finite element for plane frame buckling analysis[1] is based on linear axial movements and a cubic polynomial for the transverse movements. This element is minimal. Bubbles can be created by adding any other functions to the transverse deflections, including fourth and/or higher order polynomials.

Two such formulations are presented here. The first, *bubble element (i)*, is based on transverse displacements generated from a quartic polynomial, leading to an element with five transverse freedoms, and seven in all. Details of the generation are given in the next section. Following initial testing, a second formulation, *bubble element (ii)*, was developed, and its details are also given in the following section.

3 GENERATION OF THE FRAME ELEMENTS

Bubble element (i) is based on transverse displacements represented by the kernel functions

$$[1 \quad x \quad x^2 \quad x^3 \quad x^4]$$

Compatible assembly requires that the nodal freedoms include the end displacements and rotations, but we are free to choose the fifth nodal freedom in many ways, with probably the most obvious choice being the deflection at midspan. However, the fifth freedom is here taken as the multiplier of x^4. With these nodal freedoms the shape functions of the element are

$$N_1 = 2(x + 0.5L)(x - L)^2/L^3 \tag{1a}$$

$$N_2 = x(x - L)^2/L^2 \tag{1b}$$

$$N_3 = -2x^2(x - 1.5L)/L^3 \tag{1c}$$

$$N_4 = x^2(x - L)/L^2 \tag{1d}$$

$$N_5 = 3x^2(x - L)^2/L^4 \tag{1e}$$

The multiplier used in N_5 is arbitrary, and is here chosen to give strain energy of a magnitude similar to that of the other shape functions.

Member stiffness and stability matrices are now given by

$$k_{ij} = EI \int N_i'' N_j'' \, dx \tag{2a}$$

$$s_{ij} = P_0 \int N_i' N_j' \, dx \tag{2b}$$

where P_0 is the member axial force.

Choosing the shape functions in this way gives two advantages. The first four shape functions are those of the conventional element, and therefore so are the first four rows and columns of the element stiffness and stability matrices. Secondly the additional submatrices are sparse — the stiffness matrix has only a diagonal non-zero added while the stability matrix has a diagonal term and essentially one off-diagonal term. The sparsity of the stiffness matrix can be explained by the work theorem, which shows that any bubble, when differentiated twice, must be orthogonal to $N_1'' \ldots N_4''$, although for the particular bubble treated here a simpler proof is to note that N_5'' is a Legendre polynomial (necessarily of higher order than $N_1'' \ldots N_4''$).

The element matrices are

$$\mathbf{k} = \frac{EI}{L^3} \begin{bmatrix} 12 & 6L & -12 & 6L & 0 \\ 6L & 4L^2 & -6L & 2L^2 & 0 \\ -12 & -6L & 12 & -6L & 0 \\ 6L & 2L^2 & -6L & 4L^2 & 0 \\ 0 & 0 & 0 & 0 & 7.2 \end{bmatrix} \tag{3a}$$

$$\mathbf{s} = \frac{P_0}{30L} \begin{bmatrix} 36 & 3L & -36 & 3L & 0 \\ 3L & 4L^2 & -3L & -L^2 & 3L \\ -36 & -3L & 36 & -3L & 0 \\ 3L & -L^2 & -3L & 4L^2 & -3L \\ 0 & 3L & 0 & -3L & 36/7 \end{bmatrix} \tag{3b}$$

These matrices show the flexural terms only. The axial terms are the usual $\pm EA/L$ in the stiffness matrix, and zeros in the stability matrix.

Tests with this element showed a performance greatly superior to that of the minimal element (see example 1 below) but also indicated that further improvement was possible, particularly for the stiffer columns. A second formulation was devised, taking the fifth shape function as a linear combination of the previous quartic and a symmetric sixth order polynomial. After some trial and error the shape function

$$(N_5 = 3(x^2(x-L)^2/L^4 - x^3(x-L)^3/L^6) \tag{4}$$

was adopted. This shape function has been designed to reduce the worst error in analysing the family of columns of example 1.

With this, bubble element (ii) has stiffness and stability matrices similar to those given above, but with

$$k_{55} = 10 \cdot 8 EI/L^3 \tag{5a}$$

$$s_{25} = (51L/14) P_0/30L \tag{5b}$$

$$s_{45} = -s_{25} \tag{5c}$$

$$s_{55} = (621/77) P_0/30L \tag{5d}$$

As before, the multiplier of 3 in the definition of N_5 is arbitrary, and was chosen to make the stiffness of this shape similar to the others.

4 PERFORMANCE OF THE FRAME ELEMENTS

4.1 Example 1 — Restrained column

This example treats a column with various degrees of rotational and translational end restraints, as is shown in Fig. 1. The column has uniform EI, and a span of L. The end conditions shown in Fig. 1(a)–(e) are five cases where the restraints are either zero or completely fixed, and are extreme examples of more general restraints. Calculated elastic buckling loads of these structures are given in Table 1, where the performance of both bubble elements can be compared to that of the conventional element, with both one and two elements being used to model the column. Figure 2 shows error envelopes for over 40 structures of the family, with various stiffnesses chosen for the restraints.

The results given in Table 1 show that bubble element (i) gives vastly superior performance to the conventional element (except for structure c, where both models give the same result, and where the conventional

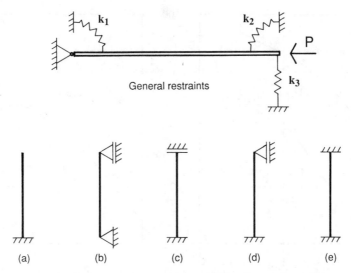

Fig. 1. Elastically restrained column: (a)–(e) five end conditions.

element is unusually accurate). The accuracy of this bubble element is much closer to that of an assembly using two conventional elements (Fig. 2). This assembly is generally considered as the minimum required to adequately represent a compression member, and such a subdivision adds one node to the structure, and hence three equations to the system (two if the axial freedom is constrained or otherwise eliminated).

TABLE 1
Predicted Buckling Loads for the Structures of Fig. 1(a)–(e)

Model	Structure				
	a	*b*	*c*	*d*	*e*
Theoretical	2·467	9·870	9·870	20·191	39·478
One element	2·486	12·000	10·000	30·000	∞
	0·75	22	1·3	49	∞
Two elements	2·469	9·944	9·944	20·709	40·000
	0·05	0·75	0·75	2·6	1·3
Bubble element (i)	2·468	9·875	10·000	20·919	42·000
	0·01	0·06	1·3	3·6	6·4
Bubble element (ii)	2·468	9·879	10·000	20·805	40·206
	0·02	0·10	1·3	3·0	1·8

Results given are values of $P_{cr}L^2/EI$ and % error.

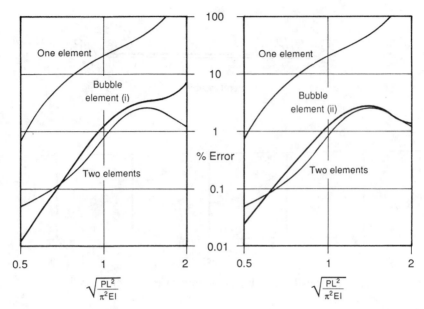

Fig. 2. Error envelopes for the calculated critical loads of restrained columns.

Member subdivision is considerably more demanding of storage space (and time) than is the use of bubbles, even without the space saving techniques treated in the Appendix.

Bubble element (ii) has been developed specifically to improve the accuracy in analysing the stiffer members of this family of columns. The basis of this element has been given previously, and its performance over a range of restraint stiffnesses is shown in Fig. 2. This element shows a worst case error of 3·0%, compared to the 6·4% worst error of bubble element (i). A worst case error of 3·0% is as good as can be realised for this problem with *any* single bubble.

4.2 Example 2 — Open-web joist

The first four buckling loads of the open-web joist shown in Fig. 3 were calculated, and the results of various models are given in Table 2.

The modes are not multiple modes but are symmetric/antisymmetric pairs at very close load values. In this example the minimal element model with one element per member is completely inadequate, as might be expected. With this model, the modes corresponding to the values in Table 2 bear little resemblance to the true modes of the structure, and no realistic detailed comparison is possible. Again, both bubble elements give useful results with only one element per member, with bubble element (ii) showing greater accuracy than bubble element (i). The

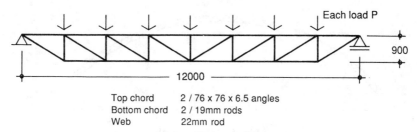

Fig. 3. Open-web joist.

Top chord	2 / 76 x 76 x 6.5 angles
Bottom chord	2 / 19mm rods
Web	22mm rod

storage used is little more than that of the minimal elements. When each compression member is modelled with two conventional elements the performance is between that of the two bubble elements, but this analysis requires considerably more equations and much more storage space. When all members are modelled with two conventional elements the result is marginally more accurate than the better bubble element, but at the cost of greatly increased storage.

TABLE 2
Predicted Buckling Loads for the Open-web Joist of Fig. 3

Model	Equations storage	P_1	P_2	P_3	P_4
Theoretical		28·79	28·79	42·05	42·07
One element	44	95·00	134·7	188·5	260·7
	358	—	—	—	—
Two elements[a]	90	30·72	30·72	44·01	44·04
	835	6·7	6·7	4·6	4·6
Two elements[b]	132	29·84	29·84	43·29	43·31
	1 279	3·6	3·6	2·9	2·9
Bubble element (i)	74	31·18	31·18	45·31	45·31
	416[c]	8·3	8·3	7·7	7·8
Bubble element (ii)	74	30·09	30·09	43·57	43·60
	416[c]	4·5	4·5	3·6	3·6

Results given are values of buckling load factor, P_{cr} (kN), and % error.
[a]Two elements used to model each compression member.
[b]Two elements used to model each member.
[c]Average storage for **K** and **S**.

4.3 Example 3 — Trussed arch

The trussed arch shown in Fig. 4 has a uniformly distributed load applied to the bottom chord. All members are hollow circular sections with 140 mm outside diameter and 5·4 mm wall thickness. The

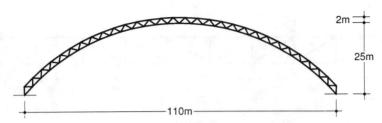

Fig. 4. Trussed arch.

distributed load is modelled as a downward load of P at each bottom chord joint. The results of several analyses are shown in Table 3, where again the first four modes are given.

Like the previous structure, this arch has symmetric/antisymmetric mode pairs at very close load values. These modes involve fairly local deformations of the bottom chords near to the supports. It also has a typical arch buckling mode at around $P = 127$ kN (this is the lowest mode predicted by the 'one element' model). Again, the one element per member model is inadequate, but all of the other models give accurate results. Bubble element (ii) is considerably more accurate than using two elements for each member even though it uses significantly fewer equations and very much smaller storage.

TABLE 3
Predicted Buckling Loads for the Trussed-Arch of Fig. 4

Model	Equations storage	P_1	P_2	P_3	P_4
Theoretical		68·46	68·46	76·71	76·71
One element	179	127·2	134·2	134·2	157·8
	1 403	—	96	96	106
Two elements[a]	251	69·12	69·12	77·83	77·83
	2 003	1·0	1·0	1·5	1·5
Two elements[b]	536	69·09	69·09	77·67	77·67
	5 042	0·91	0·91	1·3	1·3
Bubble element (i)	298	69·24	69·24	78·23	78·23
	1 641[c]	1·1	1·1	2·0	2·0
Bubble element (ii)	298	68·53	68·53	77·23	77·23
	1 641[c]	0·10	0·10	0·68	0·68

Results given are values of buckling load factor, P_{cr} (kN), and % error.
[a] Two elements used to model the 25 most heavily loaded compression members.
[b] Two elements used to model each member.
[c] Average storage for **K** and **S**.

5 CONCLUSIONS

Finite elements with a bubble displacement freedom predict frame buckling loads that are far more accurate than those obtained using the conventional minimal element. The accuracy is of the same order of magnitude as is given by an assembly of two conventional elements — an assembly that requires considerably more space (and solution time) than does the bubble element representation.

While this investigation has been restricted to frame structures, there is no reason to doubt that similar benefits will be found with bubble formulations for other problems. Since bubble displacements are very localised displacements, local buckling stands out as a particularly promising area of application.

REFERENCES

1. Przemienieki, J. S., *Theory of Matrix Structural Analysis*, Prentice-Hall, Englewood Cliffs, New Jersey, 1968.
2. Lawther, R. & Kabaila, A. P., Modification of the power method for the determination of eigenvalues, *Proc. 4th Int. Conf. FEM in Aust.*, University of Melbourne, Melbourne, 1982.
3. Aitken, A. C., Studies in practical mathematics, *Proc. Roy. Soc. Edinburgh*, **57** (1937).
4. Wilkinson, J. H., *The Algebraic Eigenvalue Problem*, Oxford University Press, Oxford, UK, 1965.
5. Jennings, A., A compact storage scheme for the solution of linear simultaneous equations, *Computer J.*, **9** (1966) 281–5.
6. Mondkar, D. P. & Powell, G. H., Towards optimal in-core equation solving, *Comput. Struct.*, **4** (1974) 531–48.

APPENDIX

This Appendix looks at the storage and manipulation of the structure stiffness and stability matrices. What follows is based on the specific forms of the element matrices given earlier. Not all bubble formulations will produce this form, so the following will not be generally applicable. However, these or similar forms are not restricted to frame elements, so their treatment is worth discussing.

The solution method used here is a modified version[2] of Aitken's power method.[3,4] The structure stiffness and stability matrices, **K** and **S**, are formed, leading to the eigenvalue equations

$$(\mathbf{K} + P_{cr}\mathbf{S})\mathbf{u} = 0 \tag{A1}$$

where P_{cr} is the buckling load factor. The stiffness matrix is factored and iteration then proceeds by the repeated solution of the equations

$$\mathbf{K}\mathbf{u}^{(n+1)} = -\mathbf{S}\,\mathbf{u}^{(n)} \tag{A2}$$

where $\mathbf{u}^{(n)}$ is the nth estimate of the buckling mode $\mathbf{u}$. The matrices $\mathbf{K}$ and $\mathbf{S}$ are stored in a symmetric, banded, re-entrant column (skyline) scheme.[5,6] The implementation adopted is to number all bubble freedoms last. Normally such a numbering would produce very poor banding of the matrices but here, because the bubble produces only a diagonal augmentation of the element matrix, all bubble freedoms produce a diagonal augmentation of the structure stiffness. The stability matrix is augmented in a similar way, but has non-zero off-diagonal terms as well. These off-diagonal terms are very simple, being a proportion of the axial force in that member, and occur once with each sign, as is seen from the last column of the member matrix $\mathbf{s}$. The off-diagonal terms are stored as the magnitude together with the row numbers for the positive and negative entries, and these are handled by sparse matrix techniques (Fig. A1).

The stability matrix $\mathbf{S}$ is stored in two parts, a compactly stored matrix $\mathbf{S_c}$ which has the same addressing as $\mathbf{K}$, and a sparse storage matrix $\mathbf{S_s}$ which contains the off-diagonal terms associated with the bubble functions. Each is multiplied by $\mathbf{u}^{(n)}$, using the appropriate algorithm, and the results added to give

$$\mathbf{S}\,\mathbf{u}^{(n)} = (\mathbf{S_c} + \mathbf{S_s})\,\mathbf{u}^{(n)} = \mathbf{S_c}\,\mathbf{u}^{(n)} + \mathbf{S_s}\,\mathbf{u}^{(n)} \tag{A3}$$

In this way the extra storage for both $\mathbf{K}$ and $\mathbf{S}$ is three reals and two integers for each member of the structure, or an average of about two reals for each member in each matrix. This is a small increase in storage when compared to the benefits that have been shown to come from the bubble formulation.

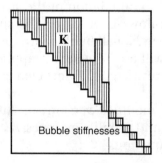
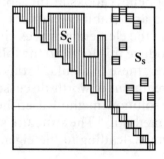

Fig. A1. Matrix storage.

It is interesting to speculate on the possibility of choosing a formulation in which both the stiffness matrix **K** and the stability matrix **S** are simultaneously augmented in a purely diagonal way. If this were possible then the system of eigenvalue equations would separate into the modes of the model without bubbles and purely bubble modes. The bubbles would be of no benefit except in those cases where the bubble functions alone gave better answers.

Thin-Walled Structures **9** (1990) 389–406

Buckling Considerations in the Design of Elevated Steel Water Tanks

Leonard R. Allen

Leonard Allen and Associates, 1 Hodgson Street, Heidelberg, Victoria 3084, Australia

Graham L. Hutchinson & Len K. Stevens

Department of Civil and Agricultural Engineering, University of Melbourne, Parkville, Victoria 3052, Australia

ABSTRACT

Improved fabrication techniques and the availability of higher strength steels have encouraged greater use of thin-walled containment vessels in recent years. A major increase in computing capability to analyse these structures for buckling modes has also occurred and this paper considers two recently constructed steel water towers. In particular, the effect of door cut-outs on buckling capacity is examined. The analysis techniques used in the paper provide powerful tools for readily estimating buckling modes and assessing the effects of various stiffener arrangements. By far the most effective stiffening element in the stem of a water tower is a horizontal diaphragm which maintains a circular cross-section.

1 INTRODUCTION

The use of relatively thin steel plate for the construction of containment vessels such as silos and water towers is being encouraged by the use of improved fabrication techniques and by the availability of higher strength steels. Accompanying these advances is a major increase in the capacity to analyse complex shapes through the application of powerful

389

Thin-Walled Structures 0263-8231/90/$03·50 © 1990 Elsevier Science Publishers Ltd, England. Printed in Great Britain

finite element computer programs. Such programs allow stress and buckling analyses to be performed for shapes and load cases which could not be attempted by manual methods.

The provisions for allowable stress-conditions that are available in most current codes of practice are based upon classical shell theory and results of tests performed mainly on scale models. Such provisions have given good results when applied with due attention to their derivation and consequential limitations of application. However, given the advances made in analytical capacity it is timely to re-examine the behaviour of structures consisting of shells of single curvature such as cylinders and cones and to reconsider the factors relevant to their design. In particular, computer results for stress distributions, buckling estimates, deformation patterns and buckling mode shapes, which can be provided numerically and graphically from finite element analyses, require evaluation as design aids. In this study, attention will be concentrated on the design of thin-walled steel shell structures so that premature failure due to buckling is avoided.

2 BUCKLING CHARACTERISTICS

2.1 Idealised behaviour under axial loading

Buckling is a mode of behaviour associated with a rapid increase in displacements out of the plane of loading which occurs after a bifurcation point has been reached in the equilibrium state. Several distinct modes may be identified for different structural systems and the material characteristics.[1, 2]

The elastic action of a line element subjected to axial compression provides the typical Euler column behaviour with undefined displacements occurring at the critical load as shown in Fig. 1. No transverse stresses can be developed in this line element to either restrain or to exacerbate the out-of-plane displacements.

The elastic action of a flat plate with restrained edges will exhibit the increasing load capacity shown in Fig. 1 beyond the buckling load due to the restraint provided by the transverse tensile stresses that are developed with the growth of out-of-plane displacements.

The elastic behaviour of axially loaded thin-walled cylinders is distinguished by the steeply descending characteristic shown in Fig. 1 after the theoretical buckling load has been reached. This characteristic reflects the delicate state of stability for a situation where transverse compressive stresses, which are induced by the axial loading, act to drive

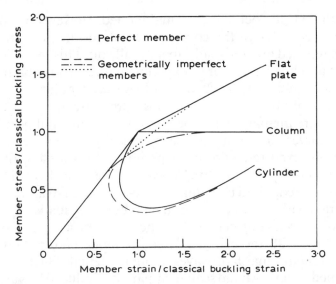

Fig. 1. Post-buckling behaviour of flat plates, columns and thin-walled cylinders (after Ref. 2).

the buckling mode further, rather than to restrain it as in the case of flat plates. This catastrophic nature of buckling of thin-walled cylinders is of particular concern for design, since failure can occur without the warnings that may be signalled to some extent in columns and flat plates.

2.2 Effects of imperfections and non-elastic action

Imperfections in columns produce an increasing rate of lateral displacements as the critical load is approached but this will be approached asymptotically if the behaviour remains elastic. However, if the stresses due to combined axial and induced flexural stresses exceed the elastic limit, the stiffness is reduced and the load capacity will fall off. This is particularly severe for materials with sharply defined yield points such as occurs for most structural steels. The maximum load capacity may then be considerably less than the Euler predicted load depending on the slenderness ratio and the magnitude of the imperfection. The greatest reduction below either the yield or Euler loads and the greatest scatter of experimental results occurs when the slenderness ratio is such that the yield and Euler load predictions are about the same.

The introduction of imperfections into plates will produce a deviation from the behaviour of the idealised system as shown in Fig. 1, but the post-buckling response will approach the idealised action asymptotically provided that elastic behaviour is maintained. However, if non-elastic behaviour occurs due to the combined axial and flexural stresses, the stiffness is reduced and the load capacity falls off. This reduction can be significant and a large scatter of experimental results is obtained when the predicted yield and elastic critical loads are similar.

The effect of imperfections is most dramatic for axially loaded cylinders where the narrow gap between the loading and post-buckling unloading curves shown in Fig. 1 can be easily bridged, leading to the very large observed reduction in experimental results for all but very stocky cylinders when squashing occurs at the yield load. This severe reduction was recognised by Donnell[3] and Timoshenko and Gere.[1] Tests were reported with values of experimental buckling loads as low as 20% of the predicted value by classical elastic theory based on axisymmetric shell buckling, with the cylinder buckling mode taking the form of a number of longitudinal half-waves along the length. Such results were accompanied by a very large scatter, apparently induced by variations in imperfections, and Timoshenko and Gere[1] illustrated the behaviour by the curves shown in Fig. 2. Non-elastic action induced by axial and flexural stresses reduces the stiffness and produces a falling characteristic with a reduction in the predicted elastic capacity.

Donnell's experimentally derived relationships and more recent studies have provided the basis for the formulation of code requirements[4] for allowable design stresses which will prevent premature failure of axially loaded thin-walled cylinders which contain practical imperfections and residual stresses due to forming and welding.

Recent work by Rotter and Teng[5] in which practical imperfections have been taken into account by large deflection finite element analyses

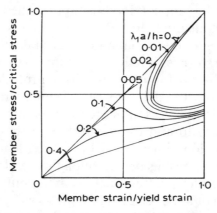

Fig. 2. Buckling of cylindrical shells: effect of imperfections. λ_1 = Numerical factor, h = shell thickness, a = radius (after Ref. 1).

have confirmed a reduction to about 30% of the classical buckling load. Residual stresses may also be expected to produce significant reductions, but there appears to be little quantified information on the effects when both imperfections and residual stresses act together.

Very little published information appears to be available on the buckling characteristics of cones other than the study reported by Timoshenko and Gere,[1] where rather sweeping assumptions had to be made in order to obtain classical solutions for elastic buckling loads of perfect systems. It has apparently been tacitly assumed that similar conditions apply to cones as have been found for cylinders and the code provisions appear to be based on this assumption.

2.3 Axial action plus flexure of cylindrical shells

The analysis of classical buckling loads for cylindrical shells subjected to axial plus flexural action was handicapped by the analytical difficulties associated with the asymmetric modes of buckling.[1] Such analytical solutions as were obtained indicated that the value of the compressive stress at buckling was comparable to that pertaining to pure axial action. However, experimental results and later theoretical work have shown that the adoption of the pure axial buckling stress is probably conservative because of the strain gradient and less unfavourable transverse stress pattern.[6] It is also possible that imperfections may have a less dramatic effect in producing reductions in the buckling load because of these factors.

Flexure may cause ovalling which will change the cross-sectional shape of very thin-walled flexible cylindrical shells, but this effect is usually not significant for most practical containment-type structures.

2.4 Effects of holes and cut-outs

Little analytical attention appears to have been given to the effects of holes and cut-outs in thin-walled cylindrical shells, although the reduction in effective area and local buckling can significantly reduce the load capacity. Codes usually require some empirically defined local edge stiffening and the replacement of the hole area to avoid any reduction in capacity.

Studies made by Little[6] on the bending strength of tubular steel lighting columns give some indication of the likely reduction in strength of a cylinder which includes a slotted hole on the compressive side. Test results were used to produce design curves of the form shown in Fig. 3 where the bending strength of a slotted tube is compared with that of a

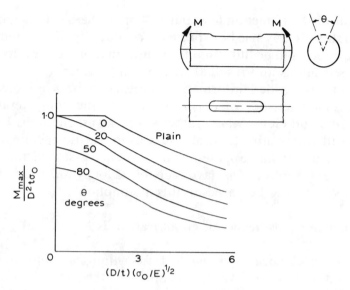

Fig. 3. Design curves for circular tubes (after Ref. 6). *D*, Diameter; *t*, wall thickness; σ_0, yield stress under uniaxial loading.

complete tube. The curve for a hole subtending a zero angle corresponds to that of a slit without any reduction in area. It is seen that there is a significant reduction in load capacity for this case, presumably due entirely to the local buckling which is permitted by the loss of circumferential continuity and membrane action. This reduction is potentially very dangerous unless adequate edge stiffening is provided along the edges of the slotted hole together with adequate transverse stiffening to retain the cross-sectional shape at the ends of the hole.

3 ANALYSIS OF BUCKLING LOADS BY FINITE ELEMENT ANALYSIS

3.1 General remarks

General finite element programs are available which will give estimates of buckling loads by extracting the eigenvalues from a small deflection stiffness analysis for a system modelled with plate elements subjected to in-plane forces.[7] Such analyses require access to a moderately large computer but are not prohibitively costly if normal stress analyses are also being performed. These eigenvalues represent the loads at which bifurcation of equilibrium conditions occur and should therefore be related to the corresponding classical values which would be obtained for idealised elastic action. Similar reductions to those applied to the classical solutions must therefore be applied to ensure that premature failure does not occur.

Special large deflection analyses, such as those developed by Rotter and Teng,[5] would have to be used with a knowledge of actual imperfections if more exact predictions of failure loads were required. However, such analyses are usually very time-consuming and are probably not warranted unless small deflection analyses give a minimum eigenvalue which indicates that doubt exists as to the safety of the system.

The choice of the factor by which the predicted classical or lowest eigen load must be divided to obtain a safe maximum value is a matter of judgement based on the structural form, the expected sizes of imperfection and the loading type. It is suggested that for practical, well-supervised cylindrical shells with small imperfections the factor should be at least 4, and desirably rather greater, if premature failure induced by buckling is to be avoided. For the case of flexure, this factor may be conservative, but the uncertainties are such that a reduction would only be warranted by a rigorous large deflection analysis. It must be emphasised that this buckling check is additional to the normal stress limits given in the appropriate codes and does not replace those requirements.

Another very major benefit for design which can be provided by a finite element analysis which gives the eigenvalues is that the corresponding buckling modes should also be available. If these can be presented graphically it is a simple matter to check that the critical lowest eigenvalue is associated with a mode consistent with that expected and that a more fundamental mode has not been overlooked.

A much more important design aid provided by the graphical presentation of buckling modes is in the assistance given for reaching decisions on the best means for suppressing an undesirable mode. If the mode shape is known it is usually obvious which action should be taken by the addition of edge stiffness or diaphragms to prevent buckling distortion and hopefully generate a new mode with a higher eigenvalue.

3.2 ABAQUS program

ABAQUS is a large multi-purpose finite element analysis computer package which incorporates the facility to estimate elastic buckling loads by eigenvalue extraction.[7] The buckling load estimate is obtained as a multiplier of the pattern of 'live' loads which are added to a set of 'dead' loads. In both the case studies presented the self weight of the tank was considered to be the dead load and the live load was taken as the combined hydrostatic load due to the contained water and the wind loading.

If the dead loads are $P^N (N = 1, 2$, etc., up to the number of degrees of freedom in the model) the elastic tangent stiffness of the structure is K_P at this 'dead' load state. If some nominal 'live' loading Q^N is now added, the load state becomes $(P^N + Q^N)$ with an elastic stiffness K_Q where

$$K_Q = K_P + \Delta K_{PQ} \tag{1}$$

in which ΔK_{PQ}, the change in stiffness going from loads P^N to $(P^N + Q^N)$, is proportional to the change in load Q^N.

This assumption essentially restricts the analysis to the elastic response of 'stiff' structures, i.e. structures which undergo only small displacements and rotations prior to buckling. Hence, the structure's tangent stiffness at a load state $(P^N + \lambda Q^N)$ is

$$K_P + \lambda K_{PQ}$$

The load rate–displacement rate relationship at this state is

$$(K_P^{NM} + \lambda \Delta K_{PQ}^{NM}) \, \mathrm{d}u^M = \mathrm{d}F^N \tag{2}$$

We seek non-trivial solutions for this system when $\mathrm{d}F^N = 0$, i.e.

$$(K_P^{NM} + \lambda \Delta K_{PQ}^{NM}) \, \mathrm{d}u^M = 0 \tag{3}$$

This is an eigenvalue problem and the eigenvalues λ_i are multipliers which provide the estimated buckling load as $P^N + \lambda_i Q^N$ while the corresponding eigenvector $(\mathrm{d}u^N)_i$ gives the associated buckling mode.

ABAQUS also has powerful graphics facilities enabling pre-processor geometry checks to be carried out as well as post-processor plots of mode shapes.

Two case studies of elevated steel water storages recently constructed in Victoria, and analysed for buckling using ABAQUS, are presented below to illustrate various points relating to shell buckling. All computations were carried out at the University of Melbourne, Faculty of Engineering Computer Aided Engineering Design Centre.

4 CASE STUDIES

4.1 Description of water towers

Both towers considered in this study have circular cross-sections and are axisymmetric. The towers have been constructed in Grade 250 steel with all joints made using full strength butt welds. Wind loadings have been determined in accordance with AS1170[8] and in both cases the tanks were assumed to be connected to a rigid foundation at the base.

4.1.1 Tower A

Tower A is located at Kalimna near Lakes Entrance in Victoria, Australia. It was designed for Tambo Water Board by Dr L. R. Allen in association with Fisher Stewart Pty Ltd and was constructed by V. G. Saunders Pty Ltd.

The tower has a water storage capacity of 1000 kilolitres and its geometry with plate thicknesses and overall dimensions is shown in Fig. 4. A substantial internal ring beam of triangular cross-section was provided at the top of the stem. Access to the tank was provided via a door at the base of the 4 m diameter stem and another in the internal cone immediately above the top of the stem. Internal service platforms were constructed at the 4·6 and 8·9 m levels within the stem.

4.1.2 Tower B

Tower B is located at Warracknabeal, Victoria, Australia. It was designed by Dr L. R. Allen and constructed by Steel and Mechanical Systems Pty Ltd for the Warracknabeal Water Board.

The tower consists of a 21 m high, 3 m diameter stem supporting a 750 kilolitre tank. Details of the geometry and plate thicknesses are given in Fig. 5. Internal service platforms were provided at the 6, 12 and 18 m levels in the stem (see Fig. 5).

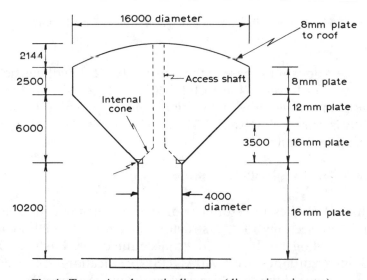

Fig. 4. Tower A: schematic diagram (dimensions in mm).

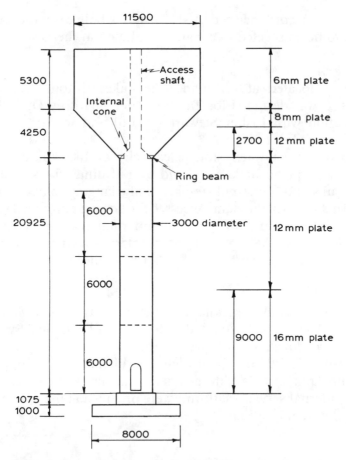

Fig. 5. Tower B: schematic diagram (dimensions in mm).

The access door at the base of the stem is identical in dimensions with that provided in Tower A (Fig. 6), but because of the reduced diameter of Tower B (3 m compared with 4 m diameter) the potential for structural instability is greater. A substantial internal ring beam was also provided at the stem/tank junction.

4.2 Finite element modelling of towers

In both case studies three-dimensional finite element models of the structures, or sections of the structures, were developed so that all possible buckling modes would be accounted for. Each model was created in accordance with ABAQUS specifications and generated taking advantage of the axisymmetric nature of the structures. Throughout the modelling extensive use was made of S8R and S4R elements. S8R

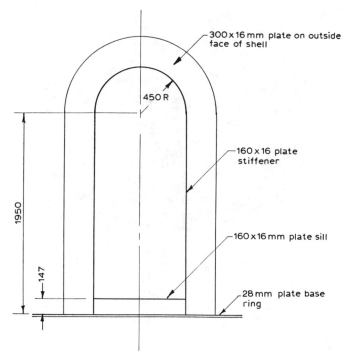

Fig. 6. Details of door cut-out at base of Tower A and Tower B (dimensions in mm).

elements possess eight nodes (four mid-side nodes) and four output integration points on each surface, near the quarter-points of the element. S4R elements possess four nodes and one output integration point on each surface at the centre of the element.

The effect of geometric imperfections in the supporting stems of the two water towers under study was also considered. The imperfection took the form of a full sine wave over the height of the stem. Various imperfection amplitudes were included, reflecting the expected construction tolerances. In each case the narrowest cross-section occurred in the lower half of the stem.

Further to account for any possible sloshing effects, and to ensure a conservative approach to the analysis, the resultant of the hydrostatic load was applied at an eccentricity of 100 mm from the central vertical axis in all analyses. Calculations showed that this load distribution was more critical than any produced by sloshing in a partially filled tank.

4.2.1 Tower A

4.2.1.1 Model of complete structure. Initially a full three-dimensional model of the tank was developed (see Fig. 7). This consisted of some 675 nodal points, 185 S8R eight-node shell elements and 150 S4R four-node

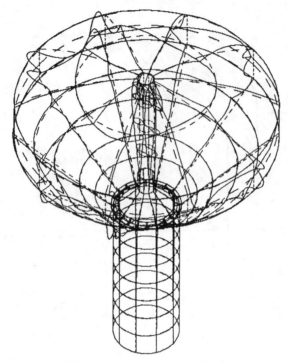

Fig. 7. Mode shape corresponding to first positive eigenvalue ($w = 8.33$) for the case of self-weight and prescribed wind loading. - - - -, Original shape; ————, displaced shape.

shell elements. Appropriate shell thicknesses determined by manual calculations were used throughout. In this model neither the access doors nor the internal service platform in the stem were included, as the effect of the stem access door would be considered in a second model and the internal service platforms were not designed to contribute to the overall buckling load capacity of the structure.

Imperfections in the stem were considered, however, and an imperfection amplitude of 20 mm was built into the finite element model. This was considered to be conservative as the construction tolerances for Tower A were substantially less than this.

For this model the self weight and hydrostatic loadings on the model were automatically calculated by the program. The wind loadings were applied as appropriate pressure loadings on the structure.

4.2.1.2 Model of stress. A three-dimensional model of the stem of Tower A was developed. This model included a door cut-out at the base of the stem (see Fig. 8). The edge stiffening beam was included in the model but neither the doubling plate around the door nor the door itself were

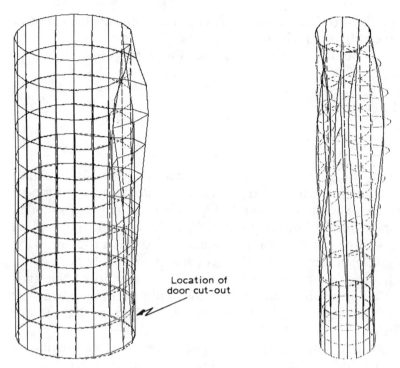

Fig. 8. Tower A stem: first buckling mode; $w = 6.8$. ----, Original shape; ——, displaced shape.

Fig. 9. Tower B stem without door cut-out; $w = 8.42$.

included. An imperfection of amplitude 10 mm was built into the model.

The resultant of the wind loading on the complete structure was applied as equivalent horizontal loadings on the nodes at the top of the stem. Further, the resultant of the hydrostatic load was assumed to be 100 mm away from the central vertical axis. In both cases these loads were positioned such that they produced maximum compressive stresses over the door cut-out.

4.2.2 Tower B

For Tower B a three-dimensional model of the stem only was constructed (see Fig. 9). The door cut-out at the base of the stem was modelled with semi-circular doorhead represented as part of an equivalent octagon.

The edge stiffening plate around the door cut-out was also included. However, the doubling plate around the door opening was disregarded. The ring beam at the top of the stem was also modelled and an imperfection amplitude of 10 mm was built into the stem. Provision was also made for the possible inclusion of extra stiffening members around the door cut-out by the inclusion of extra nodal points.

A model of the Tower B stem without the door cut-out was also generated.

4.3 Typical results

4.3.1 Tower A

4.3.1.1 Using the model of the complete structure. Various buckling analyses were conducted for different load combinations using the model of the complete structure as shown in Fig. 7. For this particular model, which did not include the door cut-out stem, nor an eccentrically applied hydrostatic loading, an eigenvalue estimate of 20 was extracted. This indicated that elastic buckling would occur at approximately 20 times the combined hydrostatic and wind loadings which comprised the 'live' loading in the eigenvalue extraction. This finding prompted further analyses involving modelling of the tank stem only and these are discussed below.

For the complete model (Fig. 7) the special loading combination of self-weight and prescribed wind loading indicated an eigenvalue of approximately 8·3 and Fig. 7 shows the corresponding buckling mode. Under these conditions buckling will occur in the tank itself.

4.3.1.2 Model of stem. The model incorporates the door cut-out, the edge stiffener and an imperfection amplitude of 10 mm. The 'live' loading condition for this analysis assumed that the resultant of the hydrostatic load acts 100 mm from the vertical axis and it was positioned along with the wind loading to produce maximum compressive stresses over the door region. The analysis yielded an eigenvalue estimate of 6·8, i.e. 6·8 times the combined hydrostatic and wind loading is required to produce an elastic buckling of the stem. The corresponding buckling mode is given in Fig. 8.

4.3.2 Tower B

All the analyses for the Tower B model used the structure self-weight as the 'dead' loading. The 'live' loading consisted of an appropriate horizontal load applied at the top of the stem to simulate wind loading and the offset hydrostatic load.

In the models which incorporated a door cut-out at the base both the wind and hydrostatic loads were positioned to produce maximum compressive stresses over the door region.

An initial analysis with the door cut-out and the door edge stiffener modelled yielded an eigenvalue estimate of 4·5. Although probably adequate, especially in view of the conservative modelling assumptions made, it was decided to investigate the effect of providing some extra stiffening around the cut-out.

A corresponding analysis of the model of the stem without the door cut-out gives an eigenvalue estimate of 8·42 with a mode shape as shown in Fig. 9.

The stiffening to be used around the door cut-out consisted of two 250 × 90 × 35·5 kg/m channel sections located vertically 900 mm apart on either side of the cut-out (see Fig. 10). An initial analysis including the stiffeners, but not the door cut-out, yielded an eigenvalue of 8·46 and a mode shape indistinguishable from that in Fig. 9, indicating that the effect of the stiffeners in this model was minimal.

However, inclusion of the vertical stiffeners and cross-members shown in Fig. 10 in the stem model with the door cut-out results in an eigenvalue estimate of 5·74 with a buckling shape as shown in Fig. 11. The effect of the stiffener in constraining the tank in the region of the door is clear. Using a large channel (300 × 90 × 40·1 kg/m) for the vertical stiffener results in the eigenvalue estimate being raised to 6·92. The corresponding mode shape is very similar to that in Fig. 11.

The effect of the ladder landings on the buckling stability of the stem with the door cut-out was also considered. Using a facility in ABAQUS the modes at this level were all forced to remain in a circular configuration, thus modelling what actually occurs because of the diaphragm action of the mid-height landing. The resulting estimate of the eigenvalue was 17·48 and the corresponding mode is as shown in Fig. 12. Clearly, the effect of these landings is to increase significantly the buckling capacity of the stem.

5 CONCLUSIONS

1. Special attention should be given to the detailed design of openings in cylindrical elements in structures subject to axial compression. In particular, at the bases of water towers careful consideration should be given to appropriate methods of offsetting the reduction in buckling capacity of the stem caused by any opening.

2. Methods of analysis such as are employed in this paper provide powerful tools for estimating buckling loads and assessing the effects of various stiffener arrangements. Moreover, imperfections

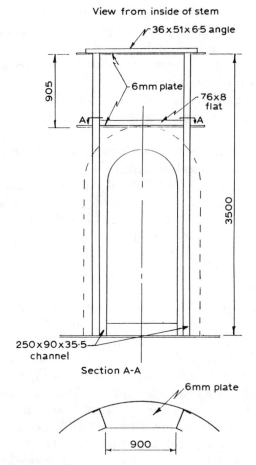

Fig. 10. Vertical stiffeners and cross members around door cut-out — schematic diagram (dimensions in mm).

may be readily incorporated into the finite element model to represent anticipated structural misalignments and geometric deviations from the theoretical shapes.

3. The graphical outputs provided by this type of analysis provide an excellent visual representation of the buckling modes and form the basis on which to design appropriate stiffening elements.

4. The practice of simply replacing the lost wall area due to the door opening with an equivalent doubling plate and edge stiffener around the opening may not be conservative.

5. In order to obtain plate thicknesses for use in a buckling analysis, the procedures outlined in Trahair *et al.*[9] appear to be appropriate.

6. By far the most effective stiffening element in the stem of a water

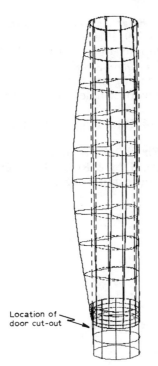

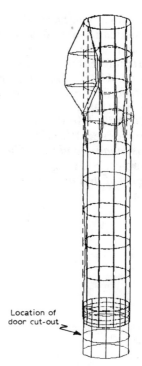

Fig. 11. Tower B stem including stiffeners: first buckling mode; $w = 5.74$.

Fig. 12. Tower B stem including stiffeners and mid-height diaphragm action: first buckling mode; $w = 17.48$.

tower is a horizontal diaphragm which maintains the circular cross-section. The restraining forces may readily be provided by appropriately designed intermediate ladder landings.

It should be noted that if a more accurate buckling analysis is required, perhaps because of an unsatisfactorily low eigenvalue being predicted, it would be necessary to conduct a detailed non-linear second-order analysis as outlined in Rotter and Teng.[5]

REFERENCES

1. Timoshenko, S. P. & Gere, J. M., *Theory of Elastic Stability*, Second Edition, McGraw-Hill, New York, 1961.
2. Stephens, M. J., Kulak, G. L. & Montgomery, C. L., *Local buckling of thin walled tubular steel members,* Department of Civil Engineering, University of Alberta, Edmonton, Alberta, 1982.
3. Donnell, L. H., A new theory for the buckling of thin cylinders under axial compression and bending, *Trans. ASME,* **56** (1934).

4. *Standard for Steel Tanks — Standpipes Reservoirs and Elevated Tanks,* American Water Works Association D100–79, 1979.
5. Rotter, J. M. & Teng, J. G., Elastic stability of cylindrical shells with circumferential lap joints, *First Nat. Struct. Engin. Conf.,* Melbourne, 1987.
6. Little, G. H., Design curves for the bending strength of circular and octagonal steel tubes including the effects of a hole, *Struct. Engr,* **628**(2) (Sept.) (1984).
7. *ABAQUS,* Hibbitt, Version 4.5, May 1984, Karlsson and Sorensen, Inc., Providence, RI, USA.
8. *Australian Standard: 1170, Part 2, Wind Forces,* 1981 Edition.
9. Trahair, N., Abel, A., Ansourian, P., Irvine, H. M. & Rotter, J. M., *Structural design of steel bins for bulk solids,* Australian Institute of Steel Construction, 1983.

SESSION 7

Thin-Walled Structures **9** (1990) 407–415

Effect of Pre- and Postbuckling Behaviour on Load Capacity of Continuous Beams

Paul Grundy

Department of Civil Engineering, Monash University, Clayton, Victoria 3168, Australia

ABSTRACT

The nonlinear moment–curvature relationship of thin-walled beams, due to a combination of non-Hookean material behaviour and local buckling, inevitably leads to a 'strain-softening' component after a peak has been reached. Representation of this relationship in continuum mechanics leads to fallacious estimates of the static or incremental collapse load capacity of continuous beams. More realistic results are obtained when it is recognised that the moment–curvature relationship can only develop over a finite length associated with the half-wavelength of the final plastic buckle. It cannot develop over an infinitesimal length.

1 ASSUMPTIONS OF LIMIT ANALYSIS

A rigorous analysis to determine the ultimate load capacity of beams, taking into account material and geometric nonlinearity, generally starts with the moment–curvature relationship. Moment–curvature relationships can be derived experimentally by applying constant moment to a length of beam which is suitably braced to prevent lateral buckling. In steel structures a distinction is made between compact and non-compact sections. In compact sections the flange and web width/thickness ratios are low enough for a large plateau to appear in the moment–curvature relationship near the full plastic moment capacity. This plateau is sufficient for the full redistribution of bending moments without loss of local moment capacity, which is required for valid application of plastic

Thin-Walled Structures 0263-8231/90/$03·50 © 1990 Elsevier Science Publishers Ltd, England, Printed in Great Britain

mechanism theory. In non-compact sections the plateau is drastically shortened or absent, through local buckling combined with yielding.

The collective wisdom appears to be that significant ductility is required before simple theory can be used for determining ultimate load capacities. This restricts plastic analysis to beams of compact section, or their equivalent. In this paper the validity of the application of moment–curvature relationships in determining ultimate load capacity is examined, and found wanting. It is also demonstrated that there are significant applications where limited ductility does not lead to a load capacity significantly less than that obtained assuming infinite ductility.

2 MOMENT–CURVATURE BEHAVIOUR

Various moment–curvature relationships and idealisations are shown in Fig. 1. Curves **a**, **b** and **c** are idealisations used to simplify analysis, representing elastic–plastic, elastic–plastic–softening, and elastic–softening (no plateau), respectively. The first is the most popular. Curve **d** is a more realistic representation of real behaviour, with a gradual transition from hardening to softening. The length of this transition depends on material properties, residual stresses and slenderness parameters with respect to local buckling. Curve **e**, in which softening is absent, can be used effectively if local buckling does not occur.

The collapse load analysis of continuous beams is only possible with curves **a** and **e**, which postulate infinite curvature capacity at ultimate moment — necessary for a plastic hinge to form. In the other cases where the structure is loaded with a monotonically increasing load, or with a moving load train, complete local failure occurs at any point where the ultimate moment, M_P, is reached. This occurs because the moment–curvature relationship passes the peak and goes down the softening path,

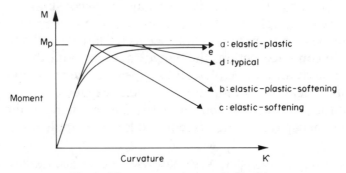

Fig. 1. Moment–curvature relationship.

over an infinitesimal length of the beam, while the adjacent lengths of the beam unload elastically. Since the inelastic behaviour is confined to an infinitesimal length of the beam, significant plastic curvature or plastic hinge rotation does not occur, preventing redistribution of moments.

This theoretical result is not in accord with all observations. Sudden collapses are not usually observed, and plastic hinges do not form. There are instead zones of high plastic curvature, the extent of the zone being dependent on the gradient of the bending moment with respect to distance along the beam.

3 MOMENT–ROTATION BEHAVIOUR

The problems associated with using moment–curvature relationships have been avoided by adopting moment–rotation curves for beams with moment gradients, where the maximum moment is at the end of the beam or at a node in the finite element analysis.

The principle is illustrated in Fig. 2. Where a beam is subjected to a gradient moment it is assumed, to simplify analysis, that the inelastic curvature can be replaced by a hinge with the same effect on displacements. Moment–rotation curves can then be derived experimentally or theoretically.

However, the derivation is sensitive to the moment gradient. This problem is overcome either by preparing standard solutions for common cases or by including the moment gradient in the parameters affecting the derivation.

A simple box beam subjected to four-point loading as shown in Fig. 3 can reach its maximum moment as characteristic local buckling occurs in the compression flange. The half-wavelength, λ, is typically the width

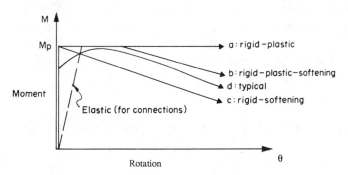

Fig. 2. Moment–rotation relationship.

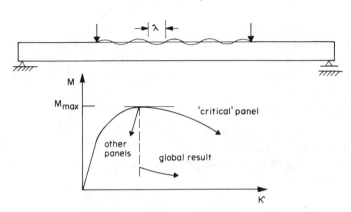

Fig. 3. Four-point loading for moment–curvature.

of the panel. For this test with a zone of constant bending moment it is false to assume that each buckling panel follows the same postbuckling (softening) path. One panel, possible including the adjacent panels, will be slightly weaker than the rest, and will indeed follow the postbuckling path, but the remainder will unload elastically. The cumulative result is a snap-through failure, creating the impression that the beam with this cross-section has no ductility of the type assumed in plastic analysis.

Even if there is constant moment over a length of the span, as in the test beam used to derive moment–curvature relationships, collapse is associated with a finite number of buckles, and it is impossible to conceive of plastic curvature being distributed over a length less than a half-wavelength of buckle at collapse. It then becomes possible to replace the moment–curvature relationship with a moment–rotation relationship. For example, assuming that there is a yield plateau of length κ_P in the moment–curvature relationship, and that this occurs over a distance λ, then there will be a yield plateau, θ_P, equal to $\lambda\kappa_P$ in the moment–rotation relationship.

With the introduction of a minimum length over which the moment–curvature relationship becomes effective, it is possible to transform the moment–curvature relationships of Fig. 1 into the moment–rotation relationships of Fig. 2. If the rotation is concentrated at a 'hinge', then the hinge is rigid until inelastic deformation occurs.

4 ANALYSIS OF A CONTINUOUS BEAM WITH FIXED LOAD POSITIONS

For the reasons just given, attempts to apply moment–curvature relationships with limited ductility to continuous beams or any frames where concentrated loads are applied in fixed positions will fail to find any further capacity once the peak moment is reached at a point in the structure. Consider the prismatic beam of Fig. 4. It has two equal spans, constant section properties, and the elastic–plastic–softening moment–curvature relationship as shown. As soon as the positive moment reaches $4.93M_P/L$, collapse occurs. This is due to the plastic curvature being limited to an infinitesimal length of the beam. No finite plastic rotation can occur for redistribution of moments.

There are many cases where practical observation conflicts with this theoretical result. There are two major reasons. The first has already been described. It is the requirement of a finite length over which the moment–curvature relationship applies. The second is the existence of an inelastic knee before the maximum moment in the moment–curvature relationship (curves **d** and **e** of Fig. 1). This knee permits the development of residual plastic curvatures before the peak load is reached. In general these curvatures tend to produce the desired residual moments in the system so that the maximum moments at all potential hinges of the collapse mechanism are approached simultaneously.

5 ANALYSIS OF A CONTINUOUS BEAM WITH MOVING LOADS

In many practical situations the gravity loads move across the structure, generating an infinite number of load cases for consideration. It can be shown that the ductility requirements may be quite minimal for achieving the ultimate plastic limit load, for either static collapse or incremental collapse. If a beam is subjected to a moving load it is possible for all the necessary plastic curvature to develop away from the location of the

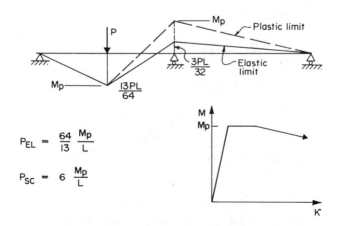

Fig. 4. Two-span beam with fixed load position.

plastic hinges of the collapse mechanism, so that ultimate load capacity is unimpaired.

Results have been obtained for the beam shown in Fig. 4 on the generation of plastic curvature, assuming ideal elastic–plastic moment–curvature, for a moving concentrated load.[1] These are shown in Fig. 5. The results are particular to the case of the maximum load moving from left to right across the beam. Any other loading history involving lesser loads being applied first, or reversing the direction of motion, will produce a different pattern of residual curvatures but the same residual moment.

These results are derived by observing the increment of plastic rotation required with an increment of movement of the load, as shown in Fig. 6. The moment at the point of load application follows the moment envelope, M_E, until it reaches the plastic moment, M_P. The moment cannot exceed this limit, so that plastic curvature develops under the load as it moves further right, sufficient to build up a residual

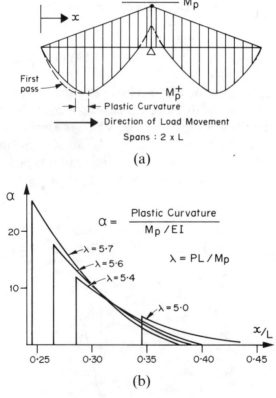

Fig. 5. Plastic curvatures developed under moving load: elastic–plastic M–κ. (a) Moment envelope for $P = 5\cdot4M_P/L$; (b) distribution of plastic curvature.

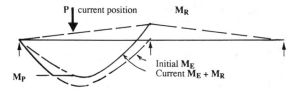

Fig. 6. Development of residual moment and plastic curvature.

moment, M_R, to maintain equilibrium. The combination of M_R with M_E moves the elastic envelope to a new position for subsequent passages of load. If the envelope lies between $-M_P$ and $+M_P$ then shakedown has occurred.

This result is obtained from the moment–curvature relationship without any requirement of hinge rotation capacity. However, if M_P was first reached over the interior support, rotation capacity would be required.

Where the plastic curvature develops under the moving load it can be shown that inelastic adaptation or shakedown will occur even when curvature softening occurs. The capacity to adapt depends on the slope of the softening curve, but it is quite possible for the plastic capacity to be undiminished by softening.

6 EFFECT OF INELASTIC MOMENT–CURVATURE

For practical cross-sections there is a 'knee' in the moment–curvature relationship between initial yield in the extreme fibres and full plastic moment. If residual stresses are present, due to the hot rolling, cold forming, or welding processes of manufacture, the initial yield point is lowered, but the full plastic moment is unchanged. In non-compact cross-sections M_P might be reduced through local buckling affected by residual stresses.

The conventional wisdom is to employ fabrication methods which minimise residual stresses. However, studies of continuous beams under fixed or moving loads reveal that the knee is beneficial in the develop of plastic curvatures such that the full plastic moment capacity can be attained. The cost is a little more permanent deflection in the beam.

Under loads in fixed positions the knee permits the development of plastic curvatures around the positions of maximum moment. The capacity of the structure to develop the theoretical plastic collapse load depends on the shape of the M-κ curve and the gradient of the moment along the beam.

(a)

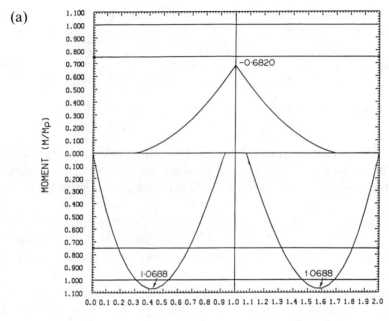

(b)

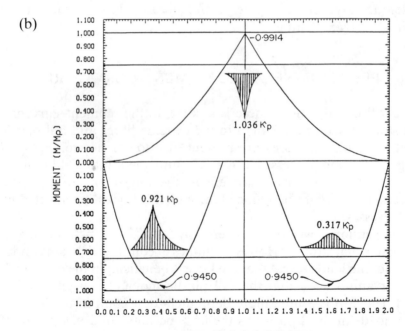

Fig. 7. Plastic curvatures developed under moving load: inelastic M–κ: (a) M_E elastic envelope; (b) $M_E + M_R$ after shakedown showing residual plastic curvature. Total uniformly distributed load: $2M_P/L$ per span; moving concentrated load: $4 \cdot 5M_P/L$; $P_{IC} = 4 \cdot 74M_P/L$; $P_{SC} = 4 \cdot 83M_P/L$; $M_Y/M_P = 0 \cdot 75$; $M/M_P = 1 \cdot 27\ (\kappa/\kappa_P)^{-3}/256$ $(M_Y < M < M_P)$.

Under moving loads similar results to those for an elastic–plastic M–κ are obtained, with reduced residual plastic curvatures. An example is given in Fig. 7 for the same two-span beam, where $M_Y = 0.75M_P$, and the M–κ curve approaches M_P asymptotically.[2]

7 CONCLUSIONS

The application of realistic moment–curvature relationships to the analysis of continuous beams and frames does not permit significant redistribution of moments leading to the development of a plastic collapse mechanism unless the finite length of development of plastic curvature is taken into account.

Where the inelastic behaviour is due to local buckling the half-wavelength of buckle provides a suitable reference length for relating the moment–curvature relationship to a realistic moment–rotation relationship at a potential location of a plastic hinge.

The collapse load derived from simple plastic theory assuming infinite ductility can often be obtained with elements considered non-ductile with respect to moment–curvature behaviour. This includes cross-sections classified as 'unsuitable for plastic action'.

The inelastic knee in the moment–curvature relationship is an important factor in the development of plastic curvatures, which in turn permit the development of a residual moment pattern necessary for the plastic collapse load to be obtained.

Under moving concentrated loads the adaptation necessary to achieve the plastic collapse load can readily be obtained with minimal moment-curvature ductility, provided that the plastic curvature is occurring under the moving load, and not at the supports. Even the softening part of the moment–curvature relationship becomes significant.

ACKNOWLEDGEMENT

Computations for Fig. 7 were made by Goh Chong Chee, Research Student, Monash University.

REFERENCES

1. Grundy, P., The application of shakedown theory to the design of steel structures. *The Michael R. Horne International Conference on Instability and Plastic Collapse of Steel Structures*, Manchester, UK, September 1983, 184–94.
2. Grundy, P., Shakedown — Theory and Applications. Notes for a Course at the International Centre for Mechanical Sciences, Udine, Italy, October 1987.

Thin-Walled Structures **9** (1990) 417–435

General Non-Dimensional Equation for Lateral Buckling

Mario M. Attard

Department of Civil Engineering, Monash University, Clayton, Victoria 3168, Australia

ABSTRACT

A new approximate non-dimensional equation for the elastic lateral buckling load of straight prismatic beams of monosymmetric cross-section with general boundary conditions and general loading, which includes the effects of initial bending curvature prior to buckling, is derived. For sections where the flexural rigidity about the axis of initial bending, EI_{zz}, is smaller than the flexural rigidity about the other principal centroidal axis, EI_{yy}, it is shown that lateral buckling is still a possibility.

NOTATION

a_y	Height of transverse load above shear centre
$A_1, \ldots, A_4$	Constants
e_y	Eccentricity of UDL
E	Young's modulus
G	Shear modulus
I_{yy}, I_{zz}	Second moment of area about the y and z axis, respectively
I_ω	Warping constant
J	Torsion constant
L	Beam length
M	Maximum bending moment
M_{cr}	Critical moment
M_y, M_z	Bending moment about the y and z axis, respectively
P	Applied transverse load
P_{cr}	Critical transverse load

Thin-Walled Structures 0263-8231/90/\$03·50 © 1990 Elsevier Science Publishers Ltd, England. Printed in Great Britain

q_y	UDL in the y direction
Vs	Displacement of the shear centre in the y direction
Ws	Displacement of the shear centre in the z direction
x	Centroidal axis
y, z	Principal centroidal axes
y_s	y coordinate of the shear centre
β_1	$1/(2I_{zz})\left[\int_A (yz^2 + y^3)\, dA\right] - y_s$
v_z	$1 - I_{yy}/I_{zz}$
ϕ	Angle of twist

1 INTRODUCTION

Industrial racking used for storage is usually produced from cold formed thin-walled sections with a profile which is often open. The cross-sectional shape can often have only one or no axis of symmetry and may not have a dominant principal axis. The analysis for lateral and/or torsional buckling for racking beams can therefore be quite complex when other than simple boundary conditions exist. Since closed form exact solutions are available for only a limited number of problems, there has been a strong motivation for the development of numerical solutions obtained by techniques such as the finite difference method, numerical integration or the finite element method.

There is also a place for non-dimensional approximate solutions which are applicable to a variety of boundary conditions, loading cases and cross-sectional shapes. Equations have been proposed by Clark and Hill,[1] Horne,[2] Maeda,[3] Nethercot and Rockey,[4] Trahair[5] and others.[6, 7] The derivations have been generally limited to symmetric cross-sections. The equations can provide a quick means of estimating the buckling load and can be helpful in pinpointing the governing parameters of a problem.

Recently, Roberts and Burt,[8] and Roberts and Benchiha[9] have presented approximate solutions for the lateral buckling loads of monosymmetric beams with simple supports and various loadings. These authors also included the effects on the torsional stiffness of the initial deflection due to bending prior to buckling.

This paper attempts to present a new approximate non-dimensional equation for the elastic lateral buckling load of straight prismatic beams of monosymmetric cross-section with general boundary conditions and general loading, and includes the effects of initial bending curvature prior to buckling.

2 DERIVATION

Consider a straight prismatic beam of length L loaded by a proportional conservative load system producing a bending moment distribution $M_z(x)$ about the z-axis of the beam as shown in Fig. 1. The loading system consists of a concentrated point load P (upward) and a uniformly distributed load q_y. The line of action of the transverse loads passes through the shear centre. The height of the concentrated load is a_y above the shear centre while the uniformly distributed load has a height of e_y above the shear centre. Conservative end moments are also considered which are applied at each end of the beam. The boundary conditions at the ends of the beam are considered to be general except that the end moments are assumed not to be applied at a free end.

A suitable stability criterion for an elastic conservative system is a

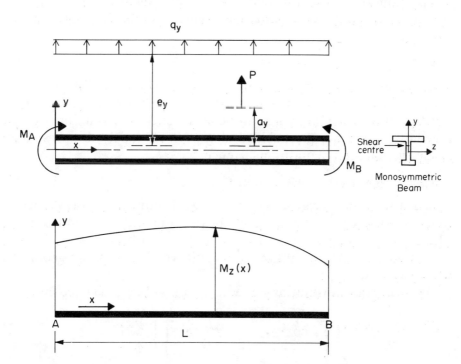

Fig. 1. Beam with unspecified boundary conditions and general loading.

positive definite second variation of the total potential energy. The following expression for the second variation of the total potential is derived in Attard:[10, 11]

$$\delta^2 V = \frac{1}{2} \int_0^L \left[EI_{yy}(\delta Ws_{,xx})^2 + EI_\omega(\delta\phi_{,xx})^2 + GJ(\delta\phi_{,x})^2 \right.$$

$$\left. + 2M_z\{v_z\delta Ws_{,xx}\delta\phi - \beta_1(\delta\phi_{,x})^2\} - \frac{M_z^2 v_z(\delta\phi)^2}{EI_{zz}} + q_y e_y(\delta\phi)^2 \right] dx$$

$$+ \frac{1}{2} Pa_y\bar{\phi}^2 \tag{1}$$

The effects of initial bending curvature prior to buckling are included in the term v_z defined by

$$v_z = 1 - \frac{I_{yy}}{I_{zz}} \tag{2}$$

The displacement $\bar{\phi}$ represents the perturbation of the angle of twist at the point of application of the concentrated load P. Equation (1) is limited to cross-sections where the torsional rigidity GJ is small in comparison to the flexural rigidity about the axis of bending, EI_{zz}.

In order to non-dimensionalize the problem, the following substitutions are made:

$$X = x/L \qquad M_z = M m(X) \tag{3}$$

where $m(X)$ is a function describing the bending moment distribution, M being the maximum bending moment along the beam. An approximate solution to the buckling load can be established by assuming a priori functions describing the buckled shape which satisfy the prescribed geometric boundary conditions. Hence, let

$$\delta Ws = \bar{W}s f(X) \qquad \delta\phi = \bar{\phi} g(X) \tag{4}$$

in which $\bar{W}s$ is the perturbation of the lateral displacement evaluated at some characteristic point along the beam; $f(X)$ and $g(X)$ are functions which are assumed *a priori* to describe the distribution of the lateral displacement and twist, respectively, and which satisfy the geometric boundary conditions.

Following the substitutions of eqns (3) and (4), eqn (1) becomes

$$\delta^2 V = \frac{1}{2} [\bar{W}s \; \bar{\phi}] \begin{bmatrix} \dfrac{EI_{yy}C_5}{L_3} & \dfrac{-Mv_zC_6}{L} \\[3mm] \dfrac{-Mv_zC_6}{L} & A \end{bmatrix} \begin{bmatrix} \bar{W}s \\[2mm] \bar{\phi} \end{bmatrix} \tag{5}$$

in which

$$A = \frac{EI_\omega C_1}{L^3} + \frac{GJC_2}{L} - \frac{2M\beta_1 C_3}{L} - \frac{M^2 v_z L C_4}{EI_{zz}} + Pa_y + q_y e_y C_7 L$$

$$C_1 = \int_0^L (g_{,XX})^2 \, dX \qquad C_2 = \int_0^L (g_{,X})^2 \, dX$$

$$C_3 = \int_0^L m \, (g_{,X})^2 \, dX \qquad C_4 = \int_0^L m^2 g^2 \, dX$$

$$C_5 = \int_0^L (f_{,XX})^2 \, dX \qquad C_6 = \int_0^L -m f_{,XX} g \, dX$$

$$C_7 = \int_0^L g^2 \, dX$$

The coefficients C_1, $C_2, \ldots, C_7$ depend on the bending moment distribution and the buckled shape.

Mikhlin[12] has shown that the point of instability can be determined by minimizing the energy functional subject to some constraint on the size of the perturbations. Employing Mikhlin's procedure on eqn (5), the following equations result:

$$\frac{EI_{yy} C_5}{L^3} \overline{W}s - \frac{M v_z C_6}{L} \overline{\phi} = 0 \tag{6}$$

$$\frac{-M v_z C_6}{L} \overline{W}s + A \overline{\phi} = 0 \tag{7}$$

The bifurcation load is determined by setting the determinant of the above system of equations to zero and solving for M. Hence

$$\frac{EI_{yy} C_5 A}{L^3} - \frac{(M v_z C_6)^2}{L^2} = 0 \tag{8}$$

When I_{yy} equals I_{zz} (i.e. $v_z = 0$), the critical moment can be obtained from eqn (8). There are numerous ways of expressing the critical moment equation and one form is presented below:

$$M_{cr} = \frac{A_1}{-2r} \left[\frac{\pi^2 EI_\omega}{(k_\omega L)^2} + GJ \right] \tag{9}$$

where

$$A_1 = \sqrt{\frac{C_2}{C_4 \pi^2}} \qquad A_2 = \frac{k_2}{2\pi \sqrt{C_2 C_4}}$$

$$A_3 = \frac{C_3}{\pi \sqrt{C_2 C_4}} \qquad\qquad A_4 = \frac{k_1 C_7}{2\pi \sqrt{C_2 C_4}}$$

$$r = A_2 a_y + A_4 e_y - A_3 \beta_1$$

$$k_1 = q_y L^2 / M \qquad k_2 = PL/M \qquad k_\omega = \pi \sqrt{(C_2/C_1)} \tag{10}$$

The coefficients $A_1, \ldots, A_4$ can be approximated numerically (see Appendix 2) by either assuming the form of the buckled shape or by solving the buckling problem numerically for the buckled shape and then integrating using the derived eigenmode shape.

The k_ω factor can be thought of as a quasi-torsional effective length factor, although there is no proof presented here that this quantity relates to the distance between points of contraflexure of the torsional buckled shape. The k_ω factor is a function of $g_{,x}$ and $g_{,xx}$, and hence would be related primarily to the shape of the torsional buckle and thus to the warping restraint at the boundaries.

The r quantity contains all the height terms of the transverse loads, i.e. a_y is the height of P above the shear centre and e_y is the height of q_y above the shear centre, as well as the monosymmetric parameter β_1 which can be related to the resultant position of the shear force (see Attard[13]).

Equation (9) can be rearranged into a non-dimensional form thus:

$$\frac{2M_{cr}L}{\sqrt{EI_{yy}GJ}} = \frac{A_1\left[\left(\dfrac{\pi K}{k_\omega}\right)^2 + 1\right]}{-\gamma} \tag{11}$$

in which

$$\gamma = r \sqrt{(EI_{yy}/GJL^2} \tag{12}$$

$$K^2 = EI_\omega/GJL^2 \tag{13}$$

The parameter defined in eqn (13) is a useful measure of the relative importance of warping.

Equation (11) indicates that a positive real solution for the buckling load is possible even if I_{yy} equals I_{zz} and occurs when γ is non-zero and negative. The γ parameter is non-zero when the cross-section is monosymmetric and is bent about the non-symmetric axis, and/or when transverse loads are applied above or below the shear centre. The γ parameter is negative when the cross-section is orientated and transverse loads are applied with a height and direction so as to destabilize the beam (for example when an I-beam is loaded at the top flange with a downward load). From eqns (6) and (7), it can be concluded that the buckling mode would be *purely torsional* ($\overline{W}s = 0$).

When $I_{yy} \neq I_{zz}$ the critical moment obtained from eqn (8) can be written in the following form:

$$M_{cr} = A_1 \left[P_f r \pm \sqrt{(P_f r)^2 + P_f P_\omega} \right] \tag{14}$$

where

$$P_f = \frac{\pi^2 EI_{yy}}{(v_z^* k_f L)^2} \qquad P_\omega = \left[\frac{\pi^2 EI_\omega}{(k_\omega L)^2} + GJ \right] \tag{15}$$

$$k_f = \frac{C_6}{\sqrt{C_4 C_5}} \tag{16}$$

$$v_z^* = \sqrt{v_z \left[v_z + \frac{I_{yy}}{I_{zz}} \frac{1}{k_f^2} \right]} \tag{17}$$

The factor k_f is a quasi-flexural effective length factor and is dependent on the boundary conditions imposed on the out-of-plane bending. Note that there are two effective length factors used in eqn (14), k_f and k_ω.

Rearranging eqn (14) into non-dimensional form, we have

$$\frac{M_{cr}(v_z^* k_f L)}{\sqrt{EI_{yy} GJ}} = A_1 \pi^2 \left\{ \gamma_f \pm \sqrt{\gamma_f^2 + \frac{1}{\pi^2} \left[\left(\frac{\pi K}{k_\omega} \right)^2 + 1 \right]} \right\} \tag{18}$$

in which

$$\gamma_f = \frac{\gamma}{v_z^* k_f} = \frac{r}{v_z^* k_f L} \sqrt{\frac{EI_{yy}}{GJ}} \tag{19}$$

Two solutions to eqn (19) are possible when γ is non-zero. The negative solution can often be related to a reversal of the transverse load direction and/or a rotation of the cross-section through $180°$. For a beam with a very low warping stiffness ($K^2 = 0$) the two solutions for M_{cr} can be vastly different, as one solution involves the subtraction of like terms while the other involves the addition of like terms. The variation in M_{cr} caused by a rotation of the cross-section through $180°$ can be very dramatic.

The form of eqn (18) is similar to the equation presented by Clark and Hill.[1] Clark and Hill do not, however, include the effects of initial bending curvature and in their derivation make the following substitution

$$EI_{yy} \delta Ws_{,xx} = -M_z \delta \phi \tag{20}$$

which is only applicable to cantilevers and to beams with supports where the lateral rotation ($Ws_{,x}$) is restrained. The more general equilibrium equation for bending about the y-axis in the buckled state would include the end moments due to any fixity about the y-axis at the supports.

For a cantilever or a beam with no restraint to the lateral rotation at the supports, the bending equilibrium equation about the y-axis is given by (see Appendix 1)

$$EI_{yy} \delta Ws_{,xx} = -M_z v_z \delta\phi \tag{21}$$

It therefore follows that

$$f_{,xx} = - \text{constant} \times mg \tag{22}$$

and hence

$$k_f = \frac{C_6}{\sqrt{C_4 C_5}} = 1 \tag{23}$$

Therefore from eqn (17) we have

$$v_z^* = \sqrt{1 - \frac{I_{yy}}{I_{zz}}} \tag{24}$$

3 EFFECT OF INITIAL BENDING CURVATURE

Qualitative conclusions about the effects of any initial bending deformations on lateral buckling can be made from an inspection of eqns (14)–(19).

Michell[14] attempted to include the effects of initial bending curvature on the buckling of rectangular section cantilevers loaded at their shear centre by a concentrated load at the free end. His equation is

$$\frac{M_{cr} L}{\sqrt{EI_{yy} GJ}} = \frac{4 \cdot 0126}{\sqrt{1 - \frac{I_{yy}}{I_{zz}}}} \tag{25}$$

This equation indicates that lateral buckling is impossible if $I_{yy} \geqslant I_{zz}$ for the case considered. Equation (25) also indicates that for sections where buckling is possible the effect of initial bending curvature is to increase the buckling load.

Many engineers are under the misapprehension that buckling is impossible if $I_{yy} \geqslant I_{zz}$ no matter what the loading, boundary conditions or cross-section shape, because of the form of eqn (25). It can be shown, however, that eqn (25) is only a specific case of the general equation, eqn (18).

For a rectangular section cantilever with a concentrated load at the shear centre ($\gamma_f = 0$, K^2 and $k_f = 1$), eqn (18) becomes

$$\frac{M_{cr}L}{\sqrt{EI_{yy}GJ}} = \frac{A_1\pi}{\sqrt{1 - \dfrac{I_{yy}}{I_{zz}}}} \tag{26}$$

This is of the same form as Michell's equation, eqn (25).

For the general problem, eqn (18) (provided $I_{yy} \neq I_{zz}$) indicates that a real solution exists for the buckling load if

$$v_z \left[v_z + \frac{I_{yy}}{I_{zz}} \frac{1}{k_f^2} \right] \geqslant \frac{-\gamma^2\pi^2}{\left[\left(\dfrac{\pi K}{k_\omega} \right)^2 + 1 \right] k_f^2} \tag{27}$$

For a cantilever and for a simply supported beam with supports which do not restrain the lateral rotation, use of eqn (24) reduces eqn (27) to the condition

$$\frac{I_{yy}}{I_{zz}} \leqslant 1 + \frac{\gamma^2\pi^2}{\left(\dfrac{\pi K}{k_\omega} \right)^2 + 1} \tag{28}$$

The term on the right of eqn (28) is always greater than or equal to unity. Further inspection of eqn (14) indicates that a real *positive* solution for the buckling load is possible even if $I_{yy} \geqslant I_{zz}$, when γ is non-zero and negative.

To determine the effects of initial bending curvature on the magnitude of the critical buckling load, first consider the case when r is zero. Hence from eqn (14) we have

$$M_{cr} = A_1 \sqrt{P_f P_\omega} \tag{29}$$

When the beam is a cantilever or where the lateral rotation is unrestrained at the boundaries, the k_f factor is unity and the P_f term is increased when initial bending curvature is considered (see eqns (15) and (24)). It follows that the critical moment is increased.

When the lateral rotation at the boundaries is restrained, the parametric study discussed later has shown that k_f is approximately 0·5. Consideration of the initial bending curvature modifies the critical moment by the factor

$$1 \Big/ \sqrt{\left(1 - \frac{I_{yy}}{I_{zz}} \right) \left(1 + 3\frac{I_{yy}}{I_{zz}} \right)} \tag{30}$$

For I_{yy}/I_{zz} below about 0·6 the critical moment will be reduced (see Fig. 2) while for $I_{yy}I_{zz}$ above 0·6 the critical moment will be increased.

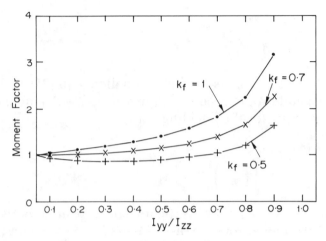

Fig. 2. Effect of initial bending curvature.

If r is non-zero, whether consideration of the initial bending curvature will increase or decrease the critical moment will depend on both the boundary conditions and the sign of r. Similar observations on the effects of initial bending deformations on the magnitude of the critical moment were also made by Vacharajittiphan *et al.*[15]

4 NUMERICAL EXAMPLES

Two examples are examined numerically. The analysis was performed using the quadratic eigenvalue finite element formulation of Attard,[16] which incorporates the effects of initial bending curvature.

The first example, shown in Fig. 3, is of a simply supported rectangular section beam with a concentrated load at the mid-span. The line of action of the applied load passes through the shear centre and is applied at various heights above the shear centre. The effect of the height of the applied load is to reduce the torsional stiffness and this can offset the effects of initial bending curvature. For zero height, no buckling is possible for sections where $I_{yy} > I_{zz}$. As the height is increased, the point at which no buckling is possible is pushed further to the right on the graph, at values where $I_{yy} > I_{zz}$. Also plotted on Fig. 3 is an approximate solution obtained using eqns (18) and (24), and estimated coefficients calculated in Appendix 2 and presented in Table 6. The approximate solution for $I_{yy} \neq I_{zz}$ is given by

$$\frac{P_{cr}L^2 v_z}{5 \cdot 39 \sqrt{EI_{yy}GJ}} = \pi^2 \left(\gamma_f \pm \sqrt{\gamma_f^2 + 1/\pi^2} \right) \tag{31}$$

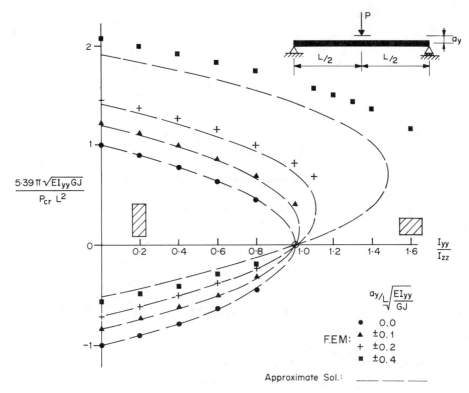

Fig. 3. Simply supported rectangular section beam.

where

$$\gamma_f = \frac{-0.56a_y}{v_z L} \sqrt{\frac{EI_{yy}}{GJ}}$$

and for $I_{yy} = I_{zz}$ by

$$\frac{P_{cr}L^2}{5.39 \sqrt{EI_{yy}GJ}} = \frac{0.5}{-\gamma_f} \tag{32}$$

The second example is of a more practical significance. Figure 4 shows a trough section girder of the form used in composite bridge construction. During construction the girder is simply supported and carries its own weight. The cross-sectional properties of the girder are listed below:

I_{yy} = 680×10^8 mm⁴ I_{zz} = 473×10^8 mm⁴ J = 101×10^5 mm⁴

I_ω = 398×10^{13} mm⁶ β_1 = 1894 mm y_s = -1399 mm

Mario M. Attard

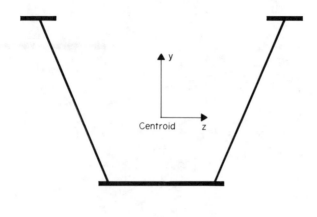

Fig. 4. Trough section.

L = 50 000 mm E = 200 000 MPa G = 80 000 MPa

I_{yy}/I_{zz} = 1·44

The self-weight of the trough beam is 6·9 kN/m. At first glance it might be thought that buckling will not be a problem since I_{yy} is greater than I_{zz}, but this would be a catastrophic assumption. The trough section is monosymmetric and hence the distribution of normal stresses due to bending will affect the torsional stiffness. The torsional stiffness is also affected by the height of the self-weight of the trough which acts through the centre of gravity well above the shear centre. The computed load factor at buckling was 0·623, indicating a very undesirable situation. The computed eigenmode was predominantly torsional with very little lateral movement.

In normal practice the trough top flange should be temporarily braced during construction until the deck slab achieves the required strength. The bracing would need to increase the torsional constant J sufficiently to achieve the required factor of safety against buckling.

5 CONCLUSION

An approximate non-dimensional equation for the elastic lateral buckling of straight beams has been presented. The equation incorporates the effects of monosymmetry and height of applied transverse loads and the effects of initial bending curvature. The form of the equation provides an insight into the lateral buckling phenomenon. For cross-sections where the flexural rigidities of the principal centroidal axes are equal, and for sections where the flexural rigidity about the axis of initial bending, EI_{zz}, is smaller than the flexural rigidity about the other principal centroidal axis, EI_{yy}, buckling is still a possibility. Buckling is possible if transverse loads are applied with a height above or below the shear centre and with a direction so as to destabilize the beam and/or if the cross-section is monosymmetric and is oriented to destabilize the beam.

Tabulated values for buckling coefficients have been presented which can be used to estimate the buckling load for various beam problems. The estimated buckling load using the presented approximate formula can provide a useful check on results obtained numerically, such as through the use of the finite element method.

ACKNOWLEDGEMENT

The writer is indebted to Associate Professor G. Hancock of the University of Sydney for suggesting the trough example and for his helpful discussion and criticisms.

REFERENCES

1. Clark, J. W. & Hill, H. N., Lateral buckling of beams, *J. Struct. Div., ASCE,* **86** (ST7) (1960) 175–95.
2. Horne, M. R., The flexural–torsional buckling of members of symmetrical I-section under combined thrust and unequal terminal moments, *Q. J. Mech. Appl. Math.,* **7**(4) (1954) 410–26.
3. Maeda, Y., Influence of web deformation upon flexural–torsional buckling of I-shaped beams, *Tech. Rep. Osaka Univ.,* **907** (Oct.) (1969) 657–77.
4. Nethercot, D. A. & Rockey, K. C., A unified approach to the elastic lateral buckling of beams, *Struct. Eng,* **49**(7) (1971) 321–30.
5. Trahair, N. S., Lateral buckling design strength of steel beams, *Trans. Inst. Engrs, Australia, Civil Engineering,* **CE26**(4) (1984) 319–26.
6. Column Research Committee of Japan, *Handbook of Structural Stability*, Corona, Tokyo, 1971.
7. Structural Stability Research Council, in *Guide to the Stability Design Criteria for Metal Structures,* ed. B. G. Johnston, John Wiley & Sons, New York, 1976, Chapter 6.
8. Roberts, T. M. & Burt, C. A., Instability of monosymmetric I-beams and cantilevers, *Int. J. Mech. Sci.,* **27**(5) (1985) 313–24.
9. Roberts, T. M. & Benchiha, M., Lateral instability of monosymmetric beams with initial curvature, *Thin-Walled Structures,* **5** (1987) 111–23.

10. Attard, M. M., *The elastic flexural torsional response of thin-walled open beams,* presented to the University of New South Wales, August 1984.
11. Attard, M. M., Nonlinear theory of non-uniform torsion of thin-walled open beams, *Thin-Walled Structures,* **4** (1986) 101–43.
12. Mikhlin, S. G., *Variational Methods in Mathematical Physics,* Moscow, Translated into English by Pergamon Press, 1964.
13. Attard, M. M., Nonlinear shortening and bending effect under pure torque of thin-walled open beams, *Thin-Walled Structures,* **4** (1986) 165–77.
14. Michell, A. G. M., Elastic stability of long beams under transverse forces, *Phil. Mag.,* **48** (1899) 298–309.
15. Vacharajittiphan, P., Woolcock, S. T. & Trahair, N. S., Effect of in-plane deformation on lateral buckling, *J. Struct. Mech.,* **3** (1974) 29–60.
16. Attard, M. M., Lateral buckling analysis of beams by the FEM, *Comput. Struct.,* **23**(2) (1986) 217–31.
17. Kitipornchai, S., Wang, C. M. & Trahair, N. S., Buckling of monosymmetric I-beams under moment gradient, *J. Struct. Enging,* **112**(4) (1986) 781–99.
18. Attard, M. M. & Lawther, R. L., Effect of secondary warping on lateral buckling, *11th ACMSM,* University of Auckland, 1988, 219–25.

APPENDIX 1

Consider a beam initially bent about the z-axis. The distribution of bending moments is given by

$$M_{\bar{z}} = M_z \qquad M_{\bar{y}} = 0 \tag{A1.1}$$

Initially only transverse displacements in the y direction are experienced and therefore

$$\phi = 0 \qquad Ws = 0 \tag{A1.2}$$

The transverse curvature can be obtained from

$$Vs_{,xx} = M_z/EI_{zz} \tag{A1.3}$$

For a cantilever or a simply-supported beam with the lateral rotation freedom unrestrained at the supports, the change in bending moment $M_{\bar{y}}$ after perturbations of the displacement field will be (assuming small angles of twist)

$$\delta M_{\bar{y}} = M_z \delta \phi \tag{A1.4}$$

From Ref. 2 we have

$$M_{\bar{y}} = -EI_{yy}[Ws_{,xx} - Vs_{,xx}\phi - \beta_2\phi_{,x}^2] \tag{A1.5}$$

After perturbations of the displacement field the perturbation of M_y is

$$\delta M_{\bar{y}} = -EI_{yy}[\delta Ws_{,xx} - Vs_{,xx}\delta\phi - \delta Vs_{,xx}\phi - 2\beta_2\phi_{,x}\delta\phi_{,x}] \tag{A1.6}$$

Substituting eqns (A1.2) and (A1.3), eqn (A1.6) reduces to

$$\delta M_{\bar{y}} = -EI_{yy}[\delta Ws_{,xx} - (M_z/EI_{zz})\delta\phi] \tag{A1.7}$$

Now, employing eqn (A1.4) and rearranging yields

$$EI_{yy}\delta Ws_{,xx} = -M_z(1 - I_{yy}I_{zz})\delta\phi$$
$$= -M_z v_z \delta\phi \tag{A1.8}$$

APPENDIX 2

Ignoring the effects of initial bending curvature by setting v_z^* to unity, eqn (14) becomes

$$M_{cr} = A_1[P_f r \pm \sqrt{(P_f r)^2 + P_f P_\omega}] \tag{A2.1}$$

where

$$P_f = \frac{\pi^2 EI_{yy}}{(k_f L)^2} \qquad P_\omega = \left[\frac{\pi^2 EI_\omega}{(k_\omega L)^2} + GJ\right] \tag{A2.2}$$

or in non-dimensional form

$$\frac{M_{cr} k_f L}{\sqrt{EI_{yy} GJ}} = A_1 \pi^2 \left\{ \gamma_f \pm \sqrt{\gamma_f^2 + \frac{1}{\pi^2}\left[\left(\frac{\pi K}{k_\omega}\right)^2 + 1\right]} \right\} \tag{A2.3}$$

in which

$$\gamma_f = \frac{\gamma}{k_f} = \frac{r}{k_f L}\sqrt{\frac{EI_{yy}}{GJ}} \tag{A2.4}$$

The coefficients A_1, A_2, A_3, A_4, k_f and k_ω depend on the shape of the buckle and the bending moment distribution. The finite element stability analysis developed in Attard[16] was used to determine the eigenmodes for specific problems and to make a parametric study of the coefficients. Since the displacement field for the finite element formulation is a cubic polynomial for the twist and the lateral displacement, a continuous function can be determined for the twist, the rate of twist, the lateral displacement and the lateral rotation. The lateral curvature and the second derivative of the twist will only be piece-wise continuous over the length of the beam.

A six-point Gaussian Quadrature procedure per element was employed to integrate for the required coefficients. A number of simply-supported beam problems were investigated using 40 elements. The

TABLE 1
Support Conditions at Each End of the Beam

Type	Freedom	
	Lateral rotation	Warping restraint
1	Free	Free
2	Fixed	Free
3	Free	Fixed
4	Fixed	Fixed

support conditions involving the lateral rotation and the warping restraint at both ends of the beam are defined in Table 1. Different combinations of geometric and material properties were used.

Tables 2 to 6 list the calculated values for the coefficients. It has been identified[17, 18] that for monosymmetric cross-sections with a very low warping stiffness such as a tee or angle, the cross-section can be prone to a localized torsional buckle. A simple formula to estimate the localized torsional buckling load is presented in Ref. 18.

TABLE 2
Buckling Coefficients

Support type	A_1	A_2	k_f	k_ω	Loading
1	1	1	1	1	
2	1·16		0·58		
	1·00	1	0·45	1	M M
3	1·09		1		
	1·12	1·12	1	0·49	
4	1·16	1·16	0·58	0·5	
1	1·31	1	1	1	
2	1·53		0·58		
	1·32	1	0·46	1	M M/2
3	1·32		1		
	1·47	1·12	1	0·49	
4	1·53	1·15	0·58	0·5	
1	1·77		1		
	0·84	1	1	1	
2	2·13		0·61		
	1·84	1	0·46	1	M
3	1·78		1		
	2·06	1·12	1	0·49	
4	2·13	1·15	0·59	0·5	

It was also discovered during the parametric study that the coefficients for support type 2 depend on the EI_ω/GKL^2 value and the sign of β_1. For negative β_1, as the warping stiffness is decreased the solution for the coefficients approached the solution obtained for support type 4. It was therefore decided that the coefficients would be calculated for two cases only:

$$\text{case 1: } K^2 = EI_\omega/GJL^2 = 0 \qquad \gamma = 0$$

TABLE 3
Buckling Coefficients

$$M/2$$

		$\dfrac{\beta_1}{L}\sqrt{\dfrac{EI_{yy}}{GJ}}$	A_1	A_3	k_f	k_ω
Support type 1	$K^2 = 0$	0	2·33		1	
		0	2·54		1	1
		0·15	2·51	0·93	1	0·95
	$K^2 = 1$	0·3	2·49	0·98	1	0·93
		−0·15	2·59	0·8	1	0·99
		−0·3	2·67	0·71	1	0·99
Support type 2	$K^2 = 0$	0	2·92		0·65	
		0	2·64		0·52	1
		0·15	2·53	0·91	0·5	0·96
	$K^2 = 1$	0·3	2·48	0·99	0·49	0·93
		−0·15	2·85	0·55	0·54	0·98
		−0·3	3·16	0·28	0·57	0·91
Support type 3	$K^2 = 0$	0	2·35		1	
		0	2·93		1	0·46
		0·15	2·92	1·11	1	0·46
	$K^2 = 1$	0·3	2·92	1·13	1	0·46
		−0·15	2·94	1·05	1	0·47
		−0·3	2·95	1·02	1	0·46
Support type 4	$K^2 = 0$	0	2·89		0·65	
		0	3·12		0·64	0·48
		0·15	3·08	1·09	0·63	0·48
	$K^2 = 1$	0·3	3·04	1·13	0·63	0·47
		−0·15	3·19	0·97	0·64	0·49
		−0·3	3·28	0·88	0·64	0·49

and

case 2: $K^2 = 1$ $\beta_1\sqrt{EI_{yy}/GJL^2} = 0, \pm0\cdot15, \pm0\cdot3$

$$e_y\sqrt{EI_{yy}/GJL^2} = 0, \pm0\cdot15, \pm0\cdot3$$

$$a_y\sqrt{EI_{yy}/GJL^2} = 0, \pm0\cdot15, \pm0\cdot3$$

In both cases $EI_{yy}/GJ = 80$. For the load cases producing single curvature (Tables 2, 5 and 6), the coefficients were fairly constant to within $\pm5\%$. In the two loading cases producing double curvature (Tables 3 and 4) the A_1 and A_3 varied with the value of β_1 and these are listed.

TABLE 4
Buckling Coefficients

		$\dfrac{\beta_1}{L}\sqrt{\dfrac{EI_{yy}}{GJ}}$	A_1	A_3	k_f	k_ω
	$K^2 = 0$	0	2·55		1	
Support type 1		0	2·72		1	1
		$\pm0\cdot15$	2·72	$\pm0\cdot29$	1	0·97
	$K^2 = 1$	$\pm0\cdot3$	2·72	$\pm0\cdot18$	1	0·99
	$K^2 = 0$	0	2·91		0·67	
Support type 2		0	2·76		0·58	1
		$\pm0\cdot15$	2·76	$\pm0\cdot44$	0·57	0·95
	$K^2 = 1$	$\pm0\cdot3$	2·76	$\pm0\cdot74$	0·57	0·88
	$K^2 = 0$	0	2·59		1	
Support type 3		0	3·46		1	0·46
		$\pm0\cdot15$	3·46	$\pm0\cdot28$	1	0·46
	$K^2 = 1$	$\pm0\cdot3$	3·48	$\pm0\cdot53$	1	0·45
	$K^2 = 0$	0	2·91		0·66	
Support type 4		0	3·63		0·73	0·48
		$\pm0\cdot15$	3·64	$\pm0\cdot31$	0·72	0·46
	$K^2 = 1$	$\pm0\cdot3$	3·64	$\pm0\cdot59$	0·72	0·47

TABLE 5
Buckling Coefficients

Support type	A_1	A_3	A_4	k_f	k_ω	Loading
1	1·13	0·54	−0·46	1	1	$M = q_y L^2/8$
2	1·16			0·61		
	1·13	0·54	−0·46	0·57	1	
3	1·13			1		
	1·23	0·86	−0·39	1	0·5	
4	1·17			0·62		
	1·24	0·89	−0·38	0·64	0·5	

TABLE 6
Buckling Coefficients

Support type	A_1	A_2	A_3	k_f	k_ω	Loading
1	1·36	−0·56	0·43	1	1	$M = PL/4$
2	1·37			0·67		
	1·36	−0·57	0·43	0·63	1	
3	1·35			1		
	1·45	−0·60	0·71	1	0·5	
4	1·38			0·67		
	1·47	−0·60	0·74	0·69	0·5	

Thin-Walled Structures **9** (1990) 437–457

Aesthetics of Thin-Walled Structures

Alan Holgate

Department of Civil Engineering, Monash University, Clayton, Victoria 3168, Australia

ABSTRACT

Thin-walled structures are assumed to include all 'surface-acting' structures. This is a brief review of the factors generally considered to influence our emotional and intellectual response to built forms. General problems arising from the strong forms and large plain surfaces of thin-walled structures are considered. A number of specific types are then treated under the headings of 'bridges', 'shells', 'silos', 'tents' and 'air-supported structures'.

1 INTRODUCTION

For the purposes of this paper, thin-walled structures are assumed to include:

(1) structures made of thin steel plates, such as box-girder bridges, cranes, pressure vessels, pipelines and steel silos;
(2) a more limited range of concrete structures such as shells, folded plates, cooling towers, silos, and some bridges;
(3) membrane structures such as tents and inflated structures.

This presents a wide range of diversity. To discuss the aesthetics of thin-walled structures, it is necessary to ask what important visual characteristics they have in common. Obviously, they are composed first and foremost of surfaces rather than linear members. As their name implies, they are sometimes two-dimensional in appearance, but as their surfaces often enclose a volume, for engineering or architectural reasons, their overall appearance is often three- rather than two-dimensional.

437

Thin-Walled Structures 0263-8231/90/$03·50 © 1990 Elsevier Science Publishers Ltd, England. Printed in Great Britain

The surfaces of thin-walled structures are frequently required to act in compression, giving rise to the danger of buckling. As a result, detailing often involves stiffeners or ribs of some sort, and this has been a particular characteristic of steel structures of this type. So far the walls of concrete structures have not been sufficiently thin to require stiffening, but developments in high-strength concretes and fibre-reinforced concrete may eventually make this necessary. The need to avoid large, laterally unsupported panels also encourages the use of frequent cross-walls, or diaphragms.

In tents it is necessary to avoid wrinkling, so form-finding becomes a matter of avoiding compression completely.

Where thin-walled structures envelop habitable space by means of a single surface only (rather than a two-skin, sandwich panel), it is necessary to minimize bending moments or even eliminate them altogether. In shells this consideration plays a large part in the determination of form. Sudden changes in direction of the surface are generally avoided, and smoothly-flowing forms result. In tents it is possible to have discontinuities where cables provide line support at edges or in the vicinity of masts.

2 A BRIEF REVIEW OF AESTHETIC THEORY

What is generally discussed under this heading is really the 'appreciation' of built form, rather than true aesthetics. However, the use of this term, especially in engineering circles, is so well established that it will be adopted here. Much has been written by engineers on the subject of aesthetics, particularly by bridge engineers. Some typical references appear below. There are also many useful introductory books on the subject of appreciation of architecture.[1-4] There is reasonable agreement on the nature of the factors which are considered to govern the observer's response to built form.

There is no need to review the principles in detail here, but a brief résumé is appropriate. The factors involved can be loosely separated under three headings: 'formal', 'psychological', and 'intellectual'.

Formal aesthetics covers the effects of light, texture, colour and pattern; the perception of proportions, scale, form, shape, and space; and concepts such as 'visual weight'. These lead on to considerations of composition such as balance, unity, harmony and duality. Many observers experience an impression of 'movement' in forms as their eye sweeps across them. As a result, they also perceive rhythm where there are repetitive elements or lines. Many theorists feel that true aesthetics is limited to these formal characteristics of objects.

Basic psychological responses to built form are considered to include feelings such as claustrophobia and agoraphobia, reactions of awe or fear inspired by strange or ugly buildings, and insecurity inspired by the perception that a building is unsafe or illogical from a structural standpoint. Satisfaction is supposed to be experienced when forms are familiar or safe, and when compositions are well-balanced and conform to expectations. Hostility may be aroused by new forms, and nostalgia by the older and more familiar. Sensual responses may be evoked by the visual texture of surfaces or by certain forms.

Buildings may provide surprises as the visitor travels from one space to another, and structural gymnastics may provide a feeling of excitement. People are seen to have conflicting desires for security, stability, and predictability on the one hand, and stimulation and excitement on the other. The tension between these two poles adds a further psychological element to the experience. Many commentators see tension in the static forms of buildings, such as the contrast between outward-bulging surfaces and inward-curving ones; between tension and compression members; between masts and ground-anchors; between smooth and highly textured surfaces; and between smooth and jagged edges. Many observers derive an intellectual as well as a visual pleasure from evidence of elegance and optimization in design.

Mental association plays a large role in response to form. Many people see similarities between built forms and animals, insects and human features. Associations sparked by historical and national styles are particularly strong, though of course they depend very much on the observer. Moral and political outlooks also play a large part. The latter need not concern us greatly here, but the commitment of engineers to minimum cost, and their tendency to demand 'truth' in structural form, and to see ornament as frivolous and wasteful are typical examples of this.

3 GENERAL OBSERVATIONS

3.1 Aesthetic problems

The forms of surface-acting structures, particularly tents and shells, tend to be sculptural and strong, and to have an interesting structure. They are therefore difficult to ignore. Their unconventional nature is likely to provoke strong reactions (awe, unease, admiration, hostility) in the average person.

There is a problem in trying to apply the principles of formal aesthetic analysis to surface-acting structures. These principles were developed for

Art, mainly paintings, and then extended to cover the 'Art' of architecture. This development has related mainly to rectilinear buildings and has little to offer regarding the flowing, homogeneous forms of tents and shells. Box-girder bridges lend themselves more readily to this traditional analysis.

Surface-acting structures generally have simple forms and plain, unarticulated surfaces. Simplicity of form may be equated with purity, elegance and beauty, but plainness is definitely out of fashion at the moment, with the development of the so-called Post-Modern movement in architecture. Architects have rediscovered visual complexity and are having great success in selling it to the general public and to clients from all walks of life. For many people, the perfection of the simple, unadorned form is too quickly and easily comprehended, and the reaction is liable to be '... and now what?'.

Antidotes suggested by engineers have included 'complexity within simplicity'. An example of this might be the elements visible on the interior of one of Nervi's domes. Another suggestion is the juxtaposition of a contrary effect such as a strikingly different shape,[5] or of a shape of different scale.[6] Berger saw the solution at the Riyadh stadium (Fig. 1) of arranging repetitive tent forms around the perimeter. The fact that each is viewed from a slightly different angle overcomes the monotony that would be present in a linear arrangement, or in a single, unified form.

'Scale' often presents a problem in plain and simple forms. In the theory of appreciation of architecture, this term refers to the apparent size of a building. The observer is supposed to start from objects of reasonably dependable size, such as trees, handrails and doors, and to work up through proportional relationships between larger architectural features, to estimate the overall size of the building. Classical architecture is held by its devotees to provide ample clues and relationships, but monolithic forms with plain surfaces obviously do not. The result is that some observers fail to apprehend the size of these structures or are misled, and when the truth is perceived, feel overwhelmed or alienated.

Another difficulty arising from strength and simplicity of form is that tents and shells often fail to blend with the more conventional

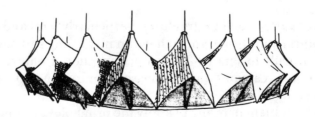

Fig. 1. Riyadh Stadium, Saudi Arabia.

substructures employed to support them and with ancillary buildings of a conventional nature. As Drew[7] puts it, 'it is very difficult to tune in conventional building forms and details to tensile structures, and hence the failure rate is high even amongst gifted architects'.

Strong forms clash with the natural, and even with the urban environment. This difficulty is increased by the fact that the colour and texture of the materials employed (white concrete and light-coloured fabrics) rarely conform to the greens and browns of the natural landscape, or the brick and timber of the suburban environment.

One of the most notable developments in steel structures has been the change, since the war, from trussed construction to thin-walled box construction for bridge decks, pylons and masts, and crane gantries. Theorists would describe this as a visual 'expression' of the change that has occurred in the relative costs of labour and materials. It has been welcomed by many as replacing the complexity and confusion of trussed members with the smooth, clean, elegant lines of the box.

However, as we have seen such forms are easily comprehended at first glance, and many find them boring. The Post-Modern movement in architecture even demands 'complexity and contradiction'. Also, there is currently a wave of nostalgia for the Victorian era which is reflected in the struts and cross-bracing of many 'High-Tech' buildings, such as the Pompidou Centre in Paris or the Lloyds Headquarters building in London. There is thus a new aesthetic of steel which is reflected in the use of trussed and braced masts for many tent structures.

3.2 Determination of form

The design of thin-walled structures is often at the 'leading edge' of technology. As a result, their forms are greatly influenced by technical considerations. Artistic or aesthetic notions must take second place. Functionalists would argue that this is the reason why their forms are often beautiful. However, most commentators, including engineers, agree that, while functional efficiency often gives rise to beautiful forms, it provides no guarantee of beauty. Many leading designers produce idiosyncratic forms which have a sound basis in technical and economic considerations, and then modify them to optimize their aesthetic appeal. Drew claims that Frei Otto resists the temptation to 'tickle' the structure in this way, but Nervi, who was a committed functionalist, and subscribed to the idea of the perfect 'form-type', did modify his designs in this way.[8] Tsuboi has expressed the opinion that architectural beauty exists at a slight deviation from structural perfection, and Leonhardt has noted that it is hard to combine good appearance with good mechanics in structures of this type.[9]

It is generally agreed that, except in the most extreme circumstances, designers have a number of economically viable forms available to meet a given requirement, and that the choice is usually made on the basis of some personal disposition.[10] Billington[11] states that in Maillart's case, this was his 'passion for thinness'.

When large-scale modern tent structures were first developed, even the choice of their boundaries, let alone their internal form, tended to be determined by technical considerations, and therefore to be in the realm of the structural engineer. This applied also to shell forms.[12] Now, as engineers have gained in analytical skills and experience, and architects have become more familiar with the potentialities of tent forms, we are beginning to see aesthetic considerations playing a much bigger role. The Riyadh Stadium (Fig. 1) and the Schlumberger Centre in Cambridge, UK (Fig. 2), are examples.

Many designers insist that structure should be honestly expressed, but in thin-walled structures this often presents a problem, either because the structural action is too complex for the layman to comprehend, or because cladding and ancillary elements conceal the main structure. It is very noticeable that shells tend to be photographed before completion of the cladding, or at night, when internal illumination makes glass walls transparent.

In the case of shells it is often quite expensive to integrate the supports into the overall form structurally and visually, but when this is done the result is very pleasing. Robin Boyd[13] noted as long ago as 1958 that the practice of sitting a strongly shaped roof on top of a conventional lower storey was a transition phase. He noted a further problem in that conventional accessories also sit uneasily with dramatic structural forms, citing as an instance the conventional, orthogonal lift wells inside the sculptural form of the TWA Terminal building at Kennedy Airport (Fig. 3).

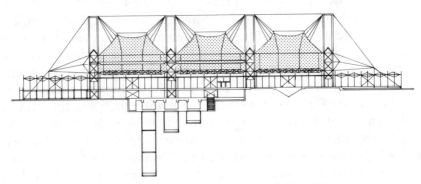

Fig. 2. Schlumberger Centre, Cambridge, UK.

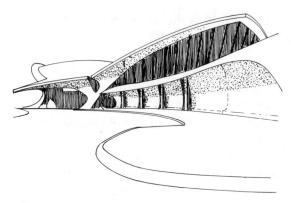

Fig. 3. TWA Terminal, Kennedy Airport, USA.

Boyd was strongly in favour of the growing use of shells at that time, seeing the new shapes as poetic, in comparison to the more rational and allegedly functional box-like forms of the Modern Movement in architecture.

Thin-walled structures tend to be unconventional, and are likely to be rejected because of this. Acceptance may grow, at least in avant-garde or professional circles. Otto has remarked that his tent structures were considered ugly when they were first introduced, but they are now considered beautiful, at least in critical circles.

4 SPECIFICS

4.1 Bridges

It is interesting to note that bridges with tubular members (Britannia and Forth) were amongst the earliest man-made structures that can be considered 'thin-walled' by modern standards.

The rectangular box is, of course, the most common form for bridges. Formerly, the steel box was characterized by rows of stiffeners and rivets or bolts. These provided clues to the scale of the structure, and helped articulate its form. With modern welding techniques, all stiffeners are now placed on the inside of the box, and much of the visual interest of steel box forms has been lost. Leonhardt[14] states: 'Modern steel girders now hardly differ from prestressed-concrete bridges in their external appearance, except perhaps in their colour. This is perhaps regrettable, because stiffeners on the outside enliven the plate-faces, give scale and make the girder look less heavy.'

Alan Holgate

The introduction of thin-walled box sections has permitted the use of greatly increased span-to-depth ratios for decks, and of slender pylons for cable-stayed and suspension bridges, thus reducing their visual impact in environmentally sensitive locations. Aerodynamically shaped boxes which reduce drag and wind-induced vibration have further contributed. The impression of slenderness can be increased by using a bright cantilevered fascia on the outside of cantilevered footpaths and by the use of sloping webs.[14]

In tall pier-and-beam bridges in Germany, great care has been taken to ensure that the view along the valley is framed in as satisfactory a manner as possible, and the spacing of the piers is varied, at some cost in construction, in order to maintain a harmonious relationship between the proportions of the individual frames (Fig. 4). In allowing the use of greater spans, the high strength and stiffness of boxes also reduces the obstruction to vision caused when the bridge is viewed from an oblique angle, as often happens when it is seen from a curving approach road. A further advantage is the torsional rigidity of the box girder, which, in cable-stayed bridges, allows the use of a single mast and a single plane of cables on the longitudinal axis. There is, of course, a premium to be paid for preferring this to the two-plane alternative.

The high strength and stiffness of box-sections used as pylons often eliminates the need for cross-bracing. At the Severinsbrücke, lateral resistance has been increased still further by the use of an A-frame.

The introduction of thin-walled box sections has had a considerable effect on the appearance of steel arch bridges. Cross-bracing is less necessary to provide stiffness, strength, and stability in the lateral direction. A number of choices still remain. At the Donaubrücke Straubing, cross-bracing has been used, allowing the arches to be made of very narrow boxes which appear very slender when viewed by the traveller. At Kaiserlai, twin booms of circular section 2 m in diameter are

Fig. 4. Mosel Viaduct, Winningen, FRG.

employed on each side. Each pair is joined together by a horizontal plate 1 m wide. At the Schwabelweis bridge, broad flat boxes are used for the arches and are presumably deck-stiffened. A final option, used in several locations, is to lean the arches together so that they touch at the crown. This has been adopted at Fehmarnsund.[14]

Although concrete boxes may not qualify as 'thin-walled', it is often difficult to tell from a distance whether a structure is of concrete or steel. It is not evident from photographs that the towers of the Humber suspension bridge are of concrete. Relatively thin walls figure prominently in a number of types. Maillart used box cross-sections in many of his bridges, as a result of exploiting the resistance of spandrel walls (Fig. 5). The thin sections of the arches of his 'stabbogen' bridges, and of the cross-walls which prop their decks (Fig. 6), demonstrate his 'passion for thinness'.[11]

4.2 Shells — architectural

Shells constitute a form of concrete 'surface-acting' structure which does have a high ratio of span to thickness. Unfortunately their overall form often gives an impression of heaviness and 'dumpiness': a good example of 'visual weight'. Treated carefully, this can give rise to impressions of stability and repose, and nobility: qualitites which critics of architecture perceive in masonry domes. However, neo-classical domes are often raised up on a drum, which may be lined with columns. Their rise is generally greater than that of a semi-circle. The brick domes of Hagia Sophia in Istanbul are sometimes criticized as being too flat, and

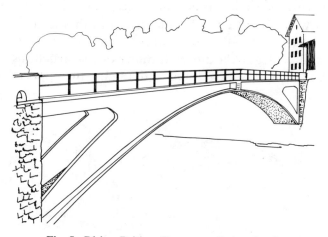

Fig. 5. Rhine Bridge, Tavanasa, Switzerland.

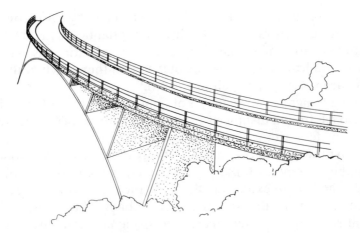

Fig. 6. Schwandbach Bridge, Switzerland.

therefore lacking the nobility of domes like that of St Peter's in Rome.

When designing his domical shell for the auditorium at MIT, Boston (Fig. 7), Eero Saarinen attempted to obviate the visual heaviness of the form by slicing the dome vertically along three planes. In doing so, he destroyed the structural efficiency of the form, and later agreed that the solution was not one of his best architecturally.

The response of many designers to this problem has been to try to make the thinness and therefore the *real* lightness of shell roofs evident to the casual observer by exposing the edge. Torroja adopted this policy in his shell for the market hall at Algeciras, extending the edges of the shell in cantilever beyond the walls. Isler, by carefully shaping his shells, and strengthening the edge zones in a way which avoids the need for edge beams, has achieved shell-forms which *appear* as light as they really are. Transparent walls are of course a major aid in this regard.

Another way to avoid edge beams is to choose forms that are inherently stiff, as Candela did with many of his structures.

It could be said that Nervi adopted a diametrically opposed approach,

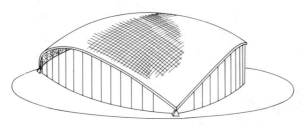

Fig. 7. Kresge Auditorium, MIT Boston, MA, USA.

and stiffened his shells at all points with a mass of ribs, which he exploited to develop intricate patterns. The ribs are so close in comparison to the span that they almost provide the structure with a special 'texture', and certainly assist in establishing scale and rhythm (Fig. 8).

In contrast, Isler is attracted by the simplicity and purity, or 'clarity', which can be attained with shell forms. In comparison with conventional structures, they have no supporting beams, no tension members, and no 'confusion of columns' to support the roof. Best of all, their inner volume is simply their outer volume minus a fine layer which may be no greater than 10 cm in thickness. Isler also notes that their unity of form causes shells to look deceptively small from the outside.[10]

According to the theorists, shells carry many powerful associations, but it is likely that these are related more to the concept of 'shell', or to the word itself, than to people's actual reactions when confronted by the real structure. Hyperbolic paraboloid umbrella shells do, however, arouse memories of Gothic vaults when used repetitively, and Candela's shell for the restaurant at Xochimilco may be reminiscent of a scallop shell (Fig. 9). It is interesting that at least two architects have 'quoted' the one really successful shell type, the hyperbolic paraboloid cooling tower, in their buildings. Le Corbusier used one above his Legislative Assembly Building (Parliament), at Chandigarh in India, and Le Couteur and Herbé used it above the Algiers Basilica (Fig. 10).

4.3 Shells — containment vessels

Shells functioning as containment vessels generally have the simple, 'Platonic' forms which delighted the architects of the early Modern Movement such as Le Corbusier. Concrete cylindrical tanks at ground

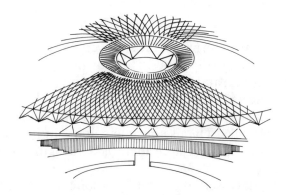

Fig. 8. Interior of Palazetto dello Sport, Rome.

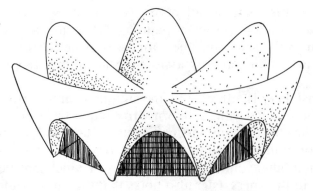

Fig. 9. Los Manantiales Restaurant, Xochimilco, Mexico.

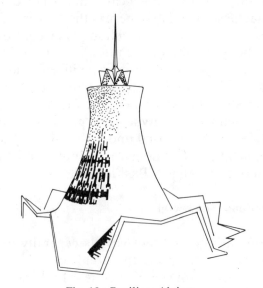

Fig. 10. Basilica, Algiers.

level attain this purity of form, but the steel version suffers from irregular patterns of joints between the plates. These do nothing for the theory that 'functional is beautiful', and no satisfactory solution seems to have been found. Now that the use of lively colours is intellectually respectable, it is possible to distract attention away from blemishes in the surface of both concrete and steel tanks. The use of such colours in industrial plants is well established in France where there is a recognized profession of 'colour consultant'.[15]

Steel containment vessels often consist of spheres, or of cylinders lying with their longitudinal axes horizontal. In these cases the simplicity of the basic form contrasts oddly with excrescences such as manhole collars and supporting cradles or props and bracing. Again the use of colour to emphasize the dominant form and provide some sort of visual logic to the appurtenances may be advisable.

Pipelines are a special case of this type of thin-walled structure. Those associated with hydro-electric power stations are usually very prominent and in stark conflict with the surrounding environment. An interesting example of the way in which an architect has coped with the conflict between a prominent pipe and associated conventional buildings, is provided by the Umlauftank at the Hydraulic Research Institute, Berlin Tiergarten, designed by Ludwig Leo (Fig. 11).

An interesting variation on the 'Platonic' forms is Ulrich Finsterwalder's purification tanks where the form is derived from considerations of fluid flow as well as structural efficiency (Fig. 12).

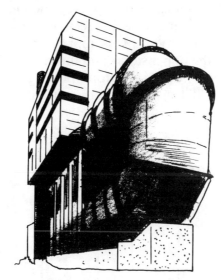

Fig. 11. Hydraulic Research Institute, Berlin.

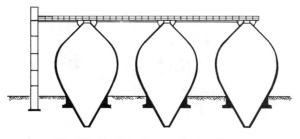

Fig. 12. Purification tanks, Berlin.

4.4 Silos

The silo is another example of 'Platonic' form, and was singled out by Le Corbusier for special praise. He was referring to concrete wheat silos seen in the United States. Strangely enough, the pure cylindrical form is rarely revealed in this type because the cells are usually grouped together to form a solid bulk.

The aesthetics of silos have already been discussed at some length.[16] Most silos have a strong vertical emphasis. Many theorists insist that in multi-storey buildings, it is essential to define visually a 'top' and a 'bottom' to terminate the movement of the eye, which tends naturally to follow the vertical line. It would seem reasonable that the same principle might apply to tall silos. Another important question is the massing of the cylinders, and the familiar problem of relating their pure forms to those of appurtenant elements, such as conveyors and their housings.

In the example shown in Fig. 13, the upper portion has the air of being precariously perched on cylinders which seem too elongated, as though they have 'shot up' like mushrooms. This impression is heightened by the close identity between the upper storey and the ground floor. In marked contrast, the silos shown in Fig. 14 are proportioned so that the 'fairing' of the upper portions is at least as powerful visually as the cylinders themselves.

Fig. 13. Grain silos, Welwyn, UK.

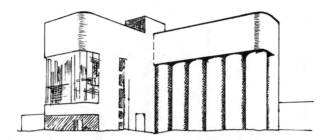

Fig. 14. Lehigh Valley Brewery, Allentown, PA, USA.

An interesting alternative solution has been employed in the group of silos shown in Fig. 15. There are two rows, each of four cylinders, and the outer walls of the bins have been continued to full height, concealing the conveyor system, and doing away with the concept of a 'top-storey' altogether. Doctrinaire formalists might find this disturbing, on the grounds that the upward line is not 'terminated' at the top by a horizontal element.

Another visual alternative occurs when the silos are allowed to stand independently, but grouped close together to form a sculptural composition. This solution is more appropriate in industrial plants such as cement works where the flow of material requires that the containers be located some distance from one another (Fig. 16).

Steel silos or 'bins' provide an interesting case study in aesthetic theory, because they conform to many of the 'rules' for good aesthetic design, yet are not particularly attractive visually (Fig. 17). They should

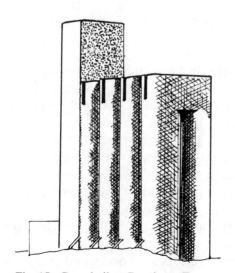

Fig. 15. Cereal silos, Romigny, France.

Fig. 16. Märker Cement Works, Hamburg, FRG.

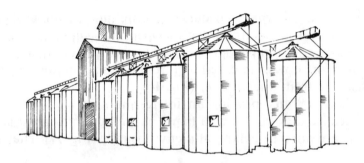

Fig. 17. Standard steel farm silos.

appeal to the formalist because they are comprised of primary geometric forms; cylinders and cones. There is ample evidence of the 'order' beloved of classicists, in the regular layout of the bins, the arrangement of the steel panels, the ribbing of the walls, and in certain aspects of the distribution systems. Other good aspects of formal arrangement include the rhythm of hand-railing, support details, and jointing, and the wealth of clues concerning scale. The bins should also appeal to the functionalist, because their characteristics are undoubtedly determined by technical and economic considerations.

Yet, it is doubtful if many people would see them as beautiful, or even as having great character. This is probably due to the ever-present emotional factor: the overtones of corrugated-iron cheapness; their air of impermanence, fragility and flexibility; and their lack of mass in both the real and visual sense. The idea that mass, preferably of masonry, signifies permanence, stability and opulence is very important for many people. The 'dumpiness' of the forms is no help in this regard, and the monotony induced by repetition must also be an important negative factor. Again, colour would undoubtedly enhance the appearance of these facilities.

4.5 Tents

The forms of tents are seen as lively, in contrast to those of shells of revolution, which are generally seen as stable, and suggestive of repose. The eye tends to follow the sweeping curves of tents, and the lines of supporting masts and cables.

Not a great deal has been written on the formal design of tents, perhaps because it has been so governed by technical considerations that architects and critics have felt excluded. Some time ago an article appeared in the *Architectural Record* entitled 'Tent structures: are they architecture?'.[17] Much can, however, be learned from case histories of the design of cable-net structures. While these are not strictly 'thin-walled', their form is governed by similar structural action.

The growing confidence of architects in modifying technically determined forms has already been mentioned. An early example was the way in which Kenzo Tange modified the form of the cable-net roofs for the Tokyo Olympic Stadiums. He felt that the natural curve of the roof was not sufficiently dramatic and wished to introduce a change of curvature along a roughly horizontal line part-way down the slope. In order to achieve this, it was necessary to introduce light trusses into the structural system, spanning from ridge to edge (Fig. 18). This of course destroyed the logic of the structural action.[18]

Berger has made the point that, as far as the structural engineer is concerned, the most efficient way to support a tent roof is to hang it from a central internal mast. In the Haj terminal tents, even though the roof of each bay rises to a peak at the centre, it was decided for architectural reasons to provide this support by means of external cables suspended from a mast at each corner of the bay.

At the Schlumberger Centre in Cambridge, UK, a great display has been made of the support structure, and the form of the tents has been made more complex by 'picking out', by means of cables, certain points on the tent surface. In some respects these appurtenances provide much of the visual interest of tents, whose plain surfaces are lacking in texture or other small scale interest, apart from the pattern of seams.

A common perception of suspended roofs is that, seen from inside, a

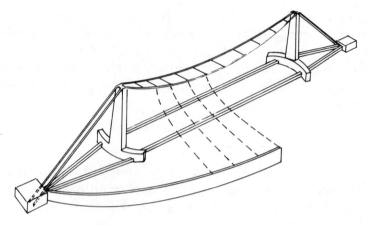

Fig. 18. Olympic Stadium, Tokyo.

sagging roof appears heavy and cumbersome, and even induces a feeling
of depression. In tents, this is counteracted by the obvious lightness of the
fabric, which is due to its translucency. The shadows of clouds and even
passing birds can be distinguished, and the level of natural lighting is
high.

Tents have of course strongly emotional associations for many people.
For west Europeans they also carry overtones of impermanence and may
be seen to provide inadequate security and protection from the elements.
Different climatic conditions and cultural expectations concerning the
impenetrability of buildings may explain their relative popularity for
large public buildings in Arab countries.

4.6 Air-supported structures

Air-supported structures have some similarities to tents, but their forms
often appear 'dumpy' or sausage-like from outside. Complex forms have
been fabricated for Expo exhibitions, but have seen little practical
application. Inflated roofs covering stadiums tend to have a very low rise
to span ratio, and their visual impact is similarly uninspiring. An

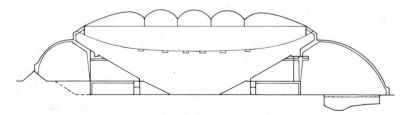

Fig. 19. O'Connell Centre, University of Florida, USA.

interesting response at the O'Connell Center at the University of Florida (Fig. 19) was to surround the central dome with subsidiary rooms roofed by fabric which is stretched over a series of concrete arches.

5 CONCLUSION

The aesthetic appreciation of structures is and must remain a highly subjective matter. However, it is believed by many people, including eminent engineers, that there is general agreement on sufficient points to permit rational discussion of aesthetic matters to a certain level.

It has been shown that thin-walled structures, consisting as they do mainly of large plain surfaces, present special problems in form-finding and in their aesthetics. Medwadowski[19] has observed that it is hard to design an ugly suspension bridge, but shells are 'easily hurt' in the hands of a 'doctrinaire constructivist' or 'drama-seeker'.

The logic of modern construction techniques often leads to totally plain surfaces which give no clues as to the contents of the envelope, or to its structural action, and which provide no visual interest for the observer. To provide artificial interest such as rows of bolts, weld lines, or formwork marks would lead us onto dangerous ground ethically and, as Torroja suggested, would be as ridiculous as indicating the structural action of a concrete structure by painting the location of reinforcement on its surface. It would seem equally wrong to introduce structural complexity simply to provide visual interest.

Perhaps the best we can hope is that, given the latitude which economic and technical constraints often allow us, a designer who has made a study of aesthetics as well as engineering design and construction will intuitively conceive structures which are satisfactory from a visual standpoint as well as an economic and technical one.

ACKNOWLEDGEMENTS

The illustrations were derived from, or based on, the following sources:

1. Philipp Holzmann Aktiengesellschaft, Technical Report, May 1987, *Internatonales Sportstadion in Riyadh/Saudi Arabien.*
2. *Archit. Rec.,* **174,** April 1986.
3. Sharp, D., *A Visual History of 20th Century Architecture*, Heinemann/ Secker and Warburg.
4. Leonhardt, F. (Ref. 14).

5, 6, 8. Billington, D. P., *The Tower and the Bridge*, Basic Books, 1983.
7. Mainstone, R., *Developments in Structural Form*, MIT Press, 1975.
9. Siegel, C., *Structure and Form in Modern Architecture*, Crosby Lockwood, London, 1962.
10. Bernier, *The Best in 20th Century Architecture*.
11. *Archit. Rev.,* **169,** June 1981.
12. Festschrift: *Ulrich Finsterwalder*, Dyckerhoff and Widmann, 1973.
13. Holme, C. G., *Industrial Architecture*, The Studio, London, 1935.
14. Hoyt, C. K. (ed.), *Buildings for Commerce and Industry*, McGraw–Hill, New York, 1978.
15. *Construction Moderne,* No. 41, March 1985.
16. Nestler, P. & Bode, P. M., *Deutsche Kunst seit 1960: Architektur,* Bruckmann, Munich, 1976.
17. Reimbert, M. L. & Reimbert, A. M., *Silos: Theory and Practice*, Clausthal, Trans. Tech., 1976.
18. *Bull. Int. Assoc. Shell Spat. Struct.* (Ref. 18)
19. *Progressive Architecture*, No. 8, 1981.

REFERENCES

1. Caudill, W. W. *et al., Architecture and You*, Watson–Guptill, New York, 1978.
2. Smith, P. F., *Architecture and the Human Dimension*, Godwin, London, 1979.
3. Gauldie, S., *Architecture*, Oxford University Press, London, 1969.
4. Rasmussen, S. E., *Experiencing Architecture*, MIT Press, Cambridge Massachusetts, 1959.
5. Tsuboi, Y., Structural design and architecture, *Bull. Int. Assoc. Shell Spat. Struct.,* **21–2** (Aug. 1980) 15–43.
6. Abercrombie, S., *Architecture as Art: an Esthetic Analysis*, van Nostrand Reinhold, New York, 1984.
7. Drew, P., Steel tendons support the Pacific Games Conference, *Architecture Aust.,* **67** (March) (1978) 42–3.
8. Nervi, P. L., *Aesthetics and Technology in Building*, Harvard University Press, Cambridge, Massachusetts 1965.
9. Leonhardt, F., Engineering structures and the environment, *Bull. Int. Assoc. Shell Spat. Struct.,* **17–1** (April) (1976) 25–8.
10. Isler, H., Typologie und Technik der modernen Schalen, *Werk, Bauen und Wohnen,* **70/37** (December) (1983) 34–41.
11. Billington, D. P., Structural art and Robert Maillart, *Archit. Sci. Rev.,* **20** (June) (1977) 44–51.
12. Medwadowski, S. J., The interrelation between the theory and the form of shells. Symposium on shell and spatial structures: the development of form. Morgantown, 1978. *Bull. Int. Assoc. Shell Spat. Struct.,* **20–2** (August) (1979) 41–61.
13. Boyd, R., Engineering of excitement, *Archit. Rev., Lond.,* **124** (1958) 295–308.

14. Leonhardt, F., *Brücken: Ästhetik und Gestaltung/Bridges: Aesthetics and Design,* Deutsche Verlags–Anstalt, Stuttgart, Architectural Press, London, 1982.
15. Porter, T. & Mikellides, B., *Colour for Architecture*, Studio Vista, London, 1976.
16. Holgate, A., The aesthetics of non-conventional structures, *Proc. Int. Conf. Design and Construction of Non-Conventional Structures*, London, Dec. 1987. London, Civil Comp Press, 1987, 1–10.
17. Anon., Tent structures: are they architecture? *Archit. Rec.,* **67** (May) (1980) 127–34.
18. Kawaguchi, M., Tension structures and their form, *Bull. Int. Assoc. Shell Spat. Struct.,* **20–2** (August) (1979) 25–39.
19. Medwadowski, S. J., Conceptual design of shells. In *Proc. Symp. Concrete Thin Shells*, ed. S. J. Medwadowski, W. C. Schnobrick and A. C. Scordelis, New York, April 1966. (ACI Pubn SP-28, ACI, Detroit, 1971, 15–39.)

Index